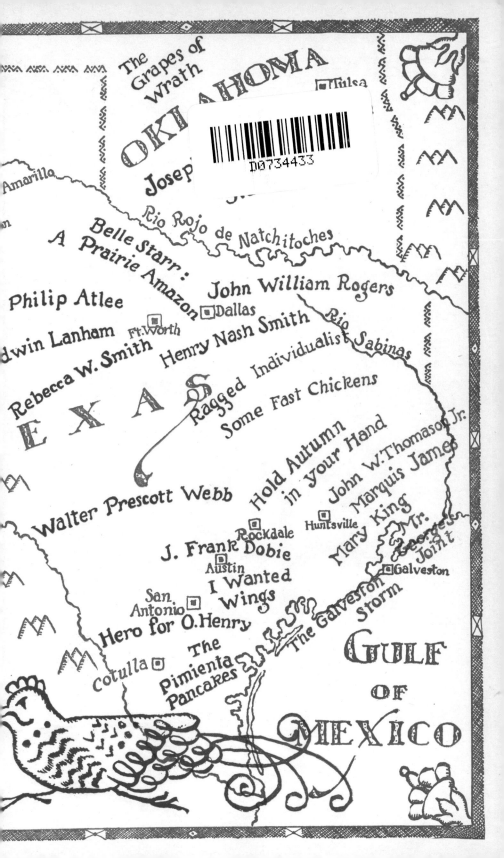

The Grapes of Wrath

OKLAHOMA

◻Tulsa

Joseph

Amarillo

Rio Rojo de Natchitoches

Belle Starr:
A Prairie Amazon

Philip Atlee

John William Rogers

◻Dallas

dwin Lanham    Ft.Worth◻

Rebecca W. Smith    Henry Nash Smith

Rio Sabinas

T E X A S    Ragged Individualist

Some Fast Chickens

Hold Autumn
in your Hand

John W. Thomason Jr.

Marquis James

Walter Prescott Webb

Rockdale
◻    Huntsville◻

Mary King

Mr.

Georges
Joint

J. Frank Dobie

Austin◻

I Wanted
Wings

◻Galveston

San
Antonio◻

Hero for O. Henry

Cotulla◻    The
Pimienta
Pancakes

The Galveston Storm

GULF

OF

MEXICO

# ROUNDUP TIME

*A Collection of Southwestern Writing*

EDITED BY
GEORGE SESSIONS PERRY

# ROUNDUP TIME

*A COLLECTION OF*
*SOUTHWESTERN WRITING*

*New York* WHITTLESEY HOUSE *London*
McGRAW-HILL BOOK COMPANY, INC.

ROUNDUP TIME

*Copyright*, 1943, *by* GEORGE SESSIONS PERRY

PUBLISHED BY WHITTLESEY HOUSE
A division of the McGraw-Hill Book Company, Inc.

*Printed in the United States of America by The Maple Press Co., York, Pa.*

This book of Southwestern writing could properly be dedicated only to the one man who has struggled longest to draw out of the people of the Southwest a full and true written picture of their lives, their problems, their joys, of the meaningful beating of their secret hearts. For that reason this book is respectfully dedicated to

John H. McGinnis

# INTRODUCTION

HESE ARE PIECES OF PROSE WHICH CONCERN THAT VAST area between the Sabine and Colorado rivers: Texas, Oklahoma, New Mexico, and Arizona; the prose writing which I happen to like, that is, and do honestly and joyfully commend to your attention. If there is any other rule of thumb by which these selections were made, I suppose it is merely the requirement that the work be honest, interesting, and, as far as possible, inspired.

This volume is not a monument to the idea of regional and/or parochial art. I am, as a matter of fact, of the belief that there is no such thing as regionalism in literature. A piece of writing, it seems to me, is either literature or it is something else. There is a core system of values that is applicable to and has meaning for all people everywhere. It is of these values, among other things, that literature is composed. And while the literature or art of a given region or nation may present those central values in one or another novel dress, it is nevertheless true (however trite) that the values of art and literature are universal.

In most cases a region is merely a place where an artist has lived long enough to have assimilated completely the various forms of behavior and the collateral conditions of human existence. By such a time he is ready to use that region as his most effective stage. For while Oklahoma unquestionably helped fashion George Milburn, and New Mexico Paul Horgan, God must also have had a little something to do with it, since states themselves are unable to dispense the essential ingredient of talent. Only in a secondary degree, then, does it matter whether a writer's homeland is marshy or dry.

But in a secondary degree which is very real, the nature of the land, the kind of people it attracted and the conditions under which they came are of more than passing interest.

What made our people inhabit this land? Well, certainly not religious persecution or anything else half so respectable. Mostly it was restlessness, and impatience with the normal processes of earning a living. A huge part of us had the constable on our heels. Then after the first edge of violence had begun to wear off of our people, oil was discovered, and there came a fantastically large new crop of riskers and swindlers and thieves. But hardly had law and what passes in the Southwest for order been restored, when the third influx of adventurers began. That was when the Southwest, with its dry, blazing weather, became the seat of military aviation.

It is true that cattle rustling is no longer as fashionable as it once was. But we still for some reason hate law and order, are still incorrigibly rugged individualists. In a land where most of us have seen fabulous fortunes made overnight by the discovery of oil—in a land which, for that matter, we just hauled off and took by force (a lot of juridical mumbo-jumbo to the contrary) —most Southwesterners want the law to remain pliable and full of loopholes, so that when the main chance comes we can charge in and get ours and never mind the "ifs" and "ands."

Most of our people, of whatever economic strata, seem to feel that either a man and his family can live off the land, or he can go and steal something. If he has neither the daring nor the energy to steal at such times, it is felt that he is a person with neither spirit nor courage, and therefore not entitled to the respect of good men. For the fact remains that what the Southwest has in large quantities is not morals, but vitality. But remember that vitality means health, as well as a number of other things, and that healthy people make good neighbors.

Consider our relations with the Mexicans. We took what they had, which was never much more than the land. Now we get along with them wonderfully. The Mexicans are good and friendly and useful citizens. (Also, incidentally, they have a personal cleanliness mania at least as violent as our own.) A life that was hell for the Okies (following the ripening fruit and vegetable crops) has been made by the Mexicans into an honorable and satisfying trade. Year in and year out the same Mexican families follow the ripening crops and perform their jobs with a nimbleness, knowledge, and skill that their northern American brothers simply do not possess. Generally speaking, these Mexican fruit and vegetable workers are a happy and, in a small way, prosperous people, with no idea that there is any reason for them to feel sorry for themselves. Yet in this business of following the fruit and vegetable crops, northern Americans almost invariably fail to compete successfully with the Mexicans, and usually wind up as "brush hogs," living on God knows what and sheltered by a scrap of burlap in a mesquite thicket—almost always utterly defeated people.

But while Southwesterners get on well with the Mexicans, they are often even more peremptory and lacking in understanding for the Negroes than, say, the people of the Old South. For the Southerners have learned that they can't get along without the Negroes, and the Southwesterners, since they live in a cattle civilization rather than a cotton one, know that they can, and do.

What kind of writing has this Southwestern environment produced? Most of it, like the people, has been virile and strong. There has been more of cows and horses and thirst and violence and guns than there has of the self-conscious discussion of letters and salons and whatever is effete and possibly decadent; for physical toughness, vitality, and stamina have been necessary attributes of our daily lives. We still have hardly licked the land and the elements and, until we do, we haven't much time for the amenities of ripened civilization. Besides, while farming is work, our people have always loved ranching, which has something of the qualities of an Indian's life. And since many of our people rode over this hard land which they loved, songs and something of literature had to be created to express their pleasure.

The two writers who probably come closest to being the natural expression of the genuine ruggedness of the people of the Southwest are Frank Dobie and John Thomason. It's fairly simple. Thomason is a martial man whose careful and stylized writing is informed with an almost constant note of arrogance.

And Dobie, who loves cows and the brush country, is himself, like the tough Southwestern flora, armed with thorns.

But time passes and younger writers are coming on the scene, younger writers expressing more recent developments of Southwestern life. Some of the first signs of self-criticism in the Southwest come from the pens of Paul Horgan, John Rogers, George Milburn, and Jim Phillips.

The universities of the Southwest become more and more interested in the expression of the native scene through writing. But the three greatest agencies in encouraging the production of literature in this area are *The Southwest Review*, which is published at Southern Methodist University under the editorship of Dr. John H. McGinnis, the Dallas *News*, and the University of Oklahoma Press. While other universities maintain their own presses, that of the University of Oklahoma is definitely outstanding. Incidentally, not only are its productions sound from the standpoint of scholarship and literature, they are models of beautiful bookmaking.

There are many crack Southwestern writers for the nation's magazines, writers whose specific purpose is often more successfully achieved than is that of some of the writers here included, but whose purpose is, for one reason or another, at variance with that of this book. Norma Patterson and Helen Topping Miller, to mention but two, both stand in the front rank among those who have mastered the extremely difficult and demanding form of magazine serial writing. Again, in the case of Dr. Eugene Barker, outstanding Texas historian and biographer of Stephen Austin, it was felt that his excellent writing was of more especial interest to the scholar than to the general reader.

Although adequate coverage of the various significant facets of life in the Southwest was a lesser objective of this collection, I was glad to find that there were pieces of first-rate writing dealing with most of them. Mary King's *Quincie Bolliver* creates for the reader the smells, the urgency, the risks of the world which grew out of the hunt for oil. Frank Dobie, in his great biography of the longhorns, will acquaint you with the ways of those tough and spirited creatures on which and with which the Southwest lived before the cotton and oil came. You will get a horse's-eye view of the more intimate aspects of the rodeo from Ross Santee's *Sleepy Black*. Elizabeth Lee Wheaton will introduce you to our colored brethren in her delightful picture of the grand opening of Mr. George's "jinte." Oliver LaFarge and Stanley Vestal have Indian tales to tell. Paul Horgan and Mabel Dodge Luhan recount the times when the red-bearded Messiah came to Taos. There is an exciting passage from Beirne Lay's *I Wanted Wings*, to give you some feeling of the times when the Southwest had a virtual monopoly on American military aviation.

But as it is not so long since the Southwest was the frontier, there are stories depicting those times: Duncan Aikman's *Belle Starr*, Owen P. White's picture of El Paso when it was young and hellish; Stuart Lake's biography of the greatest gunman of them all, Wyatt Earp. And since it was as difficult to reach the frontier as to exist there, you will find a fine story by Edwin Lanham of a pioneer family crossing the Red River on their way to Texas.

As the reader would have expected, even demanded, there is a chapter from Marquis James's brilliant biography of Sam Houston. Not only is there a story by O. Henry but a splendid account of his ranch experiences; a piece written not by himself but by Dora Neill Raymond and extracted from her *Captain Lee Hall of Texas*. There is an inspired chapter from John Steinbeck's great human document of the trials and migrations of the Okies. There is George Milburn to tell of the plain people who dream into mail-order catalogues and wear flour-sack drawers. Finally, there is Jim Phillips to see that we do not take our neighbors too much at face value; in short, that nobody gets away with anything.

So much for the subjects covered, for the background and influences which have acted upon the editor and the artists whose work is collected here. I hope that in reading them you will find as much pleasure as I have found.

GEORGE SESSIONS PERRY.

# CONTENTS

~~~~~~~~~~~~~~~~~~~~~~~~~~~~~~~~~~~~~~

# Biography

# Criticism

# ACKNOWLEDGMENTS

Grateful acknowledgment is made to the following publishers and authors for permission to reprint copyrighted material:

To Don Brown and *The Southwest Review* for "Ragged Individualist." Reprinted by permission.

To Paul Horgan and *The Saturday Review of Literature* for "So Little Freedom." Reprinted by permission.

To Harcourt, Brace and Company, for "Imogene Caraway," from *Oklahoma Town*, copyright, 1931, by George Milburn; and for "María Concepción," from *Flowering Judas and Other Stories*, copyright, 1935, by Katherine Anne Porter. Reprinted by permission.

To Doubleday, Doran & Company, Inc., for "The Pimienta Pancakes," from *Heart of the West*, by O. Henry, copyright, 1904, 1932, by Doubleday, Doran & Company, Inc. Reprinted by permission.

To Alfred A. Knopf, for "Early Marriage," from *Early Americana*, by Conrad Richter, copyright 1934, 1935, 1936 by The Curtis Publishing Company; and for a selection from *Lorenzo in Taos* by Mabel Dodge Luhan, copyright, 1932, by Alfred A. Knopf. Reprinted by permission.

To *The Southwest Review* for "Some Fast Chickens," by Archie Steagall. Reprinted by permission.

To Charles Scribner's Sons for "A Name and a Flag," from *Lone Star Preacher*, by John W. Thomason, copyright, 1938, 1939, 1940, by The Curtis Publishing Company; copyright, 1941, by John W. Thomason, Jr.

To Stanley Vestal and *The Southwest Review* for "Dakotah Courtship." Reprinted by permission.

To D. Appleton-Century Company, Inc., for "A Pair of Red-topped Boots," from *Dust of the Desert*, by Jack Weadock, copyright, 1936, by D. Appleton-Century Company, Inc. Reprinted by permission.

To Houghton Mifflin Company for a selection from *Quincie Bolliver*, by Mary King, copyright, 1941, by Mary King; selection from *Laughing Boy* by Oliver La Farge, copyright, 1929, by Oliver La Farge; for a selection from *Wyatt Earp, Frontier Marshal*, by Stuart N. Lake; copyright, 1931, by Stuart N. Lake; and for the preface from *The Texas Rangers* by Walter Prescott Webb, copyright, 1935, by Walter Prescott Webb. Reprinted by permission.

To Edwin Lanham for "The River of Blood," from *The Wind Blew West*, copyright, 1935, by Edwin Lanham. Reprinted by permission.

# Short Stories &

# EARLY MARRIAGE

*by* CONRAD RICHTER

Conrad Richter was born in Pennsylvania but has lived much of his life in New Mexico and the adjacent Southwest. In the 1920's, when he came, there were still alive a large number of old-timers who had lived through the early days before the railroad; and from his talks with many of these grew a fund of notes of early life out of which his stories came. Also, his own experience has given him an intimate understanding of life on the range. His books are: *Early Americana,* from which this story was taken; *The Sea of Grass,* a short novel of the Southwest; *The Trees,* a novel of the pioneer when the Northwest Territory was "the West"; *Tacey Cromwell,* a novel of the mining camps of Socorro and Bisbee; and *The Free Man,* a short novel of the days when the frontier was in Pennsylvania. As can be seen from the following story, Mr. Richter is a careful stylist and technician.

---

FOR TWO DAYS THE LEATHERY FACE OF ASA PUTMAN HAD been a document in cipher to anyone who could read the code. Since Saturday but one traveler had passed his solitary post, a speck of adobe and picket corrals lost on the vast, sandy stretch of the Santa Ana plain. Far as the eye could see from his doorway, the rutted El Paso trail, unfenced, gutterless, innocent of grading, gravel, culverts or telephone poles, imprinted only by iron tires, the hoofs of horses and oxen, sheep and cattle, and the paw of the loping lobo wolf, lay with dust unraised.

Ordinarily, there were freighters with cracking whips and trailers rumbling on behind. Army trains to and from the forts set up their tents for the night beyond the springs. The private coaches of Santa Fé and Colorado merchants, of cattle kings and Government officials, stopped long enough for the Putman children to admire the ladies, the magnificent woodwork and the luxurious cushions inside. Trail herds of gaunt red steers bawled for the water in the earthen tank, and pairs and companies of horsemen rode up and down.

But since Saturday not even a solitary buckboard from the far settlements in the Cedar country had called for supplies or letters. Only a girl from the Blue Mesa had ridden in for her and her neighbors' mail. She had eaten dinner with the Putmans, refused to stay overnight and started her long ride home.

A stranger from the East would have spoken about the stillness, the deadly waiting, and asked uneasily why Uncle Gideon hadn't come as promised. But in the Putman household it was not mentioned.

Asa deliberately busied himself about the post, filling the bin beneath the counter with navy beans and green coffee, leafing through the packet of letters in the drawer and making a long rite out of feeding the occupants of the picket corrals—four horses of which were fresh for the next stage.

Rife, just turned fifteen, carried water and gathered cow chips in an old hide dragged by a rope to his saddle horn. Ignacita, the Mexican housekeeper, spat sharply on her heavy irons in the torrid kitchen and kept glancing over her shoulder and out of the open door and windows.

And Nancy Belle, going on seventeen, packed and repacked the high, ironbound trunk that her father had bought for her at Santa Fé and sang softly to herself in the way that women sang fifty and sixty years ago.

Saturday she was being married at Gunstock, two hundred miles away—five days' journey in a wagon, four in a saddle or buckboard.

For six months she had thought of little else. The almanac fell apart at June as naturally as her mother's Bible did at the Twenty-third Psalm. So often had she run her finger down the page that anyone might tell from the worn line of type the very day she and Stephen Dewee would be man and wife. The Dewees lived four hundred miles west across the territory in the Beaverhead country. She and Stephen were taking a mountain ranch near his people, and the wedding had been compromised at Gunstock, nearly equidistant to both families and convenient to friends scattered up and down the Rio Grande.

She had lighted a candle in the dusk, when a figure appeared reluctantly in her doorway. Asa Putman had never been at ease in his daughter's bedroom. A tall, rawhide man in an unbuttoned, sagging vest, any furnishings that suggested refinement visibly embarrassed him. Invariably he kept his hat on in the house. He had it on now, a flat top and a flat brim, not so much like the Western hats you see now. Nancy Belle knew that her mother's people had never forgiven him for bringing his young wife and their two small children to this lonely post, at the mercy of outlaws and the worse Apaches.

Tonight she could see that something bothered him. He gave her a sidewise glance, so sharp and characteristic.

"I don't expect, Nancy Belle, you could put off your weddin'?"

The girl stood quietly gazing at him with a face like the tintype of her mother. But under her sedate gray dress, with tight waist and full skirts to the instep, she had frozen. She looked much older than her years. Her air of gentlefolk and her wide-apart gray eyes came from her mother. But the chin, tipped up with resolute fearlessness, was her father's.

"No, papa!" Her two clear words held all the steady insistence of the desert.

"I figured how you'd feel," he nodded, avoiding her eyes. "I just wanted to put it up to you. I'd 'a' covered the *jornada* on foot to be on time at my own weddin', but I didn't have to count on Gideon to hold me up."

"Are you telling me, papa, that you can't go to Gunstock tomorrow?" Her voice remained quiet, but a coldness had seized her. Of all the people she had visualized at her wedding, the one next to Stephen she could least spare was the tall, grave figure of her father.

"I reckon I kind of can't, Nancy Belle," he said soberly. "Rife could tend to the stage all right and do the feedin'. But they's men come to this post no boy can handle." He shifted his position. "I figured once on closin' up the post till I got back. But the stage is comin' and the mail. And the freighters count on me for feed and grub. Then I got to protect my own property and the mail and freight for the Cedar Country that's in the storage room."

"I know," Nancy Belle said steadily. "I can get to Gunstock all right."

Far back in her father's assaying eyes, she fancied she saw a glint of pride.

"You're pretty nigh a woman now, Nancy Belle. And Rife's a good slice of a man. It's a straight trail to the Rio Grande, once you turn at the old post. Both you and Rife's been over it before. Of course, I'd like to be at the weddin', but the boy can tell me about it." He went to the window. "Rife!" he called.

Nancy Belle's brother came in presently. A slight boy, with his father's blue eyes, he seldom made a fuss over anything, even when he shot a stray duck on the tank or when they braked down the last cedar hill into Santa Fé with all the open doors of the plaza shops in sight. And when his father told him now, he showed neither enthusiasm nor regret—merely straightened.

"Sure. I can take you, Nancy Belle," he said.

Something pulled under his sister's tight basque. She remembered the long miles they would have in the wagon, the camps at lonely places, the ugly shadow ever hovering over the outposts of this frontier country and the blight that, since Saturday, seemed to have fallen on the trail. Her eyes swam. Now, at the last minute, she yielded.

"If you'll let me ride, papa, I'll wait another day for Uncle Gideon," she promised.

Her father's eyes moved to the ruffled red calico curtains at the shadeless windows.

"I don't hardly count on Gideon comin' any more, Nancy Belle. Besides, it's too long in the saddle to Gunstock—especially for a girl to get married. You'd be plumb wore out, and you wouldn't have your trunk. You couldn't get dressed for your weddin'."

He turned thoughtfully and went out, Rife close behind. Nancy Belle could hear her father's tones, slow and grave, coming from near one of the picket corrals.

It was too far to catch the words; but when they came in, she saw that her brother's features looked a little pale under the tan.

"You better get some sleep, Nancy Belle," her father said. "You and Rife are startin' before daylight. If Gideon comes, I'll ride after."

They had scarcely gone from the room when Ignacita came in from the kitchen, her black eyes glittering over a pile of freshly starched white in her arms.

"Nancy Belle, *chinita!*" she whispered, plucking at the girl's sleeve. "You don't say to your *papacito* I talk to you! I have promise I don't scare you. But I can't see you go so far in the wildness alone, *pobrecita!* Sometimes people go safe from one place to the other, oh, *si!* But sometimes, *chinita*, they don't come back! You have not the oldness like Ignacita. Ay, I tell you these old eyes have seen men and women quartered from a tree like sheep or maybe tied over a stove like I don't have the words to say to you."

Nancy Belle did not answer except to lay, one by one, the ironed pieces in her trunk—a bride's muslin underwear trimmed with red-and-blue feather stitching; long petticoats stiffly flounced with ruffles, and nightgowns long in the sleeve and high in the neck, with ruffles at wrist and throat. The Mexican woman went on hoarsely. The girl folded away her winter's cashmere dress, buttoned up the front and with a white fichu. She unwrapped and wrapped again in crumpled white tissue the red slippers the old gentleman on the stage had sent her as a wedding present from Philadelphia.

When Ignacita had left, she opened her keepsake box covered with colored shells. The mirror on the inside lid turned back a face as calm as the little golden clouds that hung of an evening over the east to catch the desert sunset. But after she had undressed and put on her nightdress, for a long time she was aware of the soft pound of her heart faintly swaying the bed on its rawhide springs.

At the first sound of Ignacita's hand on the kitchen stove, Nancy Belle sprang out of bed. She dressed on the brown pool of burro skin, the only carpet on her adobe floor. Through the west window she could see the morning star burning like a brilliant candle. It hung, she told herself, over Gunstock and the Beaverhead, where Stephen, at this moment, in their new log ranch house, lay thinking about her.

They ate in the kitchen by lamplight. She had never been so conscious of every detail—the great white cups and saucers, the familiar steel knives, the homy smell of the scorched paper lamp shade, the unreadable eyes of her father, Rife and Ignacita.

Asa Putman himself carried out the trunk. There was already hay in the wagon, a gunny sack of oats, food in a canned-tomato box and utensils in another, a water keg, bed roll tied in a wagon sheet, an ax, a bridle and her own sidesaddle made to order over a man's tree. Her eyes caught the gleam of a rifle leaning up against the seat in the lantern light. Tethered to the rear of the wagon stood her saddle mare, Fancy, with pricked ears. She was going along to their new ranch home. Nancy Belle felt that she was still among intimate things, but outside the little circle of light lay darkness and the unknown.

When she said good-by to her father he kissed her—something he had not done for years.

"You haven't changed your mind, Nancy Belle?" he asked.

She climbed quickly up over the wheel to the spring seat of the wagon before he might see that she was crying. Rife swung up like a monkey on the other side and pushed the rifle into the crevice behind the seat cushion. The lines tautened and the wagon lurched.

"*Dios* go with you safe to your husband, Nancy Belle!" she heard Ignacita cry after her.

The morning star had set. They moved into a world of silent blackness. Nancy Belle could not see how the horses remained on the trail. When she looked back, the only light in all these square miles of black, unfriendly earth was the yellow window of her father's post.

It was almost a vision, golden and far away, like all beautiful things. She didn't trust herself to look again.

Two hours later the wagon was a lonely speck of boat rocking in an illimitable sage-green sea beneath the sun. The canvas wagon sheet fastened over the bows was a kind of sail, and eastward the sandy water did not stop rolling till it washed up at the foot of the faintly blue ramparts of the distant Espiritu Range.

Just before they turned west on the cross trail to the Rio Grande, a heavy wagon with a yoke of oxen in front and a cow behind toiled around the crumbling adobe walls of the old, abandoned post house. A bearded man and a thin woman with a white face sat on the seat. She held a baby in her arms, and three black-eyed children peered from under the wagon sheet.

The bearded man saluted and stopped his willing team. Rife did likewise. The woman spoke first. Her tongue was swift and slightly acid.

"You better turn around and follow us if you want to save your hair!" she called. "Yesterday a sheep herder told us he saw—"

A sharp word from the bearded man caused her to relapse into sullen silence. He asked Rife where he might be going, then climbed down to the trail and said he wanted to talk to him a little. The boy followed reluctantly behind his wagon. Nancy Belle could hear the bearded man's tones coming slow and grave like her father's, while the woman made silent and horribly expressive lip language.

Rife came back, walking stiffly. The bearded man climbed up beside the woman.

"They got to go on," he told her in a low tone, then saluted with his whip. "Good luck, boy! And you, miss!"

Rife raised his whip in stiff acknowledgment. The wagons creaked apart. Nancy Belle saw in front of her the trail to the Rio Grande, little more than a pair of wheel tracks, that lost itself on the lonely plain. Rife seemed relieved that she did not ask what the bearded man had said. But it was enough for her not to be able to forget the woman's fearful signs and mouthings and the still horror in the curious eyes of the staring children.

Sister and brother talked very little. Nancy Belle saw her brother's eyes keep sweeping the country, scanning the horizons. Bunches of bear grass that might have been feathers pinioned his blue gaze, and clumps of cane cactus that seemed to hold pointing gun barrels. At arroyos thick with chamiso and Apache plume she could see his feet tighten on the footboard. Once he pulled out the rifle, but it was only a herd of antelopes moving across the desert page.

They camped for the night when the sun was still high. Nancy Belle asked no questions as the boy drove far off the trail into a grassy *cañada*. She sang softly to herself as she fried the salt side bacon and put the black coffeepot to boil.

Rife hobbled Anton Chico and the Bar X horse and staked out Fancy close to the wagon.

She pretended not to notice when, before dark, he poured earth on the fire till not a spark or wisp of smoke remained. Out of one eye she watched him climb the side of the *cañada* and stand long minutes sweeping the country from the ridge, a slight, tense figure against the sullen glow of the sunset.

"It's all right," he said when he came down. "You can go to bed."

"What's all right?" she asked him.

"The horses," he said, turning away, and Nancy Belle felt a stab of pain that so soon this boy must bear a man's responsibilities and tell a man's lies.

She prayed silently on her blankets spread on the hay in the wagon box, and lay down with her head on the side saddle, her unread Testament in her hand. She heard Rife unroll his camp bed on the ground beneath the wagon. It was all very strange and hushed without her father. Just to feel the Testament in her hand helped to calm her and to remember the day at the post when she had first met Stephen.

Her father had never let her come in contact with the men

of the trail. Always, at the first sign of dust cloud on the horizon, he would tell both children to heap up the chip box, fill the water buckets and carry saddles and bridles into the house. But this day Asa Putman and Rife had gone to Fort Sumner. And to Nancy Bell, Uncle Gideon could seldom say no.

It had been a very hot day. She had been sitting in the shade of the earthen bank of the tank, moving her bare feet in the cool water, watching the ripples in the hot south wind. The leaves of the cottonwoods clashed overhead, and she heard nothing until she looked up, and there was a young man on a blue-gray horse with dust clinging to his hat brim and mustache. His eyes were direct as an eagle's. Firm lines modeled his lean face. But what she noticed most at the time was the little bow tie on his dark shirt.

Instantly she had tucked her bare, wet legs under her red dress. Her face burned with shame, but the young stranger talked to her about her father coolly, as if she, a girl of fifteen, had not been caught barefooted. Then he did what in her mind was a noble thing. When Uncle Gideon came out, he magnificently turned his back for her to run into the house and pull on shoes and stockings.

She thought of Stephen constantly next day and the next. She had grown a little used to the journey without her father now—the still, uncertain nights under the wagon sheet, sitting, lying, listening, waiting; the less uncertain days with the sun on the endless spaces; her never-quiet perch on the high spring seat under the slanted bow; the bumps, creaks and lumberings of the wagon; the sand sifting softly over the red, turning wheels; all afternoon the sun in their faces; ahead the far haze and heat waves in which were still lost Gunstock and the Rio Grande. Almost she had forgotten the bearded man with the oxen and the curious, detached horror in the eyes of his children.

Since morning of the third day their progress had been slower. The trail seemed level, except for the heavy breathing of the horses. But when Nancy Belle glanced back she could see the steady grade they had been climbing. Abruptly, in mid-afternoon, she found that the long, blue Espiritu Range had disappeared, vanished behind a high pine-clad hill which was its southernmost beginning. It was like the lizard that swallowed itself, a very real lizard. At this moment they were climbing over the lizard's tail.

"Cedars!" Rife said briefly, pointing with the whip to dark sprawling growths ahead.

"You breathe deep up here!" Nancy Belle drank in the light air.

Rife took a sniff, but his blue eyes never ceased to scan the high, black-thatched hill under whose frowning cliff they must pass.

"Soon we can see the Gunstock Mountains," Nancy Belle said.

"And Martin Cross' cabin," Rife nodded. "It's the last water to the Rio Grande."

"He's a nice old man," Nancy Belle ventured casually. "It would be nice to camp by his cabin tonight and talk."

The boy inclined his head. After a few moments he started to whistle softly. At the first cedar, Nancy Belle leaped off the moving wagon and climbed back with an evergreen branch. The twig, crushed in her hand, smelled like some store in Santa Fé.

They gained the summit. A breeze was sweeping here from the southwest, and the horses freshened. But Rife had suddenly stopped whistling and Nancy Belle's sprig of cedar lay on her lap. The frowning cliff of the pine-clad hill was still there. But Martin Cross' cabin had turned to a desolate mound of ashes. As they stared, a gust of wind sent wisps of smoke scurrying from the mound, and a red eye opened to watch them from the embers. Nancy Belle felt an uncontrollable twitching in the hair roots at the base of her scalp.

Where Martin Cross' eastbound wheel tracks met the trail, Rife reluctantly halted the horses and wet his air-dried lips.

"The water keg's dry, and the horses. If papa was here, he'd drive over."

· 12 ·

"I'm the oldest." Nancy Belle found her voice steady. "I'll ride over. There might be something we can do."

The boy rose quickly. His eyes seemed to remember something his father had said.

"You can drive the wagon over if I wave."

He had thrown her the lines and slipped back through the canvas-covered tunnel of wagon box, picking up Fancy's bridle and the rifle. Barebacked he rode toward the smoldering ashes at the foot of that frowning hill. The chestnut mare's tail and mane streamed like something gold in the wind.

When she looked back to the trail, her eyes were pinioned by a light object in the wheel track ahead of the Bar X horse. It was a long gray feather. Instantly she told herself that it had come from some wild turkey Martin Cross had shot, and yet never had air anywhere become so suddenly horrible and choking as in this canyon.

Rife did not signal her to drive over. She saw him come riding back at full speed. The mare was snorting. As he stopped her at the wagon, her chestnut head kept turning back toward what had once been a cabin. Rife slipped the lead rope about her neck and climbed into the seat with the rifle in his hands.

"The water—you wouldn't want it!" he said thickly. His cheeks, she noticed, were the color of *yeso*.

"Rife"—Nancy Belle touched his arm when she had driven down the canyon—"what did you see at the cabin?"

The boy sat deaf and rigid beside her, eyes staring straight ahead. She saw that his young hands were still tortured around the barrel of his rifle.

Far down on the pitch-dark mesa she stopped the horses in the trail and listened. There were no stars, not a sound but the flapping of the wagon sheet in the wind and the clank of coffeepot and water bucket under the wagon. Half standing on the footboard, she guided the team off the trail in the intense blackness. Her swift hands helped the trembling boy stake out the mare and hobble the team. They did not light a lantern. Rife declined to eat. Nancy Belle chewed a few dry mouthfuls.

The wind came drawing out of the blackness with a great draft. It hissed through the grass, sucked and tore at the wagon sheet and whistled through the spokes and brake rigging. Rife did not take his bed roll under the wagon tonight. He drew the ends of the wagon sheet together and lay down in the wagon box near his sister. For a long time they were silent. When she heard his heavy breathing, she lifted the rifle from his chest.

The storm grew. Sand began pelting against the canvas and sifted into the wagon box. An invisible cloud of choking dust found its way into eyes, mouth, ears and lungs. Nancy Belle laid down the rifle a moment to pull a blanket over the face of the boy. He tossed and muttered pitifully, but he slept on.

Magically the rain, when it came, stopped the sand and dust. The girl drank in the clean-washed air. At daylight she slipped out to the ground. The mesa, stretching away in the early light, touched here and there with feathers of mist, would have been beautiful except for a sharp new loneliness. The horses were gone!

At her exclamation, Rife appeared from the wagon box. His shame at having slept through the night was quickly over-shadowed by their misfortune.

Together they found where Fancy's stake had been pulled out and dragged. Yards farther on they could tell by Anton Chico's tracks that his hobbles had parted.

Nancy Belle made her brother come back to the wagon and stuff his pockets with cold biscuits and antelope jerky. She said she would have a hot breakfast until he returned. The horses, perhaps, were just down in some draw where they had drifted with the wind.

When he had gone with the rifle, she filled the coffeepot from a clearing water hole in the nearest arroyo. She fried potatoes and onions in the long-handled skillet. And when he did not come, she set fresh biscuits in the Dutch oven. Each biscuit held a square of salt side bacon in its top, and as it baked the fat oozed down and incased it in a kind of glazed tastiness.

At noon she thought she heard a shot. Nowhere could she see

him on the endless sweep of mesa. By late afternoon she was still alone. She read her Testament and wondered how many women over the world had read it in hours like this. Sitting in the shadow of the wagon, facing the direction he had gone, she looked up every few minutes. But all her eyes could find were cloud shadows racing across the lonely face of the mesa. All she could hear were the desolate cries from the unseen lark sparrows.

Darkness, stillness settled down on the empty land. She climbed back into the wagon and sat on the chuck box, hands rigid on her knees. Again and again she convinced herself that the horses could not have been driven off or she would have seen the drivers' tracks. When wild, sharp barks shattered the stillness and set wires jerking in her limbs, she talked to herself steadily, but a little meaninglessly, of the post—on and on as the darkness was filled with the ringing and counter-ringing of shrill, cracked yappings—not long tones like a dog's, but incredibly short syllables rising, rising in a mad eternal scale and discord.

"I wish papa had given me two of the chairs," she repeated. "Mamma said they were post oak from Texas. She said they had got white from scrubbing. I liked the laced rawhide seats with the hair left on. It made them soft to sit on. The seats in the parlor were black. And the ones in the kitchen were red. But I liked the brockle one in my room best."

The insane din around the wagon had become terrific. There were only two or three of the animals, Nancy Belle guessed, but they threw their voices and echoes together to make a score.

"When I was little I liked to go in the storage room," her voice went on, scarcely intelligible to her own ears. "It was dark and cool, and smelled of burlap and kerosene and whisky and sweetish with brown sugar. I can see the fat sacks of green coffee. And the round tins of kerosene had boards on the side. The flour sacks were printed Rough and Ready in red letters. Mamma once used to make our underwear out of the sacking. I can smell the salt side bacon in the gunny sacks."

She could tell from the sounds that one of the animals was

running insanely back and forth near the wagon tongue. She had never noticed before that they yelped both when breathing in and out. Suddenly came silence. It warned her. Instinctively she felt for the ax.

"Nancy Belle!" a boy's far, anxious voice called from the darkness.

She hallooed and leaned out over the tailboard. Three shadowy forms were coming across the mesa in the starlight. Never had horses looked so good.

"Were you scared?" Rife greeted. "Anything bother you?"

"Nothing," Nancy Belle said. "Just coyotes."

"I had to give Fancy her head after it got dark." He slid wearily to the ground. "She brought us straight back to the wagon."

Nancy Belle had wanted to put her arms around her brother. Now she hugged the mare instead. Rife ate fresh biscuits and a tin plate piled with cold potatoes. He drank several tin cups of coffee. Nancy Belle had slipped the oats-laden gunny-sack *morrals* over the horses' heads.

"I had to walk halfway to the mountain," Rife said.

"Just help hitch up; then you can sleep all night," she promised.

It rained again heavily toward midnight. Flashes of lightning lit the drenched plain. For minutes at a time, quivering fingers of blue phosphorescence stood on the ears of the toiling horses. At dawn Nancy Belle still held the reins as the mud-splashed wagon crawled through a world bathed in early purple splendor.

Four days they had been crossing a hundred and seventy miles of desolate plain. Now the end waited in sight. To the west lay a land broken and tumbled by a mighty hand. Hill shouldered hill and range peered over range, all indescribably violet except where peaks tipped by the unseen sun were far-off flaming towers of copper.

It was a new land, her promised land, Stephen's land, Nancy Belle told herself, where nobody burned cow chips, but snapping cedar and pine, where cold water ran in the wooded canyons and the eye, weary of one flat circle the horizon round, had endless geometric designs to refresh the retina.

She sang softly as the wagon lumbered to the edge of a long, shallow valley, brown and uninhabited, running north and south, and desolate except for a winding ribbon that was white with sky and narrowly bordered with green.

"Rife!" Nancy Belle cried. "The Rio Grande!"

An hour afterward they pulled out of the sun into the shade of the long cottonwood *bosque*. Nancy Belle wasn't singing now. Where she remembered wide sand bars glistening with sky and tracked by water fowl, a chocolate-red flood rolled. Where had been the island, tops of tule and scrub willow swung to and fro with the current.

Anton Chico and the Bar X horse stopped of their own accord in the trail, ears pricked forward at the swirling brown wash. While Rife turned the three horses loose to graze, Nancy Belle silently fried bacon and made coffee. When she had washed skillet and tin dishes in the river, the boy had wired the wagon box to the brake rigging. Now he was tying securely one end of his rope to the center of the coupling pole under the wagon. The other end she knew he would fasten to the inadequate upper horn of the sidesaddle.

"I wouldn't mind the river if I just had my own saddle," he mourned.

They hitched up the team silently. Rife cinched the side-saddle on Fancy and straddled it, the single stirrup useless to a man. Nancy Belle climbed into the wagon and picked up the lines. The other bank looked as far away as the Espiritu Range from the post. She wanted to say something to her brother— some last word, in case they didn't make it. But all she did was cluck her tongue to the horses.

Gingerly, one slow foot at a time, the team moved down the trail into the water.

"Give 'em their heads!" Rife called from the right rear.

Nancy Belle held a rein in each hand. The red channel water came to the wagon tongue, covered it, reached the horses' bellies.

The team wanted to stop. Nancy Belle swung her whip, a stick tipped with a long rawhide lash. The wagon went on. The collars of both horses kept dipping, but never entirely out of sight. Still barely wading, the slow team reached the firmer footing of the island.

Two-thirds of the river still rolled in front of the wagon. The west bank did not seem to have grown much closer, but the east bank behind them had moved far away. The team had to be whipped into the violent current. The water churned white through the wagon wheels. Suddenly both horses appeared to stumble and drop out of sight. Their heads came up wildly, spray blowing from their nostrils. The muddy water hid their legs, but by their bobbing motions Nancy Belle knew that they were swimming.

"Keep 'em pointed up the river!" Rife shouted.

Already she felt the wagon floating. It swung downstream with the current; then Rife's rope from Fancy's saddle snubbed it. The team was snorting with every breath. The Bar X horse swam high in the water, his withers and part of his back out of the chocolate current. But all she could see of Anton Chico were his nose and ears.

Down between her ankles she saw water in the wagon box. She thought of the hemstitched sheets at the botton of her trunk, the towels and pillow cases crocheted with shell lace. Her blue-velvet corduroy dress was probably wet already, and all the cunning print aprons with dust caps to match. River water couldn't hurt the little yellow creamer, sugar bowl and covered butter dish that had been her mother's. And the gingham dresses could be washed. What worried her were her wedding dress and the keepsake box, especially the tintypes, one of which was Rife in a child's suit edged with black braid, his brand-new hat on his knee.

An older Rife was shouting something behind her now. She couldn't catch the words. Then she found what it was. The neck and withers of Anton Chico raised suddenly out of the water and both horses were scrambling up the steep bank below the

· 18 ·

ford. Only quick work with the lines saved the wagon from turning over. Safe and blowing on the high bank, the dripping horses shook themselves like puppies.

Nancy Belle couldn't go on until she had opened the trunk and appraised the damage. Rife unsaddled Fancy and drove on with the refreshed team. Behind his light back in the wagon box, the girl changed to her blue-velvet corduroy, which was hardly wet at all. Then she combed her hair and rolled into a cranny of her trunk the old felt hat that had been too large for her father.

A half-dozen riders met the wagon some miles down the Gunstock Canyon. All of them, Nancy Belle noticed, carried guns. Stephen wore a new white shirt and a gray hat with curled brim she had not seen before. He stood in his stirrups, and swung her down in front of him on the saddle, where he kissed her. She had never felt his lips press into such a straight line.

"Papa couldn't come," she said. "So Rife brought me."

She felt Stephen's rigid arm around her.

"We just got in from the Beaverhead ourselves."

"He means they never get any news out in the Beaverhead or he'd 'a' come further east to meet you!" Uncle Billy Williams put in. He had a lovable, squeaky voice. "The Apaches been breakin' loose again. Funny you didn't hear anything over in your country."

Nancy Belle gave him an inscrutable look with her gray eyes. Uncle Billy pulled out his bandanna and blew his nose.

"They got my old friend, Judge Hower, and his wife and kid in a buggy on the Upper Espiritu. The man that found what they did to 'em, they say, cried like a baby."

"That's all right, Uncle Billy," Stephen said in a gentle voice.

Nancy Belle glanced at Rife. Her brother's face looked gray and the eyes staring as when he had ridden in the late afternoon sunlight from the smoking ashes of Martin Cross' cabin.

Nearly fifty people, gathered in the big parlor upstairs at the hotel, greeted Nancy Belle. An old man whose young black eyes twinkled out of a bearded face said he was glad to see that she had her "hair on straight." Rife stopped with the trunk before driving to the livery, and Stephen's mother showed Nancy Belle to a room to dress.

The guests stopped talking when she came into the parlor in her white wedding dress. Her basque came to a point in the front and back. It fitted like a glove. The silk underskirt came to her instep and the ruffled overskirt to her knees. She had parted her hair from side to side and brushed the bangs down on her forehead. She felt very light-headed. The wagon still seemed to be jerking under her.

She glimpsed Rife gazing at her, a rapt expression in his reticent blue eyes. She was glad to see that he had brushed his hair. The brass swinging lamp had been lighted and the dark woodwork of the parlor festooned with evergreen branches. White streamers from the wall met in a papier-mâché bell in one corner. She noticed two children peering eagerly from the dark hall.

Stephen came to her, very straight in a long coat and stand-up collar with a black tie. He led her up beneath the papier-mâché bell. In a sibilant, churchlike whisper, the Gunstock preacher made sure of her full name. Then he coughed and began the ceremony. He had a deep voice, but Nancy Belle didn't hear all of the service. Her mind kept going back to a tall, grave man in a lonely adobe post on the wide Santa Ana plain. And after she had said "I do," her lips moved, but she was not praying for Stephen, her husband.

# IMOGENE CARAWAY

*by* GEORGE MILBURN

George Milburn, an Oklahoman, is the author of *Catalogue* and numerous excellent short stories. He was a remarkably constant contributor (a story a month for many months on end) to the *American Mercury*, in those lively times when the Sage of Baltimore, H. L. Mencken, was its editor. Mr. Milburn is a highly satisfying writer both in the realms of realism and of farce. An example of Mr. Milburn's powers as a realist may be seen in such stories as "Heel, Toe, and a One, Two, Three, Four." Yet there are spots in his novel, *Catalogue*, which are apt to set a person of normal risibilities laughing so violently as to strain his viscera dangerously near to the bursting point. For that matter, the simple, straightforward little story of Imogene Caraway is one that has always, in memory, afforded the editor much fun.

---

OLD MAN FARNUM, WHO RAN THE IRON CLAD STORE, HAD been having a lot of complaints about a brand of flour he was handling. The farmer's wives said that it wasn't any good for light bread and that it wasn't any good for biscuits, and that about the only thing they could use it for was to make flour gravy. Old Man Farnum guaranteed his flour, and he had had so many half-used sacks of the Bar-None brand brought back to him that he was about to stop handling it.

One day he said to Gabe Caraway, "Gabe, I see you always call for Bar-None flour. I've been having a lot of complaint about that flour, but you-all seem to like it. I guess your woman must get good results with it?"

"Well, to tell you the truth, Mr. Farnum, I ain't noticed. We use it for sody biscuits and I cain't notice no difference. But my woman likes Bar-None because it comes in such good sacks. They use a good grade of cloth in them Bar-None sacks. My woman has

· 21 ·

made a sight of garments out of them sacks, and they wear better than any cloth we could buy by the yard."

"We ought not to have no trouble making a deal then, Gabe. I've got a lot of Bar-None sacks on my hands. The most of them is about half-used and opened, but they ain't nothing wrong with them. I'll make that flour to you at half price. That would give your woman more sacks to rip up and sew than she would get by buying full sacks."

Gabe bought eight half-filled sacks of Bar-None flour from Old Man Farnum.

The day he bought the flour was a Saturday and that same night his oldest girl, Imogene, got religion at the Baptist revival. The revival was the first that the Baptists had had since they moved into their new church, and it hadn't been very successful until Imogene got saved. It was being conducted by an evangelist named Foster, a young man who had got the call to preach in Omaha, Nebraska, the year before. The Reverend Foster's meeting had been dragging along for two weeks and the Baptists were beginning to get dissatisfied with him. Up until then he had saved only three souls, and the Baptists had all that big debt for their new church hanging over them.

The Reverend Foster had preached a very strong sermon that Saturday night and the choir was singing *Why Not Now?* and the young evangelist was down in the aisle with his arms stretched out, pleading, "Won't you come? Won't you come? Jesus is calling you. Tomorrow may be too late. Are you going to spurn Christ Jesus?"

All of a sudden the Caraway girl let out a shriek in the back of the church and came running down the aisle. She got down and clasped the Reverend Foster's knees and commenced to weep and babble all the sins she had ever commited. The Reverend Foster prayed with her, but she was too excited to talk plainly and there were so few people there, not many got to hear what she was saying. So the Reverend Foster said that if she wanted to be washed whiter than snow she must signify that she was ready for Jesus by confessing her sins before the whole community.

The next night the Baptist Church was so crowded you couldn't get a seat and people were standing up out in the vestibule, craning and trying to get a sight of Imogene Caraway. The congregation sang a few hymns, and the Reverend Sweasy, the resident Baptist minister, prayed and read from the Scriptures. Then the Reverend Foster got up and read his text from Luke, "And behold a woman in the city which was a sinner . . . ," and he said that before he began his sermon there was a young woman in the church, come like another Mary Magdalene to bare herself before her saviour. He made a sign and Imogene stood up.

She was weeping, but she talked in a loud voice. She told about the times she had sinned with men. She told about the time she had played hookey from high school and driven down to Muskogee with Kaye Chalmers, and how they had put up at a hotel for the afternoon. After she sat down the Reverend Foster preached and twenty souls were saved that night.

The Baptist revival turned out to be successful after all. Two weeks later they had their baptizing in Chalmers' cotton-gin pond. The Reverend Foster preached on the bank. The subject of his sermon was "The Sheep and the Goats."

"Baptism by water signifies that a person is ready to give up his or her old life of sin," he said, "but there must be a baptism of the spirit, too. Don't think you can just let this old muddy water here wash your sins away. You got to be pure in heart, too. Don't try to hold nothing back on God. God taketh all the sheep into the fold, but if you're still a goat, don't you think you're going to slip by, 'cause you ain't! God has his brand on all you old goats, don't think he ain't! It's all written right here in the Grand Old Book. If you're still a goat just making out like you're a sheep it won't do you no good. 'Cause before God's All-Seeing Eye you're still a goat and your brand is writ in words of fire."

The Reverend Foster waded his way into the pond, feeling the depth with a staff. The Reverend Sweasy marshaled the converts. Imogene Caraway was first in line.

"In the name of the Father, the Son, and the Holy Ghost!" said the Reverend Foster, plunging her under.

She came to the bank and stood there alone, weeping and shivering.

"Oh, Lord God my witness, looky there!" shrieked Mrs. Sweasy, the preacher's wife. "It's the mark of the goat!"

The water had pasted Imogene's white voile dress against her flanks. The wet cloth was transparent against her flour-sack underskirt. Across her broad buttocks in large red letters had appeared the brand, Bar-None.

# MARÍA CONCEPCION

*by* KATHERINE ANNE PORTER

Katherine Anne Porter was reared near San Antonio, Texas. Some of her most effective stories are set in the Southwest, but her art rises above the limitations of any specific region. Incredible as it may seem (in view of the masterful simplicity with which it is written), "María Concepción" was Miss Porter's first published short story. Though Miss Porter is celebrated as a stylist, the very absence of any invidious stylism is one of the most striking qualities in her work. No list of the greatest American story writers would be complete without her name.

---

MARÍA CONCEPCIÓN WALKED CAREFULLY, KEEPING TO the middle of the white dusty road, where the maguey thorns and the treacherous curved spines of organ cactus had not gathered so profusely. She would have enjoyed resting for a moment in the dark shade by the roadside, but she had no time to waste drawing cactus needles from her feet. Juan and his chief would be waiting for their food in the damp trenches of the buried city.

She carried about a dozen living fowls slung over her right shoulder, their feet fastened together. Half of them fell upon the flat of her back, the balance dangled uneasily over her breast. They wriggled their benumbed and swollen legs against her neck, they twisted their stupefied eyes and peered into her face inquiringly. She did not see them or think of them. Her left arm was tired with the weight of the food basket, and she was hungry after her long morning's work.

Her straight back outlined itself strongly under her clean bright-blue cotton rebozo. Instinctive serenity softened her black eyes, shaped like almonds, set far apart, and tilted a bit endwise. She walked with the free, natural, guarded ease of the primitive woman carrying an unborn child. The shape of her body was easy, the swelling life was not a distortion, but the right inevitable proportions of a woman. She was entirely contented. Her husband was at work and she was on her way to market to sell her fowls.

Her small house sat half-way up a shallow hill, under a clump of pepper-trees, a wall of organ cactus enclosing it on the side nearest to the road. Now she came down into the valley, divided by the narrow spring, and crossed a bridge of loose stones near the hut where María Rosa the beekeeper lived with her old grandmother, Lupe the medicine woman. María Concepción had no faith in the charred owl bones, the singed rabbit fur, the cat entrails, the messes and ointments sold by Lupe to the ailing of the village. She was a good Christian, and drank simple herb teas for headache and stomachache, or bought her remedies bottled, with printed directions that she could not read, at the drugstore near the city market, where she went almost daily. But she often bought a jar of honey from young María Rosa, a pretty, shy child only fifteen years old.

María Concepción and her husband, Juan Villegas, were each a little past their eighteenth year. She had a good reputation with the neighbors as an energetic religious woman who could drive a bargain to the end. It was commonly known that if she wished to buy a new rebozo for herself or a shirt for Juan, she could bring out a sack of hard silver coins for the purpose.

She had paid for the license, nearly a year ago, the potent bit of stamped paper which permits people to be married in the church. She had given money to the priest before she and Juan walked together up to the altar the Monday after Holy Week. It had been the adventure of the villagers to go, three Sundays one after another, to hear the banns called by the priest for Juan de Dios Villegas and María Concepción Manríquez, who were actually getting married in the church, instead of behind it, which was the usual custom, less expensive, and as binding as any other ceremony. But María Concepción was always as proud as if she owned a hacienda.

She paused on the bridge and dabbled her feet in the water, her eyes resting themselves from the sun-rays in a fixed gaze to the far-off mountains, deeply blue under their hanging drift of clouds. It came to her that she would like a fresh crust of honey. The delicious aroma of bees, their slow thrilling hum, awakened a pleasant desire for a flake of sweetness in her mouth.

"If I do not eat it now, I shall mark my child," she thought, peering through the crevices in the thick hedge of cactus that sheered up nakedly, like bared knife blades set protectingly around the small clearing. The place was so silent she doubted if María Rosa and Lupe were at home.

The leaning jacal of dried rush-withes and corn sheaves, bound to tall saplings thrust into the earth, roofed with yellowed maguey leaves flattened and overlapping like shingles, hunched drowsy and fragrant in the warmth of noonday. The hives, similarly made, were scattered towards the back of the clearing, like small mounds of clean vegetable refuse. Over each mound there hung a dusty golden shimmer of bees.

A light gay scream of laughter rose from behind the hut; a man's short laugh joined in. "Ah, hahahaha!" went the voices together high and low, like a song.

"So María Rosa has a man!" María Concepción stopped short smiling, shifted her burden slightly, and bent forward shading her eyes to see more clearly through the spaces of the hedge.

María Rosa ran, dodging between beehives, parting two stunted jasmine bushes as she came, lifting her knees in swift leaps, looking over her shoulder and laughing in a quivering, excited way. A heavy jar, swung to her wrist by the handle, knocked against her thighs as she ran. Her toes pushed up sudden spurts of dust, her half-raveled braids showered around her shoulders in long crinkled wisps.

Juan Villegas ran after her, also laughing strangely, his teeth set, both rows gleaming behind the small soft black beard growing sparsely on his lips, his chin, leaving his brown cheeks girl-smooth. When he seized her, he clenched so hard her chemise gave way and ripped from her shoulder. She stopped laughing at this, pushed him away and stood silent, trying to pull up the torn sleeve with one hand. Her pointed chin and dark red mouth moved in an uncertain way, as if she wished to laugh again; her long black lashes flickered with the quick-moving lights in her hidden eyes.

María Concepción did not stir nor breathe for some seconds. Her forehead was cold, and yet boiling water seemed to be pouring slowly along her spine. An unaccountable pain was in her knees, as if they were broken. She was afraid Juan and María Rosa would feel her eyes fixed upon them and would find her there, unable to move, spying upon them. But they did not pass beyond the enclosure, nor even glance towards the gap in the wall opening upon the road.

Juan lifted one of María Rosa's loosened braids and slapped her neck with it playfully. She smiled softly, consentingly. Together they moved back through the hives of honey-comb. María Rosa balanced her jar on one hip and swung her long full petticoats with every step. Juan flourished his wide hat back and forth, walking proudly as a game-cock.

María Concepción came out of the heavy cloud which enwrapped her head and bound her throat, and found herself walking onward, keeping the road without knowing it, feeling her way delicately, her ears strumming as if all María Rosa's bees had hived in them. Her careful sense of duty kept her moving toward the buried city where Juan's chief, the American archeologist, was taking his midday rest, waiting for his food.

Juan and María Rosa! She burned all over now, as if a layer of tiny fig-cactus bristles, as cruel as spun glass, had crawled under her skin. She wished to sit down quietly and wait for her death, but not until she had cut the throats of her man and that girl who were laughing and kissing under the cornstalks. Once when she was a young girl she had come back from market to find her jacal burned to a pile of ash and her few silver coins gone. A dark empty feeling had filled her; she kept moving about the place, not believing her eyes, expecting it all to take shape again before her. But it was gone, and though she knew an enemy had done it, she could not find out who it was, and could only curse and threaten the air. Now here was a worse thing, but she knew her enemy. María Rosa, that sinful girl, shameless! She heard herself saying a harsh, true word about María Rosa, saying it aloud as if she expected someone to agree with her: "Yes, she is a whore! She has no right to live."

At this moment the gray untidy head of Givens appeared over the edges of the newest trench he had caused to be dug in his field of excavations. The long deep crevasses, in which a man might stand without being seen, lay crisscrossed like orderly gashes of a giant scalpel. Nearly all of the men of the community worked for Givens, helping him to uncover the lost city of their ancestors. They worked all the year through and prospered, digging every day for those small clay heads and bits of pottery and fragments of painted walls for which there was no good use on earth, being all broken and encrusted with clay. They themselves could make better ones, perfectly stout and new, which they took to town and peddled to foreigners for real money. But the unearthly delight of the chief in finding these wornout things was an endless puzzle. He would fairly roar for joy at times, waving a shattered pot or a human skull above his head, shouting for his photographer to come and make a picture of this!

Now he emerged, and his young enthusiast's eyes welcomed María Concepción from his old-man face, covered with hard wrinkles and burned to the color of red earth. "I hope you've brought me a nice fat one." He selected a fowl from the bunch dangling nearest him as María Concepción wordless, leaned over the trench. "Dress it for me, there's a good girl. I'll broil it."

María Concepción took the fowl by the head, and silently, swiftly drew her knife across its throat, twisting the head off with the casual firmness she might use with the top of a beet.

"Good God, woman, you do have nerve," said Givens, watching her. "I can't do that. It gives me the creeps."

"My home country is Guadalajara," explained María Concepción, without bravado, as she picked and gutted the fowl.

She stood and regarded Givens condescendingly, that diverting white man who had no woman of his own to cook for him, and moreover appeared not to feel any loss of dignity in preparing his own food. He squatted now, eyes squinted, nose wrinkled to avoid the smoke, turning the roasting fowl busily on a stick. A mysterious man, undoubtedly rich, and Juan's chief, therefore to be respected, to be placated.

"The tortillas are fresh and hot, señor," she murmured gently. "With your permission I will now go to market."

"Yes, yes, run along; bring me another of these tomorrow." Givens turned his head to look at her again. Her grand manner sometimes reminded him of royalty in exile. He noticed her unnatural paleness. "The sun is too hot, eh?" he asked.

"Yes, sir. Pardon me, but Juan will be here soon?"

"He ought to be here now. Leave his food. The others will eat it."

She moved away; the blue of her rebozo became a dancing spot in the heat waves that rose from the gray-red soil. Givens liked his Indians best when he could feel a fatherly indulgence for their primitive childish ways. He told comic stories of Juan's escapades, of how often he had saved him, in the past five years, from going to jail, and even from being shot, for his varied and always unexpected misdeeds.

"I am never a minute too soon to get him out of one pickle or another," he would say. "Well, he's a good worker, and I know how to manage him."

After Juan was married he used to twit him, with exactly the right shade of condescension, on his many infidelities to María Concepción. "She'll catch you yet, and God help you!" he was fond of saying, and Juan would laugh with immense pleasure.

It did not occur to María Concepción to tell Juan she had found him out. During the day her anger against him died, and her anger against María Rosa grew. She kept saying to herself, "When I was a young girl like María Rosa, if a man had caught hold of me so, I would have broken my jar over his head." She forgot completely that she had not resisted even so much as María Rosa, on the day that Juan had first taken hold of her. Besides she had married him afterwards in the church, and that was a very different thing.

Juan did not come home that night, but went away to war and María Rosa went with him. Juan had a rifle at his shoulder and two pistols at his belt. María Rosa wore a rifle also, slung on her back along with the blankets and the cooking pots. They joined the nearest detachment of troops in the field, and María Rosa marched ahead with the battalion of experienced women of war, which went over the crops like locusts, gathering provisions for the army. She cooked with them, and ate with them what was left after the men had eaten. After battles she went out on the field with the others to salvage clothing and ammunition and guns from the slain before they should begin to swell in the heat. Sometimes they would encounter the women from the other army, and a second battle as grim as the first would take place.

There was no particular scandal in the village. People shrugged, grinned. It was far better that they were gone. The neighbors went around saying that María Rosa was safer in the army than she would be in the same village with María Concepción.

María Concepción did not weep when Juan left her; and when the baby was born, and died within four days, she did not weep. "She is mere stone," said old Lupe, who went over and offered charms to preserve the baby.

"May you rot in hell with your charms," said María Concepción.

If she had not gone so regularly to church, lighting candles before the saints, kneeling with her arms spread in the form of a cross for hours at a time, and receiving holy communion every month, there might have been talk of her being devil-possessed, her face was so changed and blind-looking. But this was impossible when, after all, she had been married by the priest. It must be, they reasoned, that she was being punished for her pride. They decided that this was the true cause for everything: she was altogether too proud. So they pitied her.

During the year that Juan and María Rosa were gone María Concepción sold her fowls and looked after her garden and her sack of hard coins grew. Lupe had no talent for bees, and the hives did not prosper. She began to blame María Rosa for running away, and to praise María Concepción for her behavior. She used to see Maria Concepción at the market or at church, and she always said that no one could tell by looking at her now that she was a woman who had such a heavy grief.

"I pray God everything goes well with María Concepción from this out," she would say, "for she has had her share of trouble."

When some idle person repeated this to the deserted woman, she went down to Lupe's house and stood within the clearing and called to the medicine woman, who sat in her doorway stirring a mess of her infallible cure for sores: "Keep your prayers to yourself, Lupe, or offer them for others who need them. I will ask God for what I want in this world."

"And will you get it, you think, María Concepción?" asked Lupe, tittering cruelly and smelling the wooden mixing spoon. "Did you pray for what you have now?"

Afterward everyone noticed that María Concepción went oftener to church, and even seldomer to the village to talk with the other women as they sat along the curb, nursing their babies and eating fruit, at the end of the market-day.

"She is wrong to take us for enemies," said old Soledad, who was a thinker and a peace-maker. "All women have these troubles. Well, we should suffer together."

But María Concepción lived alone. She was gaunt, as if something were gnawing her away inside, her eyes were sunken, and she would not speak a word if she could help it. She worked harder than ever, and her butchering knife was scarcely ever out of her hand.

Juan and María Rosa, disgusted with military life, came

home one day without asking permission of anyone. The field of war had unrolled itself, a long scroll of vexations, until the end had frayed out within twenty miles of Juan's village. So he and María Rosa, now lean as a wolf, burdened with a child daily expected, set out with no farewells to the regiment and walked home.

They arrived one morning about daybreak. Juan was picked up on sight by a group of military police from the small barracks on the edge of town, and taken to prison, where the officer in charge told him with impersonal cheerfulness that he would add one to a catch of ten waiting to be shot as deserters the next morning.

María Rosa, screaming and falling on her face in the road, was taken under the armpits by two guards and helped briskly to her jacal, now sadly run down. She was received with professional importance by Lupe, who helped the baby to be born at once.

Limping with foot soreness, a layer of dust concealing his fine new clothes got mysteriously from somewhere, Juan appeared before the captain at the barracks. The captain recognized him as head digger for his good friend Givens, and dispatched a note to Givens saying: "I am holding the person of Juan Villegas awaiting your further disposition."

When Givens showed up Juan was delivered to him with the urgent request that nothing be made public about so humane and sensible an operation on the part of military authority.

Juan walked out of the rather stifling atmosphere of the drumhead court, a definite air of swagger about him. His hat, of unreasonable dimensions and embroidered with silver thread, hung over one eyebrow, secured at the back by a cord of silver dripping with bright blue tassels. His shirt was of checkerboard pattern in green and black, his white cotton trousers were bound by a belt of yellow leather tooled in red. His feet were bare, full of stone bruises, and sadly ragged as to toenails. He removed his cigarette from the corner of his full-lipped wide mouth. He removed the splendid hat. His black dusty hair, pressed moistly to his forehead, sprang up suddenly in a cloudy thatch on his crown. He bowed to the officer, who appeared to be gazing at a vacuum. He swung his arm wide in a free circle upsoaring towards the prison window, where forlorn heads poked over the window sill, hot eyes following after the lucky departing one. Two or three of the heads nodded, and a half dozen hands were flipped at him in an effort to imitate his own casual and heady manner.

Juan kept up this insufferable pantomime until they rounded the first clump of fig-cactus. Then he seized Givens' hand and burst into oratory. "Blessed be the day your servant Juan Villegas first came under your eyes. From this day my life is yours without condition, ten thousand thanks with all my heart!"

"For God's sake stop playing the fool," said Givens irritably. "Some day I'm going to be five minutes too late."

"Well, it is nothing much to be shot, my chief—certainly you know I was not afraid—but to be shot in a drove of deserters, against a cold wall, just in the moment of my home-coming, by order of that . . . "

Glittering epithets tumbled over one another like explosions of a rocket. All the scandalous analogies from the animal and vegetable worlds were applied in a vivid, unique and personal way to the life, loves, and family history of the officer who had just set him free. When he had quite cursed himself dry, and his nerves were soothed, he added: "With your permission, my chief!"

"What will María Concepción say to all this?" asked Givens. "You are very informal, Juan, for a man who was married in the church."

Juan put on his hat.

"Oh, María Concepción! That's nothing. Look, my chief, to be married in the church is a great misfortune for a man. After that he is not himself any more. How can that woman complain when I do not drink even at fiestas enough to be really drunk? I do not beat her; never, never. We were always at peace. I say to her, Come here, and she comes straight. I say, Go there, and she goes quickly. Yet sometimes I looked at her and thought, Now I am married to that woman in the church, and I felt a sinking inside, as if something were lying heavy on my stomach. With María Rosa it is all different. She is not silent; she talks. When she talks too much, I slap her and say, Silence, thou simpleton! and she weeps. She is just a girl with whom I do as I please. You know how she used to keep those clean little bees in their hives? She is like their honey to me. I swear it. I would not harm María Concepción because I am married to her in the church; but also, my chief, I will not leave María Rosa, because she pleases me more than any other woman."

"Let me tell you, Juan, things haven't been going as well as you think. You be careful. Some day María Concepción will just take your head off with that carving knife of hers. You keep that in mind."

Juan's expression was the proper blend of masculine triumph and sentimental melancholy. It was pleasant to see himself in the rôle of hero to two such desirable women. He had just escaped from the threat of a disagreeable end. His clothes were new and handsome, and they had cost him just nothing. María Rosa had collected them for him here and there after battles. He was walking in the early sunshine, smelling the good smells of ripening cactus-figs, peaches, and melons, of pungent berries dangling from the pepper-trees, and the smoke of his cigarette under his nose. He was on his way to civilian life with his patient chief. His situation was ineffably perfect, and he swallowed it whole.

"My chief," he addressed Givens handsomely, as one man of the world to another, "women are good things, but not at this moment. With your permission, I will now go to the village and eat. My God, *how* I shall eat! Tomorrow morning very early I will come to the buried city and work like seven men. Let us forget María Concepción and María Rosa. Each one in her place. I will manage them when the time comes."

News of Juan's adventure soon got abroad, and Juan found many friends about him during the morning. They frankly commended his way of leaving the army. It was in itself the act of a hero. The new hero ate a great deal and drank somewhat, the occasion being better than a feast-day. It was almost noon before he returned to visit María Rosa.

He found her sitting on a clean straw mat, rubbing fat on her three-hour-old son. Before this felicitous vision Juan's emotions so twisted him that he returned to the village and invited every man in the "Death and Resurrection" pulque shop to drink with him.

Having thus taken leave of his balance, he started back to María Rosa, and found himself unaccountably in his own house, attempting to beat María Concepción by way of reëstablishing himself in his legal household.

María Concepción, knowing all the events of that unhappy day, was not in a yielding mood, and refused to be beaten. She did not scream nor implore; she stood her ground and resisted; she even struck at him. Juan, amazed, hardly knowing what he did, stepped back and gazed at her inquiringly through a leisurely whirling film which seemed to have lodged behind his eyes. Certainly he had not even thought of touching her. Oh, well, no harm done. He gave up, turned away, half-asleep on his feet. He dropped amiably in a shadowed corner and began to snore.

María Concepción, seeing that he was quiet, began to bind the legs of her fowls. It was market-day and she was late. She fumbled and tangled the bits of cord in her haste, and set off across the plowed fields instead of taking the accustomed road. She ran with a crazy panic in her head, her stumbling legs. Now and then she would stop and look about her, trying to place herself, then go on a few steps, until she realized that she was not going towards the market.

At once she came to her senses completely, recognized the thing that troubled her so terribly, was certain of what she wanted. She sat down quietly under a sheltering thorny bush and gave herself over to her long devouring sorrow. The thing which had for so long squeezed her whole body into a tight dumb knot of suffering suddenly broke with shocking violence. She jerked with the involuntary recoil of one who receives a blow, and the sweat poured from her skin as if the wounds of her whole life were shedding their salt ichor. Drawing her rebozo over her head, she bowed her forehead on her updrawn knees, and sat there in deadly silence and immobility. From time to time she lifted her head where the sweat formed steadily and poured down her face, drenching the front of her chemise, and her mouth had the shape of crying, but there were no tears and no sound. All her being was a dark confused memory of grief burning in her at night, of deadly baffled anger eating at her by day, until her very tongue tasted bitter, and her feet were as heavy as if she were mired in the muddy roads during the time of rains.

After a great while she stood up and threw the rebozo off her face, and set out walking again.

Juan awakened slowly, with long yawns and grumblings, alternated with short relapses into sleep full of visions and clamors. A blur of orange light seared his eyeballs when he tried to unseal his lids. There came from somewhere a low voice weeping without tears, saying meaningless phrases over and over. He began to listen. He tugged at the leash of his stupor, he strained to grasp those words which terrified him even though he could not quite hear them. Then he came awake with frightening suddenness, sitting up and staring at the long sharpened streak of light piercing the corn-husk walls from the level disappearing sun.

María Concepción stood in the doorway, looming colossally tall to his betrayed eyes. She was talking quickly, and calling his name. Then he saw her clearly.

"God's name!" said Juan, frozen to the marrow, "here I am facing my death!" for the long knife she wore habitually at her belt was in her hand. But instead, she threw it away, clear from her, and got down on her knees, crawling toward him as he had seen her crawl many times toward the shrine at Guadalupe Villa. He watched her approach with such horror that the hair of his head seemed to be lifting itself away from him. Falling forward upon her face, she huddled over him, lips moving in a ghostly whisper. Her words became clear, and Juan understood them all.

· 37 ·

For a second he could not move nor speak. Then he took her head between both his hands, and supported her in this way, saying swiftly, anxiously reassuring, almost in a babble:

"Oh, thou poor creature! Oh, madwoman! Oh, my María Concepción, unfortunate! Listen. . . . Don't be afraid. Listen to me! I will hide thee away, I thy own man will protect thee! Quiet! Not a sound!"

Trying to collect himself, he held her and cursed under his breath for a few moments in the gathering darkness. María Concepción bent over, face almost on the ground, her feet folded under her, as if she would hide behind him. For the first time in his life Juan was aware of danger. This was danger. María Concepción would be dragged away between two gendarmes, with him following helpless and unarmed, to spend the rest of her days in Belén Prison, maybe. Danger! The night swarmed with threats. He stood up and dragged her up with him. She was silent and perfectly rigid, holding to him with resistless strength, her hands stiffened on his arms.

"Get me the knife," he told her in a whisper. She obeyed, her feet slipping along the hard earth floor, her shoulders straight, her arms close to her side. He lighted a candle. María Concepción held the knife out to him. It was stained and dark even to the handle with drying blood.

He frowned at her harshly, noting the same stains on her chemise and hands.

"Take off thy clothes and wash thy hands," he ordered. He washed the knife carefully, and threw the water wide of the doorway. She watched him and did likewise with the bowl in which she had bathed.

"Light the brasero and cook food for me," he told her in the same peremptory tone. He took her garments and went out. When he returned, she was wearing an old soiled dress, and was fanning the fire in the charcoal burner. Seating himself cross-legged near her, he stared at her as at a creature unknown to him, who bewildered him utterly, for whom there was no possible explanation. She did not turn her head, but kept silent and

· 38 ·

still, except for the movements of her strong hands fanning the blaze which cast sparks and small jets of white smoke, flaring and dying rhythmically with the motion of the fan, lighting her face and darkening it by turns.

Juan's voice barely disturbed the silence: "Listen to me carefully, and tell me the truth, and when the gendarmes come here for us, thou shalt have nothing to fear. But there will be something for us to settle between us afterward."

The light from the charcoal burner shone in her eyes: a yellow phosphorescence glimmered behind the dark iris.

"For me everything is settled now," she answered, in a tone so tender, so grave, so heavy with suffering, that Juan felt his vitals contract. He wished to repent openly, not as a man, but as a very small child. He could not fathom her, nor himself, nor the mysterious fortunes of life grown so instantly confused where all had seemed so gay and simple. He felt too that she had become invaluable, a woman without equal among a million women, and he could not tell why. He drew an enormous sigh that rattled in his chest.

"Yes, yes, it is all settled. I shall not go away again. We must stay here together."

Whispering, he questioned her and she answered whispering, and he instructed her over and over until she had her lesson by heart. The hostile darkness of the night encroached upon them, flowing over the narrow threshold, invading their hearts. It brought with it sighs and murmurs, the pad of secretive feet in the near-by road, the sharp staccato whimper of wind through the cactus leaves. All these familiar, once friendly cadences were now invested with sinister terrors; a dread, formless and uncontrollable, took hold of them both.

"Light another candle," said Juan, loudly, in too resolute, too sharp a tone. "Let us eat now."

They sat facing each other and ate from the same dish, after their old habit. Neither tasted what they ate. With food half-way to his mouth, Juan listened. The sound of voices rose, spread, widened at the turn of the road along the cactus wall. A spray of lantern light shot through the hedge, a single voice slashed the blackness, ripped the fragile layer of silence suspended above the hut.

"Juan Villegas!"

"Pass, friends!" Juan roared back cheerfully.

They stood in the doorway, simple cautious gendarmes from the village, mixed-bloods themselves with Indian sympathies, well known to all the community. They flashed their lanterns almost apologetically upon the pleasant, harmless scene of a man eating supper with his wife.

"Pardon, brother," said the leader. "Someone has killed the woman María Rosa, and we must question her neighbors and friends." He paused, and added with an attempt at severity, "Naturally!"

"Naturally," agreed Juan. "You know that I was a good friend of María Rosa. This is bad news."

They all went away together, the men walking in a group, María Concepción following a few steps in the rear, near Juan. No one spoke.

The two points of candlelight at María Rosa's head fluttered uneasily; the shadows shifted and dodged on the stained darkened walls. To María Concepción everything in the smothering enclosing room shared an evil restlessness. The watchful faces of those called as witnesses, the faces of old friends, were made alien by the look of speculation in their eyes. The ridges of the rose-colored rebozo thrown over the body varied continually, as though the thing it covered was not perfectly in repose. Her eyes swerved over the body in the open painted coffin, from the candle tips at the head to the feet, jutting up thinly, the small scarred soles protruding, freshly washed, a mass of crooked, half-healed wounds, thorn-pricks and cuts of sharp stones. Her gaze went back to the candle flame, to Juan's eyes warning her, to the gendarmes talking among themselves. Her eyes would not be controlled.

With a leap that shook her her gaze settled upon the face of

María Rosa. Instantly her blood ran smoothly again: there was nothing to fear. Even the restless light could not give a look of life to that fixed countenance. She was dead. María Concepción felt her muscles give way softly; her heart began beating steadily without effort. She knew no more rancor against that pitiable thing, lying indifferently in its blue coffin under the fine silk rebozo. The mouth drooped sharply at the corners in a grimace of weeping arrested half-way. The brows were distressed; the dead flesh could not cast off the shape of its last terror. It was all finished. María Rosa had eaten too much honey and had had too much love. Now she must sit in hell, crying over her sins and her hard death forever and ever.

Old Lupe's cackling voice arose. She had spent the morning helping María Rosa, and it had been hard work. The child had spat blood the moment it was born, a bad sign. She thought then that bad luck would come to the house. Well, about sunset she was in the yard at the back of the house grinding tomatoes and peppers. She had left mother and babe asleep. She heard a strange noise in the house, a choking and smothered calling, like someone wailing in sleep. Well, such a thing is only natural. But there followed a light, quick, thudding sound—

"Like the blows of a fist?" interrupted an officer.

"No, not at all like such a thing."

"How do you know?"

"I am well acquainted with that sound, friends," retorted Lupe. "This was something else."

She was at a loss to describe it exactly. A moment later, there came the sound of pebbles rolling and slipping under feet; then she knew someone had been there and was running away.

"Why did you wait so long before going to see?"

"I am old and hard in the joints," said Lupe. "I cannot run after people. I walked as fast as I could to the cactus hedge, for it is only by this way that anyone can enter. There was no one in the road, sir, no one. Three cows, with a dog driving them; nothing else. When I got to María Rosa, she was lying all tangled up, and from her neck to her middle she was full of knife-holes. It was a sight to move the Blessed Image Himself! Her eyes were—"

"Never mind. Who came oftenest to her house before she went away? Did you know her enemies?"

Lupe's face congealed, closed. Her spongy skin drew into a network of secretive wrinkles. She turned withdrawn and expressionless eyes upon the gendarmes.

"I am an old woman. I do not see well. I cannot hurry on my feet. I know no enemy of María Rosa. I did not see anyone leave the clearing."

"You did not hear splashing in the spring near the bridge?"

"No, sir."

"Why, then, do our dogs follow a scent there and lose it?"

"God only knows, my friend. I am an old wo—"

"Yes. How did the footfalls sound?"

"Like the tread of an evil spirit!" Lupe broke forth in a swelling oracular tone that startled them. The Indians stirred uneasily, glanced at the dead, then at Lupe. They half expected her to produce the evil spirit among them at once.

The gendarme began to lose his temper.

"No, poor unfortunate; I mean, were they heavy or light? The footsteps of a man or of a woman? Was the person shod or barefoot?"

A glance at the listening circle assured Lupe of their thrilled attention. She enjoyed the dangerous importance of her situation. She could have ruined that María Concepción with a word, but it was even sweeter to make fools of these gendarmes who went about spying on honest people. She raised her voice again. What she had not seen she could not describe, thank God! No one could harm her because her knees were stiff and she could not run even to seize a murderer. As for knowing the difference between footfalls, shod or bare, man or woman, nay, between devil and human, who ever heard of such madness?

"My eyes are not ears, gentlemen," she ended grandly, "but upon my heart I swear those footsteps fell as the tread of the spirit of evil!"

· 42 ·

"Imbecile!" yapped the leader in a shrill voice. "Take her away, one of you! Now, Juan Villegas, tell me—"

Juan told his story patiently, several times over. He had returned to his wife that day. She had gone to market as usual. He had helped her prepare her fowls. She had returned about mid-afternoon, they had talked, she had cooked, they had eaten, nothing was amiss. Then the gendarmes came with the news about María Rosa. That was all. Yes, María Rosa had run away with him, but there had been no bad blood between him and his wife on this account, nor between his wife and María Rosa. Everybody knew that his wife was a quiet woman.

María Concepción heard her own voice answering without a break. It was true at first she was troubled when her husband went away, but after that she had not worried about him. It was the way of men, she believed. She was a church-married woman and knew her place. Well, he had come home at last. She had gone to market, but had come back early, because now she had her man to cook for. That was all.

Other voices broke in. A toothless old man said: "She is a woman of good reputation among us, and María Rosa was not." A smiling young mother, Anita, baby at breast, said: "If no one thinks so, how can you accuse her? It was the loss of her child and not of her husband that changed her so." Another: "María Rosa had a strange life, apart from us. How do we know who might have come from another place to do her evil?" And old Soledad spoke up boldly: "When I saw María Concepción in the market today, I said, 'Good luck to you, María Concepción, this is a happy day for you!'" and she gave María Concepción a long easy stare, and the smile of a born wise-woman.

María Concepción suddenly felt herself guarded, surrounded, upborne by her faithful friends. They were around her, speaking for her, defending her, the forces of life were ranged invincibly with her against the beaten dead. María Rosa had thrown away her share of strength in them, she lay forfeited among them. María Concepción looked from one to the other of the circling, intent faces. Their eyes gave back reassurance, understanding, a secret and mighty sympathy.

The gendarmes were at a loss. They, too, felt that sheltering wall cast impenetrably around her. They were certain she had done it, and yet they could not accuse her. Nobody could be accused; there was not a shred of true evidence. They shrugged their shoulders and snapped their fingers and shuffled their feet. Well, then, good night to everybody. Many pardons for having intruded. Good health!

A small bundle lying against the wall at the head of the coffin squirmed like an eel. A wail, a mere sliver of sound, issued. María Concepción took the son of María Rosa in her arms.

"He is mine," she said clearly, "I will take him with me."

No one assented in words, but an approving nod, a bare breath of complete agreement, stirred among them as they made way for her.

María Concepción, carrying the child, followed Juan from the clearing. The hut was left with its lighted candles and a crowd of old women who would sit up all night, drinking coffee and smoking and telling ghost stories.

Juan's exaltation had burned out. There was not an ember of excitement left in him. He was tired. The perilous adventure was over. María Rosa had vanished, to come no more forever. Their days of marching, of eating, of quarreling and making love between battles, were all over. Tomorrow he would go back to dull and endless labor, he must descend into the trenches of the buried city as María Rosa must go into her grave. He felt his veins fill up with bitterness, with black unendurable melancholy. Oh, Jesus! what bad luck overtakes a man!

Well, there was no way out of it now. For the moment he craved only to sleep. He was so drowsy he could scarcely guide his feet. The occasional light touch of the woman at his elbow was as unreal, as ghostly as the brushing of a leaf against his face. He did not know why he had fought to save her, and now he forgot her. There was nothing in him except a vast blind hurt like a covered wound.

He entered the jacal, and without waiting to light a candle, threw off his clothing, sitting just within the door. He moved with lagging, half-awake hands, to strip his body of its heavy finery. With a long groaning sigh of relief he fell straight back on the floor, almost instantly asleep, his arms flung up and outward.

María Concepción, a small clay jar in her hand, approached the gentle little mother goat tethered to a sapling, which gave and yielded as she pulled at the rope's end after the farthest reaches of grass about her. The kid, tied up a few feet away, rose bleating, its feathery fleece shivering in the fresh wind. Sitting on her heels, holding his tether, she allowed him to suckle a few moments. Afterward—all her movements very deliberate and even—she drew a supply of milk for the child.

She sat against the wall of her house, near the doorway. The child, fed and asleep, was cradled in the hollow of her crossed legs. The silence overfilled the world, the skies flowed down evenly to the rim of the valley, the stealthy moon crept slantwise to the shelter of the mountains. She felt soft and warm all over; she dreamed that the newly born child was her own, and she was resting deliciously.

María Concepción could hear Juan's breathing. The sound vapored from the low doorway, calmly; the house seemed to be resting after a burdensome day. She breathed, too, very slowly and quietly, each inspiration saturating her with repose. The child's light, faint breath was a mere shadowy moth of sound in the silver air. The night, the earth under her, seemed to swell and recede together with a limitless, unhurried, benign breathing. She drooped and closed her eyes, feeling the slow rise and fall within her own body. She did not know what it was, but it eased her all through. Even as she was falling asleep, head bowed over the child, she was still aware of a strange, wakeful happiness.

# RAGGED INDIVIDUALIST

*by* DON BROWN

Don Brown was born in Taylor, Texas, in 1899. He studied at the College of Marshall, at Marshall, Texas, and at Centenary College, at Shreveport, Louisiana. He studied art at the Art Students' League in New York and worked on various New York newspapers. He learned to fly in 1928 and became aviation editor for North American Newspaper Alliance. In this same period he also contributed articles to the *New Republic*.

In 1929 he went to Paris, where, in 1923, he had done a short stretch as desk man on the Paris edition of the Chicago *Tribune*. Again he worked for the same journal, while at the same time continuing his painting. He held his first one-man show in Paris in 1931. The depression brought him back to East Texas in 1932, and he began teaching art at Centenary College. Though still at that job, he is also completing a book on the Cajun people of the southern Louisiana bayou country.

---

BILL BONNER WAS A BOOTLEGGER AND AN ILLEGAL FISHERMAN, and the preacher prayed for him but it didn't do any good. The law tried to catch him, but it never succeeded. It took the New Deal and a country prank to make a respectable citizen of him.

Bill's schooling had stopped when he left the sixth grade and his father's scrawny cotton patch to live in a shack in the swamp. "What I mainly wanted was to stop raising cotton," he said. "I left home so that I could quit raising cotton, and Paw was fighting mad; but now, will wonders never cease, the United States Government is paying me cash *not* to raise cotton on Paw's land."

He built his swamp shack into a sizable camp and brought a wife there, and they had two children. Fishing and trapping came to him as naturally as lawbreaking, and his uncle taught him to brew corn mash and run it through a still.

To hide his illegal sales of trapped game fish, Bill made a listless pretense of operating a commercial camp, where city fishermen could buy minnows for bait and rent boats. But his customers seldom returned. One spring day I saw a family party arrive at his camp. The young women teetered along the boatwalk and squealed that they were going to fall in and drown. Bill was bored.

One of the women caught a glimpse of the broad lake and wanted to know how deep it was "everywhere."

"Two feet deep fur as you can see, and after that it's eight feet," said Bill. His gray old mongrel squirrel dog ambled over and sniffed at the visitors.

"What kind of a dog is he?" asked one of the women.

"Lady, his mama was half hound and half bulldog, and his papa was ten of the biggest dogs in Cajun County!"

The men, their eyes shining with the eager look of indoor workers out for their first fishing trip of the spring, asked if he had minnows to sell.

"Yes, I got minners, but you won't ketch nothing with 'em. Fish just ain't biting this week." The party stood around a few minutes more and then drove on to another camp.

The state game commission turned loose four hundred deer in the swamp and a five-year closed season was declared. The wardens who released the deer spent the night at one of the camps on the lake. Early next morning they drove back to town. Stuck on a pole in the middle of the road they saw the head of a freshly killed deer.

Bill cut the venison up, changed its name to young beef and had it canned at the county cannery.

Showing off like this and frequently boasting to his friends about the efficiency of his outlaw fish traps made Bill a marked man. The law tried many tricks to catch him. There were times when wholesale raids occurred, and all the moonshiners in that end of the county were rounded up, but they never did catch Bill.

One day two innocent-looking, slightly inebriated fishermen landed their boat at his camp and gave him a note signed with the name of one of his friends. The note read: "These men are all right. Give them anything they want."

They wanted whiskey. To save trouble they had brought a two-gallon keg to hold the whiskey. Bill said he didn't sell whiskey and didn't even know where it could be bought. One of the men winked and said:

"How about a ten dollar bill for a two-gallon keg of Cata-houla lake water?"

"Well, that's a funny way to do business," said Bill, "but if you'll put the keg in that old hollow stump over there and go on away for half an hour, I might be able to find a feller who can put some in there for you."

When the men returned they sniffed at the keg, put it in their boat and handed Bill ten dollars. Then they told him he was under arrest. They took him to the county seat and brought him into court. The two revenue agents were told to produce their evidence. They forced the bung and sampled it. It was Catahoula lake water.

Bill had poured a little whiskey over the keg to give it the right smell, but the keg held just what they ordered.

"I drove the bung in good so they couldn't get it out and take a drink before they got to town," said Bill. "I know them fellers."

Bill kept the ten dollars.

I was away from the swamp country for several years. I saw the dark Atlantic and the clear blue bathtub-waters of the Swiss lakes, and I was homesick for a little muddy water and a few moccasins and mosquitoes. When I got back to the bayou, they told me Bill Bonner was the new sheriff. Somebody nominated him for a joke, they said.

"And then we figured he knew more about lawbreaking than anybody in the county and everybody voted for him. Yep, he's about the best sheriff we ever had. He's really stopped law-breaking in this neck of the woods."

# ...SO LITTLE FREEDOM

*by* PAUL HORGAN

Paul W. Horgan, author of *The Fault of Angels* and *The Common Heart*, also worked in collaboration with Maurice Garland Fulton on new Gregg papers for an annotated *Commerce of the Prairies*. He is now an officer in the United States Army. His story "So Little Freedom" is manifestly a record of his own encounter with the English writer, D. H. Lawrence. The two women in the story would appear inescapably to be Frieda Lawrence and Mabel Dodge Luhan (whose own record of her relationship with Lawrence appears in the "Biography" section of this book). The two stories afford the reader a sort of stereopticon view of these people and proceedings. None of Lawrence's work appears in this book, because he was, first and last, an Englishman. But the impact of his dynamic presence upon the Southwestern literary scene, particularly among the artists of Taos, was terrific; and the mark he left on many of them was indelible, as may be seen here in the case of Paul Horgan.

## I

THERE WERE HORRIBLE SCENES, AS HE ALWAYS KNEW THERE would be; but he resolved to get through them, and stick to his point, and stick to it, until they said yes. He wished he could roar and bellow like his grandfather; even if he could swear and sulk with that smoky, brooding power which his father had, it would help. As it was, he looked too much like his mother, talked exactly like her, and was too sensitive about what others might feel, to get what he wanted, *right off*. But if he was like his mother, then he must have something of her private, tenacious strength, too. How else could she have managed to *live* here, and in spite of everything, stay so pretty, and seem still so much in love with Daddy? It wasn't just that they were rich, lots of other people in Whitewater, Texas, had money, though

· 49 ·

nobody had as much as the Warringtons, what with grandfather's bank which Daddy was running now, while the old man lived out on one of the ranches, and stayed drunk from Friday to Monday every week, so's he wouldn't have to "see" the folks that Daddy and Texas-Anne (which was Mother's name) brought out for barbecue sometimes. Roger Warrington could only take refuge in the conviction that Texas-Anne understood him, and that Daddy didn't, and that meant that if he kept at it, and kept at it, and didn't let them change him *off*, then to get rid of him, they might let him have his way, just this once.

Roger ("Little Roger") was twenty years old, a tall, golden-haired boy with pink clouds under his eyes, and a slow, dreamy way of drifting through his days which made his father ("Big Roger") hump with shame and disgust every time he looked at his son. As for what grandfather said, you couldn't put it down. It was all Texas-Anne could do, at times, to keep Little Roger from doing something "drastic," as she would say on the phone later, telling about "this mo'nin'," or "this evenin'," or whenever the latest scene had happened.

The boy wanted to "paint."

In spite of everything: the pony they tied him to when he was four, which ran away with him; the six-gun his grandfather tried to teach him to shoot when he was six, and which deafened him forever in his left ear; the roundup his father had taken him to ride on when he was nine, when the cows had bumped up close to his horse, and then flared in another direction, running like mad and carrying the little boy along for miles; the scoldings over how his thin little arms got tired when he couldn't learn to rope a steer because he didn't care; the stories grandfather told, when there were no women around, about what *he* used to do; the smothering gusts of love which Texas-Anne visited upon him at times, and the absent, somehow taunting indifference she showed toward him at other times; the time Big Roger had taken him down to Lily's, on South San Jacinto street, and had "had a man made of him" in a bewildering cloud of sweaty perfume, laughing reassurance, and playful admiration of his pink cheeks and golden hair—in spite of everything, the Warrington family had to face the failure of their efforts to make a millionaire cow-hand out of Little Roger.

Grandfather wept over it when he got drunk, out on the ranch, and recited long truculent histories of the male valor of the Warrington line. Through his moist drawling there appeared, faintly, and from long ago, the far-off images of his own achievement. He saw again, and tried to make the others see, the plains in winter, showing and fading through bitter blowing snow, and the measure of distance by weeks, not miles on fat tires, and the gun-to-gun courage a man needed plenty of times then, and how it felt to be *right*, and to make the law yourself, because there was no other law to appeal to, and the dearness of such a foolish beast as a steer which had won the old cowboy's affection because he had outwitted it so often, saved it, fattened it, driven it a thousand miles to Dodge City, sold it, and got rich off it. . . .

Big Roger drank too, but it did something a little different, and worse, to him than it did to grandfather. Big Roger got surly and brooded and began to hate everyone, even Texas-Anne, mocked her Woman's Club parties, her book review clubs, her beauty treatments, the enormous diamonds he gave her for Christmas in 1914, reminded her of the fact that except for the Warrington money, she'd still be waiting tables in Amarillo. He broke things when he was drunk. She was terrified of him, and her heart jumped into her throat with passion at the sight of him brawling with the furniture, and wrecking it, a black-haired, marble-muscled, troubled giant whom she loved.

Little Roger dimly felt that he was the crowning failure of three retrogressive generations. He didn't see that each met instinctively what the times called for: the old man had whipped the wilderness; the son was turning that conquest into commerce; and the third stage of settlement was always cultural, and this was Little Roger's turn.

There was nobody in Whitewater, Texas, for him to talk to. He spent his time reading books, when he could *get alone*. They threatened to cut off his allowance unless he spent it for more "other" things than books and red seal opera records for his phonograph. The next thing they knew, he was cutting lawns Saturday mornings to get money for his own nourishing delights. It was a sad commentary on the original Warrington character that he was forbidden to do this, too, because it reflected on the Warrington "standing."

They gave him back his allowance.

He bought everything he could get by the British writer, Edward St. David, in whose books he found the companionship of an original and fiery soul who had won his way to a sort of freedom in world fame, after a hideous boyhood in Welsh mines, brutalized, his spirit nearly extinguished, his heart wrung by the mean life to which the mother he adored was condemned. Little Roger would stare at the book jacket photographs of St. David, that bearded face with the defiant eyes and the thick cap of uncut hair, and say to himself that sometimes even a weak person could prove himself stronger than all those authorities accepted by the world. In St. David's novels, he could read through the caprice and bitterness and lust of the human relationships described there, and see the solitude of the life out of which those books were born. Little Roger felt that it was almost a call, and he ardently answered it with his devotion to St. David's works.

One day one of his favorites was missing from his shelf in his attic playroom. Texas-Anne admitted taking it, to show Big Roger, who read a page she had turned down, and then threw the book into the burning fireplace. Such language! In Print! *Telling it right out*, thataway, if that was what her son was reading, he said thickly, it was even worse than he was afred of. When Little Roger found his book half burned up, in the fireplace, he burst into tears. He was then eighteen. His father was so enraged at such sensitiveness that he seized the boy and hit him with his fist in the face. Little Roger stopped crying and turned so white and green and sick-looking that they thought they might have to call the doctor. They were relieved to see him get over it. Texas-Anne wrote to Dallas and got another copy of the book and replaced it in the upstairs bookshelf, without telling Big Roger anything about it.

It was such blasting alternates of strength and weakness in the family that made Little Roger sure that he was going to get his way, eventually, about going to Taos that summer, where all the art was, and all the artists, and everyone could go right into any of the studios, and see artists "at work," and take lessons, if they had the money, and wear any old thing they liked, and live any old way that suited them, and nobody cared what anybody did, life was free, and a person could be themselves, no matter what. So he kept at it, and kept at it, and finally Big Roger swore and said give him the money and git him out of here, I'm goin crezy havin' to look at him moonin' and droopin' aroun', but mind, now, just for a week or two, didn't want him getting *into* anythin' up there in a crezy place like Taos, New Mexico. . . .

## II

Little Roger promised anything, just to get there, and they gave him too much money, and Texas-Anne had one of her bursts of heart-breaking love for her son just before he left, but he was over that by the time he got to Taos, on the bus from Santa Fé, and saw that signboard by the road four miles out, made like a huge artist's-palette, advertising the Studio Tea Room—Artists Supplies—Souvenirs—Originals by Local Artists for Sale, Low Prices. It struck him in some odd way a blow under the breastbone, it was Taos at last, and here was proof of it.

His joy was like drunkenness, in which he had a glimmer of sympathy for Grandfather. He roamed the sunny mud streets all day, staring at all the faces, thrilled when he saw what obviously were artists, and hanging around the Studio Tea Room as much as he dared. He had a room in an adobe house practically out in a field, and the red chili peppers hanging by the door were like a badge of freedom to him. He went to the pueblo and sketched, but every time anybody came near, he hid his drawing, having a horror of showing how poor he was to any of the talented people who lived here. He bought some oil tubes and a small oval palette and some academy board at the Studio Tea Room, and did his first oil sketch of Taos Mountain, sitting in the middle of the field behind his lodging. When he was through, he was trembling. It was a great experience for him. The picture was thickly painted and the colors went on almost pure, except for lots of delicious white mixed in the sky-blue. He set it up in his room where he could see it first thing in the morning when he woke up.

He didn't make friends easily, and the sandalled, bare-throated young men in blue jeans and beards and plaid shirts were like a race of gods, apart, whom he could watch but not accost in the plaza, or the drug store, or anywhere. But he was far from lonely, for he felt *accounted for* just being among kindred spirits.

The woman who ran the Studio Tea Room was named Mrs. Truesdale. She told Roger a remarkable thing, and said she was writing a book about it. She said there were only three places in the world which had what she called the Occult Maximus, and that it was all because of the way the sun's rays struck the earth, so that when they were reflected back, at a particular angle, conditions were precisely right for the Occult Maximus. The three places—she named them and said her book would leave nothing unsaid about the wonderful powers open to those who lived near a Maximus—the three places were Tibet, Death Valley, and Taos. She said it was really this which drew the artists and other "sensitives," as she called them, to Taos, however much they thought it was other things that interested them, like clarity of light, beautiful mountains, or paintable Indians willing to hire out with their property blankets and *ollas*. Mrs. Truesdale said the artists instinctively *knew* that the "vibrations" here were "special," and she indulgently rattled her painted wooden bracelets and promised to enlighten everyone with her book.

Roger had the disturbing and exciting belief that anything could happen in Taos. Drifting up and down the dried mud streets, he conceived of himself as living the most adventurous possible life. It took so little freedom in the realm of the possible to make him happy. . . .

## III

The morning he went into the Plaza Drug Store for a chocolate soda about half past ten and saw in the mirror the two rather large women come in, followed by the small, spring-footed man with the fiery red beard, he could hardly believe his eyes. The three people sat down noisily at one of the drug store tables, and ordered soft drinks, and sat regarding each other. There was quite a crowd in the Plaza Drug, nobody paid them any mind but Roger, but his heart was beating fast, and he felt almost weak, because it was unmistakably Edward St. David, especially now that he had pulled off his ten-gallon hat, and the thick hair fell fox-red over his incandescent white brow. The soda-jerker took them their drinks, and one of the women said in a comfortable voice, unconsciously loud so everyone could hear, but in a German accent, "Ja! the chocolate soda is yours, St. David, it vill give you cr-r-amps again."

This must be his German wife. Roger had read all about their romance, and he gazed at her and felt somehow comfortable about her. St. David screwed up his eyes and merely stared at her, but with his whole face, and took the straw into his mouth like a greedy child.

The other woman was impassive; she almost seemed like a governess for the two of them. Roger suddenly knew who she was, it was that rich woman from Boston who had built a medieval castle of adobe out near the pueblo, with a high wall, where at night the lanterns shone deep in the roadway leading to the door, and now everybody came to Taos to visit her, from everywhere, famous writers and painters and publishers and symphony conductors, her name was Mrs. Gerald Boree. Most everybody in Taos was always saying her name, "Mrs. Boree, M'sssB'ree," a sort of refrain of curious respect, except that the young painters who idled in the Plaza spoke of her with comic intention and effect simply as "Bertha." She had left her husband, Gerald Boree, the artist, in Rapallo, to come here alone and "find herself."

St. David sucked air at the bottom of his soda glass, and began to speak to Mrs. Boree, who appeared to be enacting the conception of *placidity*.

"A new kind of manorial bad manners," he sneered. "My ancestors used to have to put up with getting beaten and robbed and starved and bastardized by the manor folk, who carried on like this in full view of the county, elevated above common decency and poor trouble, as if just and right. This is a new dimension of the same thing. Moving in and taking over a whole town, a damned whole contented and centuries-old secure people, and putting them on like a new rag to wear around your shoulders, to show to the rich and famous and talented and frightful people you drag here from all over the world, to see your show, your personal mountains, your private desert, the spiritual reservoir which you did not fill, but only saw others filling and taking from."

Roger lowered his eyes in embarrassment from the big soda fountain mirror where he had seen all.

The drug store was full of the mid-morning glisten and drift of casual life. Everybody could hear. Roger was blushing, his ears were like red lampshades, he knew, with light coming through them. When he dared to look again, he was astonished to see the group at the round iron table sitting in simple composure. Mrs. Boree was gazing at the great man without resentment, almost with love? do you think? and her face was like a daytime moon under her banged black hair. Mrs. St. David looked almost bored, a bored lioness, sleepily licking the sweet edge of her chocolate glass. St. David himself was hunched bonily down, sucking on the straw, scowling. And even then, he looked up, and smiled sort of washily, his resentment free, his blue eyes striking out with a look of misery and power which gave Roger a pang in the breast. But the shrill, bitten voice was not yet able to be quiet.

"And do not sit there *understanding* me with possessive tolerance," he said. "I won't have it. Whatever I owed you I have paid you. I came, did I not? You have exhibited me, have you not? We have had our thrust and parry, I like your damned insolent wonderful landscape, and I shall flee it the moment I can afford it, and you shall have suitable credit for discovering my inner appropriateness with it."

"St. David!" said his wife, richly chiding in her German accent, "I be-leefe it is *your* manners which are too bad. You are too *bad*, to sit here in vront of all these beople, and show your temper like a stomach-ache."

"Ha!" he cried, turning on her, "if there is one thing worse than to be mooned over, it is to be shut off, like a doll! I know you! Mocking me with your big female calm, waiting . . . "

"Come, Bertha," said Gerda St. David, rising. "He is going to be dreadful all day."

Roger saw the three of them leave the drug store, St. David in the rear of the two large women, his new blue jeans sticking stiffly out behind where his bony hams failed to fill them, his head dwarfed like a rabbit's by the tall, ear-like rise of his ten-gallon hat, his rough woolen lumberjack shirt, bright red plaid, bagging pitifully around his thin shoulders and arms with a sort of childish pretension and failure. St. David coughed as he disappeared into the blazing sunshine of the sidewalk crowd. It shook him throughout his whole skeleton. Roger Warrington swallowed in sympathy. Then even genius itself was not free? Could look ridiculous? Was tortured and had to cry out, over even the silliest things?

No matter. Roger's youthful loyalty was truer than that. He had actually set eyes on Edward St. David, and if he never accomplished another thing, his trip to Taos that summer was already worthwhile.

## IV

But his hungers, too, were truer, harder to satisfy than by such a glimpse. He went out to the country where Mrs. Boree's house was, and hung around one whole afternoon, and sure enough something happened. Mrs. St. David came walking out alone, toward the dirt highway, and before he knew it, they were talking together, and he never felt so easy with anybody in his life. She had him saying in two minutes that her husband was his idol, and it didn't make her laugh, or be modest, or anything, she simply said he must come back with her to the house and meet him. Her warmth, her *allowance* of him, right off, made Roger a little blurred with joy, after all, look who she was, a German countess, and the wife of the greatest living writer, and she said she thought she had seen Roger before, at the drug store? drinking a *so-da? Ja?*

He was too scared to go with her to meet St. David. But he wrung her hand, and she smiled broadly, said she had two sons of her own, and hoped he was a happy boy, "—are you content, here, in Ta-os?" But she didn't wait for him to reply, but went on to say, that he must not break his heart if he didn't have any *tal-ent*, but go home, and be happy with good, and dear, kind, things at home, sometimes they were hard to find, but *ja!* they existed, everywhere. She blinked both her light blue eyes at him, and went back up the long road to the house, of which so many mysteries were reported in the village, and left him staring after her, startled and moved.

No talent?

It had never occurred to him.

That would mean *they* were right, the others, who were ashamed of him, and of the love he had in him and could not conceal, but had to reveal as art. Yet how kindly, how immediately, Mrs. St. David seemed to know him!

He didn't know which one he loved more, St. David or his wife.

When he got back to his room by the alfalfa field, he found a letter from Texas-Anne. It was an edict. Big Roger said if he did not take the next bus out of Taos, they would never send him any more money, and they were going to settle once and for all about this thing. And Grandfather had deeded his stock in the Bank over to Little Roger, and if he came right home, and went to work in the Bank, and learned the business, they'd put him on the Board of Directors on his twenty-first birthday. So wouldn't he do this, hon? just for her? She missed her little baby boy, and was sure he couldn't bear to refuse Texas-Anne the only thing she ever asked of him?

His exultation vanished. He bitterly thought of how both Mrs. St. David and his mother had in effect asked him to do the same thing. How could they both be right about him? He dawdled for several days, not even answering the letter. He still had enough money for a while, even if they never gave him another cent. He said to himself that he was too upset to paint. He found himself hanging around the road in front of Mrs. Boree's gateway; or out in the fields beyond her house; or down in an arroyo from which everything was out of sight but the tip of the blue mountain. Approaching there, one afternoon, he heard St. David talking, and he could not go away. In a moment he saw St. David, and that he was talking to a large, sandy-looking cow.

"Life uncritical; life absolute; life abstract," he was saying, almost in song. "You ruminate and gestate and let your generous bag to whomsoever desires it. Oh purity of un-thought! Heavenly vacuity! Obedience without inquiry!"

But he knew whenever anyone was looking, and he turned swiftly on Roger, and slitted his blue-eyed glance suspiciously. Roger stammered something, and started away, but St. David began to laugh, a high, delighted laugh.

"The drug store baby!" he cried, "Gerda told me you came to call the other day and then dwindled off in a storm of nerves. . . . I wouldn't bite you. . . . I have been having the sweetest of all arguments, with my cow here, a one-sided argument. Come here."

St. David took his hand.

"Why is your hand cold?"

Roger explained that—that he was excited, meeting this way, after years of admiring him from afar.

"Rot."

St. David sat down on a clump of salt grass and waved Roger down before him. In a twinkling, Roger was pouring out his troubles, and St. David was nodding, as if ahead of him in the tale. His eyes smouldered and began to fire. His spirit always burned at the news of cruelty, of anyone's hope being maimed, and he interrupted Roger by jumping up and walking away and coming back.

"Never, never, never, never give in!" he almost shrieked. It took all his momentary strength, and he began to cough. He hugged his wracking ribs and bent over, and the coughs travelled up from the ground and shook him as if he were a fiery red cat in the grasp of a huge dog. Roger was alarmed but St. David managed to wave off his concern, and in a little while the seizure was over, and in the sun-lit silence they met each other with little smiles. In that recuperative quiet, another voice then sounded. It came from the rim of the arroyo above them. It said, coolly, musically, "Well, if you need proof, there it is, Edward. If you will waste yourself on everything else but the one thing that matters, which is your work, which I could protect for you."

It was Bertha Morgan Boree, looking down upon them impassively. But her eyes had lights of ire in them, and she looked from the boy to the man and back again. Roger thought she even looked jealous, but he at once said to himself that that was a crazy idea.

St. David seemed for a moment to be too outraged to speak. When at last he could, he was so controlled that he was more terrifying than he was in his outbursts.

"You have been watching me in secret," he said. His voice was thin with contained rage. "When will I ever learn to believe my wife! Nobody could have seen me come here otherwise. It is all I needed to know. . . . Come along, you, lad, we will finish talking in the fields, in broad view of a purer heaven."

He turned and scrambled up the opposite slope of the arroyo with costly energy. The dirt flew down under his hands and feet.

Roger clambered after him, astonished at the powers within that delicate frame.

"Edward! Oh, *do* be sensible and careful," said Mrs. Boree, raising her voice but still sounding most cultivated. "How you misunderstand me! I only feel a *duty*—"

He turned on the opposite edge of the red arroyo and made an obscene gesture at her across the gap, and then fled to the fields, walking loosely and with incredible speed. Words trailed back over his working shoulders to Roger, angry, foul, execratory. At last, a long way across the field, they stopped, and turned, and looked. The bulky figure of the woman was still at the arroyo. Her hands were to the sky. She was posed like a priestess. Roger was impressed. Feeling that, St. David said to him, "She knew we would turn to look."

They walked on in silence for a quarter of an hour, and the calm of the day, the desert scent, wry and pungent, the peace of the looming mountain, the gold of the wheat in fields before the pueblo, which was darker gold in the sunshine, came back into them, and St. David finally said to the boy, "Well, *I* never, never, never, never gave in, and I never shall, *I would rather be killed by what I am than by what somebody else wants me to be.*"

His eyes in the white face, under the dark red bang, raked and swept Roger with a sort of rough compassionate tenderness. He seized the boy's hand and crushed it in his, and then he nodded, and saying "Goodbye, goodbye, we know each other now, those things keep, goodbye," he turned and walked throwingly away in a solitude which defied further intrusion.

Roger went back to his room.

## V

That night he slept out on the roof of the adobe house where he was living. It was a sort of ritual, under the stars of Taos, a farewell, made of joy and grief both. One thing he was sure of. It took a "genius" to say that about *never, never, never, never:* and he vaguely felt that he had been *through* something, but wasn't quite clear about what it was. He lay awake a long time, thinking about everything he had seen and done there in Taos. He loved the busy, commercial, gregarious to-do about "art."

But he knew, too, after those brief but somehow total glimpses of the St. Davids, yes, and of Mrs. Boree, that there were trials which he had never suspected about art in the souls where it lived, and required delivery. He fell asleep at peace, knowing that he carried no such fires within him as were consuming Edward St. David, and the next day he went back to White-water, Texas, and the Bank.

# A PAIR OF RED-TOPPED BOOTS

*by* JACK WEADOCK

Jack Weadock did the following autobiographical note. It is so interesting that it is printed here in full:

"As to the autobiographical material for which you asked, that is a short do and quickly skinned. I am Ohio born, of Irish descent, and raised a stockman. From that I wandered into the Army at the advanced age of sixteen years, fresh out of high school, and thence to Texas and the Border country near El Paso, following Pershing. With him as a guide, I saw something of Chihuahua, and returned packing no other scars than saddle callouses. I returned to the East to catch up on some interrupted education, only to have another war, this time of larger proportions, loom up. Education, of the formal type, again took a back seat, and I shoved off as an infantry scout to Alabama and then to Europe. Four major engagements and several minor ones in France and Belgium gave me a series of lessons not learned from books; but the Irish luck held and, aside from some minor cuts and bruises and a bit of gas, I returned all in one piece.

"The East no longer held much of an attraction, and I went back to the Texas Border and the seventh Cavalry, this time with the intention of getting an appointment to West Point. I was well on my way toward that goal when a Mexican, down along the river, shot at a noise in the dark. I was the noise. For a guy that was working by moonlight and who undoubtedly had to guess at the location of his hind sight, he did very well. When the docs released me, I was in no shape for West Point. I was shy part of one foot. But I finished my Cavalry enlistment and was commissioned in the Reserve.

"I decided to try newspaper work, starting in El Paso. This panned out O. K., and I spent some time there, later moving to Tucson and a general assignment job here on the *Star*. Since then I have been reporter, news editor, city editor, and managing editor of this paper. I now hold a job called assistant-to-the-editor, and neither he nor I have ever figured out what it means; but I like it. During my time in Arizona I have wandered back along the fringes of the livestock business. I am executive secretary of the cattle association here in Southern Arizona, and consider the time I have spent with those boys some of the best

· 63 ·

fun I have ever had. I am married, have a son somewhere in the Pacific with the sub fleet and a seventeen-year-old daughter. *No mas, amigo.*"

---

THE SHERIFF SAT IN HIS OFFICE IN THE PIMA COUNTY COURT-house and gazed through the window at the light but steady fall of rain. Its constant patter on the metal roof of the pail across the areaway and the damp, fresh breeze that came through the open window were a refreshing change from the mid-July heat which had preceded the downpour.

Cattleman as well as officer, the sheriff was content. The summer rains meant fall grass and fat cattle. In Arizona, that meant comfort and relief from worry. The sheriff smiled as he rolled tobacco between his palms, preparing it for his pipe, and listened appreciatively to the doleful strains of a Mexican voice accompanying a guitar in the jail.

As he swung in his chair to reach for his pipe on the desk, the sheriff saw a figure in the doorway. The big, dark-skinned man who stood silently watching the officer almost filled that door-way. His huge body held with a certain native dignity, his large, round face calm and unruffled, Ignacio Flores, sub-chief of the Papago Indians, waited for the sheriff to speak the first word.

"Hello, 'Nacio," said the sheriff, who had been slightly startled by the Indian's sudden appearance. "How are you and what are you doing in town?"

"*Buenos días, señor,*" answered the Indian, "I have come to tell you I have killed a man."

The sheriff came erect in his chair, his eyes no longer dreamy with thoughts of the rain and the range.

"What's that, 'Nacio?" he asked.

"I have just killed a man," said the Indian. "He was *muy malo* and deserved to die, but the law says I must tell you."

"Who was the man? Where did you kill him? Why?" questioned the sheriff, but did not wait for answer. "Come in here," he went on, "and sit down and tell me about it."

· 64 ·

Hat in hand, the big Indian stepped forward and seated himself near the sheriff, who finished tucking the tobacco into his pipe and struck a match, puffing a bit and leaning back to listen.

"I killed the man that is called Texas Jack," said the Indian. "Often you see him here in Tucson; many times you see him in San Xavier. You know him, sheriff?"

The sheriff nodded. He knew Texas Jack for a turbulent, bullying man given to bragging of his own badness, quick to threaten unarmed men and often accused, although never convicted, of having ill-treated Mexican and Indian girls. The sheriff frowned and spat as if freeing his mouth of a bad taste. Assuredly Texas Jack, as the Indian said, was *muy malo* and deserved to die. Others, not Indians, had given that idea serious thought. Nevertheless, a killing was a killing and something would have to be done about it.

"When did this happen and where?" the sheriff asked.

"Last night, señor, on the Rio Santa Cruz near San Xavier. It was there that I buried the man. Then I came to tell you as the law says must be done."

"Yes, 'Nacio, that's right. Now we'll go out there and you'll show me what happened," said the sheriff, reaching for his hat and a slicker.

"*Sí, amigo,*" said the Indian. "I will show you all."

Followed by the Indian, the sheriff walked out into the rain; and soon, side by side, they were riding south from Tucson to where, ten miles away, the white dome of the Mission of San Xavier marked the Papago country.

Arriving at the Indian village, Ignacio took the lead. The sheriff followed him down a trail which led past a number of the adobe huts of the Indian people toward the banks of the Santa Cruz, already swollen from the rains in the hills. As they passed the Indian homes, other Papagos joined them, and on their arrival at the riverbank the party numbered almost a score.

Ignacio, who had been looking at a grove of mesquite trees at the river's edge, shook his head. "It is too late now," he told the sheriff. "We must wait until the river falls. The water covers the place where I buried him. When the rains stop we will find him. But now these people can tell you it was all just as I said."

With the other Indians listening gravely and from time to time nodding assent, Ignacio told the sheriff some of the details. Texas Jack, who had been drinking, had come to the village, made trouble there and refused to leave. When Ignacio had ordered him away, he had threatened the Indian. Ignacio had forced him out of the Indian hut in which the men were, the two men had fought, and in the struggle the Indian had killed Texas Jack with one blow from a club. Having buried the body near the river, he had ridden to Tucson to tell the sheriff what had happened. The other Papagos affirmed that Ignacio was telling the truth, but neither he nor they would tell the sheriff what actually had caused the first trouble between Texas Jack and the Papagos. The sheriff, recalling certain incidents in Texas Jack's career, surmised that an Indian girl had been the reason for the fracas.

He took Ignacio back to his office in Tucson, where he explained to him that under the law he must file a charge of murder against him. Ignacio nodded. The sheriff further explained that under the law Ignacio must stay in jail. Again the Indian nodded, but a look of regret flitted across his calm face as he saw the bars.

Yet to the Indian the sheriff's word was law. The officer filled out the necessary papers, Ignacio was taken before the justice of the peace, the charge was filed, and the stolid Papago was put into a cell. When he had locked him in, the sheriff said, "'Nacio, you're just an Indian, but I'm damned if I know a single white man who would have done what you've done."

In the days that followed preceding his trial Ignacio, already the sheriff's friend, became the friend of every man about the courthouse. Deputy sheriffs, clerks, visitors—all learned to know and admire the huge Papago. So he was not long confined in a cell. Soon as a trusty he had the run of the place, doing chores for the sheriff, caring for the latter's horse at a near-by stable, and waiting quietly in the office for a chance to be of service. He became known as "the sheriff's Indian" and was accepted as an important fixture.

But when the date of the Indian's trial arrived, fate stepped in. A wave of reform had struck the desert city. Train robberies, in which several men had lost their lives, had brought a feeling of revulsion against killers of all kinds. As this wave reached its crest, Ignacio went to his trial.

Before a jury his calm unruffled manner, the very way in which he simply told the truth, as he had told it to the sheriff that rainy July morning, hurt rather than helped him. The prosecutor, hammered at by the reform group, set out to make an example of this stolid murderer. The sheriff, although he felt that Ignacio undoubtedly was justified in what he had done, could not help his Indian friend, but was forced to stand by and watch the Indian's own honesty bring him closer and closer to the noose.

The defense attorney, paid by the sheriff himself, did the best he could with his difficult task. In the face of the Indian's confession he emphasized the fact that the victim's body had never been found. When the river had receded, the waters had carried away with them all evidence except the defendant's word. But Ignacio's confession to the sheriff and his repetition of it in the court of justice, supported by the unwilling statements of the other Indians, balked the defense attorney's every effort. As one man the Papagos steadfastly refused to give the real cause of the quarrel that led to the death of Texas Jack. Ignacio confined himself to his original statement: "He was *muy malo* and deserved to die."

The jury returned a verdict of murder in the first degree. The Indian was sentenced to hang, and the reform element was appeased.

The sheriff took Ignacio back to the jail, but despite the

death sentence he made no change in the Indian's routine. He was still a trusty. Political enemies of the sheriff declared that he was giving the prisoner every chance to escape. They charged the officer with neglect of duty and made threats as to what would happen if the Indian did escape.

In answering one of these critics the sheriff answered all. To this one he said, "'Nacio has given me his word that he will be here when I want him. You wouldn't understand that, but he and I do. Now get the hell out of here and stay out."

In the meantime the defense attorney filed an appeal. But after weeks, during which the mild-mannered Indian daily added to his horde of well-wishers, the appeal was denied. The date for the execution was set. The hammers of the carpenters rang in the courthouse yard, building the scaffold upon which to hang Ignacio.

Ignacio viewed it all without comment. To him it seemed that his friend the sheriff had done all that could be done. What was to happen would happen.

But the sheriff could not see it the same way.

The huge Indian had become a close friend. His simple dignity had earned him not only the affection of the sheriff but that of all the sheriff's deputies also. The former faced mutiny among his own men. To a man they refused to have anything to do with the execution of Ignacio. They had erected the scaffold, but more than that they would not do. If the sheriff wanted their badges, he could have them. That was final.

The day before the hanging the sheriff went to tell his friend that there was no hope. "'Nacio," he said, "I can do nothing more. Tomorrow you must die. It is the law. But today I can give you anything you want. Decide what you want most, and I'll see that you get it."

In the Mexican quarter on Meyer Street, where he had been on errands, Ignacio had seen a pair of magnificent boots in a store window. They were black, with the uppers stitched in many flowery designs in brilliant red. It was a pair of boots of which a warrior might be proud. He wanted those boots.

The sheriff took him down to the bootmaker on Meyer Street and bought them for him. The Indian wore them as he and the sheriff walked back to the jail. All that day, as he worked about the jail and the courthouse, he wore the boots and took much pride in showing them to all his friends.

The gray light of the dawn of the day of execution found men gathered about the scaffold in the courthouse yard. It was a silent crowd. There were some officers, but not one of the sheriff's deputies.

From the courthouse door, walking side by side, came the sheriff and Ignacio. The Indian's hands were free as he crossed the yard in his new boots and mounted the scaffold with his friend. Standing under the dangling rope, he put one hand on the officer's shoulder, spoke to him in a tone so low that none but they two could hear, then held his arms still for the sheriff to strap them to his sides.

This done, the sheriff adjusted the black cap on the Indian's head and the noose around his neck. Stepping back he waved his hand in silent farewell and with tears streaming down his face descended from the scaffold.

At the foot of the steps he picked up a hatchet he had placed there and with one blow cut the rope which, acting as a trigger, sprung the trap. As the trap-door fell open and the suddenly taut rope hummed, the sheriff, his face set and his head high, strode across the courthouse yard without a backward glance at his dying friend.

# DAKOTAH COURTSHIP

*by* STANLEY VESTAL (W. S. CAMPBELL)

"Stanley Vestal," known in academic circles as Dr. W. S. Campbell, teaches English at the University of Oklahoma. He is an authority
on the Plains Indian, and has held a Guggenheim Fellowship for study
in this field. He writes under both his names. As W. S. Campbell, one
of his latest books was a textbook called *Professional Writing*. As Stanley
Vestal, he has written *Kit Carson, Sitting Bull, Warpath, The Old Santa
Fé Trail*, etc. His most recent is his biography of Big-Foot Wallace. He
is also a frequent contributor to the *Southwest Review* and the name
"Stanley Vestal" is carried on its masthead as one of its editors.

---

JOE LONE BEAR WAS A CONFIDENT YOUNG MAN WITH A LONG
reach and a steady eye, and plenty proud of his battered,
stripped-down car, daubed all over with what Joe believed
were the latest collegiate mottoes: MEN AT WORK, CHICKEN COOP,
THAT MAN IS HERE AGAIN, SOCKO, SO LONG, EXCUSE MY DUST. But
as Joe gradually approached the gate of Chief Hardtack's allotment, his young heart missed almost as often as his chugging
engine. Lillie Fineweather lived there.

That motor trouble in Joe's fighting heart was not entirely
due to Lillie's near presence, however. Lillie and Joe had mostly
got along fine—at the Indian Boarding School. The pocket of
his blue shirt contained a well-thumbed letter in her firm Spen-
cerian hand, assuring him, in a curious mixture of school slang
and Indian poetry, that she loved him: "Hurry up, Big Boy. I'm
crazy about you. All time you way off in South Dakota, my lips
are still on your lips."

Lillie was okay. One in a million. But now he had to face old
Mrs. Hardtack and her stuffy old man, and hurdle their objec-
tions. Dakotah and Crow had been enemies from away back.

When a Dakotah boy came courting a Crow girl, there was likely to be trouble.

Lillie had warned Joe that her grandma was terrible old-fashioned. Lillie said Joe couldn't wrangle the old lady single-handed. So Joe had brought along his own grandparents to make the match in the old-time way. But now, as he rolled in through Hardtack's gate, Joe began to get cold feet about that.

Anxiously, he shouted to caution the aged warrior at his elbow. Chief Lone Bear sat braced against the gale, clutching his splintered stiff straw hat with gnarled fingers, staring fiercely through the windshield. "Grandfather," Joe yelled, "the wars are over. We are friends with these people now. Remember that!"

The old Dakotah shifted his moccasins to a firmer position upon the hot floorboards, turned red-rimmed eyes upon his grandson, and showed his yellow teeth in a grin of pleasurable anticipation. "Make your heart strong, my grandson," he quavered. "I know how to handle the Crows. I have killed plenty of them in my day, and made them run like rabbits. *He-han!* Who is this Hardtack? He has seen only seventy-six winters. I have nothing to fear from that boy!"

The old man's words upset Joe. Then and there he killed his engine. The car jolted to a stop.

It was a good long hundred yards across the blistering prairie to Hardtack's unpainted shack and the brush arbor alongside. But Joe was too disheartened to try to start the car again. Chances were it wouldn't start, anyhow, and he did not want the visit to begin by Lillie's folks having the laugh on him. It would be less humiliating to pretend that he had meant to stop right there, and walk the rest of the way.

Joe jumped out, landing on the heels of his tan Oxfords. Chief Lone Bear stepped down, catlike, in the manner of a man who has worn moccasins all his life. Old Mrs. Lone Bear, after a moment's silent dismay at the distance to be covered afoot, heaved her two hundred pounds up from the rumble-seat and slowly clambered to the ground.

The spry old man went first, bright-eyed, bow-legged, stooping over his polished cane. Joe nervously hitched up his blue jeans and followed. The old woman pulled her bright new blanket—the price of her participation—over her meaty shoulders, and plodded along behind.

Just as they started, Joe saw Lillie leave the arbor and hurry into the shack. It was clear that the Hardtacks knew what was up. Nobody came from the arbor to greet them. The three Dakotahs halted and stood in a row just outside.

Joe lowered his head and peered in. Chief Hardtack, hatless and barefoot, lay at his ease in the checkered shadows of the arbor, puffing his long pipe and looking out indifferently through horn-rimmed spectacles. The frames held no glass, but Joe was in no mood to laugh. Hardtack was a big, vital man, and tough as a mule.

But when Joe laid eyes on the old woman, he held his breath. Mrs. Hardtack was formidable. She sat upright on the ground— one leg stretched straight out before her. Her flat, uncompromising face was painted red. She had a short hooked nose, like the beak of an owl, and her dark gaze was so searching and hostile that Joe wondered what ailed him. She wore an old-time calico dress with open flaps for sleeves. A regular squaw—even if she was Lillie's grandma.

Nobody moved. Nobody spoke. Each party waited for the other to make the first move. Chief Lone Bear would not enter until the Crow had made him welcome. The Hardtacks were ready to sit still forever rather than welcome a Dakotah on such an errand. In the silence, Joe heard the dog scratching himself.

Joe couldn't stand it. He broke the ice. "*How!*" he said.

At that word, old Mrs. Hardtack drew herself up triumphantly. Her hard face set in lines of scorn. "Dakotah!" she sneered.

Hardtack now came suddenly to life. "*Sho-da-gee!*" he cried, in hospitable greeting now that the others had begun the talk. Chief Lone Bear stepped over the pots and firewood, grasped Hardtack's hand quickly, and seated himself on his host's left side—the side nearest his heart. Mrs. Lone Bear, making a purring sound of pleasure, waddled in and found a place beside her hostess. All four of them seemed to be in high good humor, eager to begin the business. All four of them completely ignored Joe.

Joe felt like a rank outsider. For a minute he stood still, not knowing what to do. Then he turned hastily and retreated. Nobody wanted him around.

Chief Hardtack's allotment was a flat, uncompromising square of short Montana grass surrounded by a sagging fence of rusty barbed wire. The sun beat down on it with all the steady purpose of an August afternoon. Joe decided to wait in the car. It would be hot—but what the hell!

To reach the car, Joe had to pass the shack. The door was open, and the aroma of boiling coffee caught his nostrils. Lillie Fineweather stood inside, looking anxiously out towards the arbor through the grimy windowpane. Joe halted in his tracks. "Hey, Lillie. Is that you?"

She turned towards him, shamefaced. "Believe it or not," she said defiantly. "Go on and laugh. I know I look awful. Grandma made me do it."

She hardly looked the bobbed-haired beauty Joe had dated and dragged to the movies at school. Her hair still had the lustre of a new gun-barrel, but it was parted down the middle now and plaited into two stubby braids made long with strands of colored yarn. Instead of her usual shirt and dungarees, she had on a red calico dress with a yoke and frill—Crow Reservation, fashion 1890—and high button shoes too big for her. Yet somehow, she was pretty in spite of it.

Joe could not help laughing. "Are you the kid I come all this way to marry?"

"You don't have to," she countered. Relenting, she added, "No kidding, Joe. I thought you were never coming. One more day in this lousy dump, and I'll be coocoo."

"Okay. Let's skip," Joe prompted.

"Nothing doing, Big Boy. Grandma's got me buffaloed. I'm scared to marry without her okay—supposing you can get it."

Joe laughed. "Me? What I got to do with it? I'm just a by-stander." He moved his pursed lips in the direction of the old folks. "Well, I guess the war is on." Joe started to enter.

Lillie raised her hand to stop him. "Keep out, Joe. If Grandma catches you alone with me, she'll sure raise hell. She'll call the whole thing off. She's terrible old-fashioned, like I told you. She don't approve of necking."

Joe halted. "Who said anything about necking?" he complained.

"Nobody. But somebody might think of it. Whyn't you set on the stoop outside? It's shady there. That way we can talk, and watch the old folks at the same time. They can't understand each other's talk. They'll have to use the sign language."

"Okay, sweetheart." Joe sat on the stoop, and ran his fingers through his shock of stiff black hair. Looking sideways he could see every movement in the arbor—not a dozen yards away. Lillie was watching through the window.

Already Mrs. Lone Bear had begun. Her thick fingers moved in the staccato sequences of the sign talk, in gestures known to all Plains Indians. "My grandson told me he wants to marry your granddaughter. Me and my man come to see this girl. We want a good wife for our grandson."

Mrs. Hardtack smiled with marked condescension. "Is that puny boy your grandson? He would be lucky, if she ever looked at him. She could marry any man in the Crow nation."

Mrs. Lone Bear settled her weight more comfortably, as if for a long session. Her plump, copper-colored fingers moved with blandly slow precision. "He is strong and brave. His lodge will be full of meat all times. He has many horses."

"How many?" Mrs. Hardtack demanded, ticking off the question dubiously on the upraised fingers of her left hand. Her deliberate gesture implied that Joe could not possess more than one, one and a half, or two horses at the outside.

Mrs. Lone Bear smiled in a superior way, ignoring the question. "He also has a fast wagon. Look."

Mrs. Hardtack laughed. "I see it. It runs slow and stops quick. I would be afraid to have my granddaughter ride in that."

Mrs. Lone Bear's smile turned a little sour. "Moreover, he learned to fight with fists like white men, wearing mittens of leather, in a rope corral. I saw him. He knocked down every young man his size in the school, and four white boys." Mrs. Lone Bear cocked her head on one side, and made a decisive gesture to end her speech: "Cut!"

"How many horses has he?" Mrs. Hardtack persisted.

"Plenty. Heaps. We come from far to see this girl. Where is she? Why is she hiding? She must be ugly."

Then Mrs. Hardtack charged. "My daughter does not think of marriage. She would not look at a Dakotah. Your grandson must be crazy to follow her. She is a wife for a chief. She can cook and sew and wash and tan hides. She makes fine beadwork. She is beautiful and modest and strong as a horse. On top of that she belongs to a family of warriors and feastmakers. Her great grandfather was a famous horsethief!"

Joe looked over his shoulder. "Attagirl, Lillie. Grandma and me think you're tops."

Lillie giggled at him. "Tune in, Big Boy. Your time's coming."

Mrs. Hardtack never faltered. "Look at my husband. He got his name stealing bread from the soldiers at the fort. He was the meanest boy we ever had. When he was little he used to steal his mother's butcher knife and slash holes in the tent. She could not stop him. He was bad. Heap bad. Always making trouble." She beamed.

"Hot dog! What a naughty boy!" Joe jeered.

Lillie stiffened. "Lay off my folks," she cautioned.

"How about mine?" Joe demanded.

"They ain't so hot, I guess," she answered, and kept her face to the window.

"Our family is related to Sitting Bull's," Mrs. Lone Bear explained with steady hands. "You Crows all remember him. He stole plenty horses from you—every winter, they say. But he was never mean to women—not even Crow women."

Mrs. Hardtack laughed unpleasantly. "He never had a chance to be."

Mrs. Lone Bear replied with emphatic gestures. "I was told his warriors gave him a Crow woman. They captured her. Sitting Bull gave her a good horse and sent her home."

"No Crow woman would have married him," Mrs. Hardtack snapped back. "She would die first." Her black eyes shone fiercely. "That is the way when Dakota and Crow marry. They are never happy."

Mrs. Lone Bear could not resist that opening. With gusto she signaled, "That was what Sitting Bull said."

Joe called to Lillie, in genuine alarm. "Hey, the old girls will be in each other's hair in a minute. Can't you stop 'em?"

Lillie scowled at him. Then her face relaxed. "Okay. Coming up. I'll give 'em coffee. But don't pull any fast ones about my folks. I can't take it."

"Cross my heart, Lil. Give 'em some eats. They can't swallow and bite at the same time. And put plenty of sugar in the coffee."

Hastily, Lillie Fineweather caught up the kettle of stew and the pot of coffee, hurried to the arbor, and placed the food before her grandmother. Then she came back. For a while there was no sound in the arbor but that of resolute mastication. Chewing, for the old folks, was a chore that demanded concentration.

The old men, having been served first, finished before the women. Hardtack was host, and had to use both hands to fill and light his pipe. Lone Bear had his chance at last. He smacked his lips, and gestured to catch Hardtack's eye. Then, making sure the women were also watching, he began to make signs.

"When I was young, there were many Crow captives among my people. The Crows were always getting killed and captured. They did not know how to take care of themselves. There is a Crow captive now living at Standing Rock Agency. He refused to go back to his people. He was happier with us. It will be so with your granddaughter."

Hardtack stopped filling his pipe, and used his hands in talk. "Crows killed plenty Dakotahs. I was not born yesterday."

· 76 ·

Hardtack went back to work, tamping in the tobacco with his thumb, firmly. Even from the shack, Joe could see how the old man's hands trembled with rage.

Lone Bear smacked his lips again and grinned. "The Dakotahs killed Long Hair and hundreds of his soldiers. Their bodies covered the hills like a big blue blanket. I saw it. I was in the fight. You were only a boy then, too young to fight. That was your good luck. But we did not kill many Crows that day. They ran away."

Joe groaned. "Zowie! Now Granddad is talking about the Custer battle."

"The Custer Massacre," Lillie corrected him, sharply.

Joe bristled. "Massacre nothing. Them soldiers came looking for trouble, and found it. They died fighting—with guns in their hands and cartridges in their belts. That was a fair fight, and no massacre."

"That's what *you* think," Lillie snapped. "I know. Some of my relatives were there."

Joe swayed with restless irritation. "They did not stay long," he countered. Then, suddenly, he whirled on her. "Hey, Lil. Don't let it get you too. We got to stand together. I'm going to marry you."

"Maybe," she said, her eyes brimming with angry tears.

"Okay, Lillie, if that's the way you feel." Joe turned his back on her.

"Oh, for the love of Mike, shut up," she scolded. "The more we talk, the worse it is. I can't help it, I tell you. I was raised that way."

Joe said no more, and watched the old men. Chief Lone Bear was clapping his hands in rapid imitation of rifle-fire. "The soldiers shot fast that day. But we made them run, we killed them. It was a great day. Every little while I picked up a feather for my cap. I cannot remember how many I killed that day."

"My relatives told me it was a hard fight to the end," the Crow objected.

Lone Bear ignored the interruption. "I was there. I saw.

We Dakotahs made the Crows who came with the white men run for their lives. I have heard that they did not stop running for three days. Some of them are running still, maybe." Lone Bear laughed.

Hardtack threw up his head. His eyes glittered. "There are too many tongues. That day the Crows fought well. They captured the ponies of your people. Long Hair told them to do that. The Crows charged ahead of the soldiers, and ran off the ponies. But they were not told to stand and die. When they saw that the soldiers could not win, they ran away. If the soldiers had been smart, they would have run away too. A good warrior knows when to charge and when to retreat. The Crows did both better than the white soldiers."

Lone Bear gave a hearty gesture of assent. "The Crows ran well that day." He laughed. "I chased them."

Hardtack sucked flame into his pipe-bowl as if he would swallow it. He inhaled two savage puffs. Then he saw that Lone Bear was preparing to make signs again. Quickly, Hardtack handed the pipe to the Dakotah—to keep his hands still.

"I have seen Dakotahs running," he signaled. "I will tell you. That was my first warpath. I had seen only sixteen winters. I was too young to be scared. There were eight of us. Big Shoulders was leader. We found a Dakotah camp on the Yellowstone River. It was winter, and the snow was deep.

"We kept hidden while Big Shoulders threw dirt on the ice to make a road for the horses. He saw five Dakotahs coming horseback. He ran back to us. Then I ran up to the hilltop and looked over. The Dakotahs sat down to smoke, and their ponies pawed the snow to find something to eat. Then one Dakotah came riding up my hill to look around. I was reckless. I stood up. The four Dakotahs who were smoking saw me. They yelled to warn their friend. Twice they yelled. But it was cold, he had a shawl tied over his ears. He could not hear them.

"Then my friend Bear-All-the-Time shot that lone Dakotah's horse. The horse did not fall, but lunged along, and its foreleg swung back and forth, loose—like a rope. The man on that horse jumped off into the snow and tried to get away. The snow was hip-deep there. We all rode after him.

"The first Crow hit the Dakotah and took his gun. The other one claimed the horse. The two of them began to wrestle for the gun. I was third. I shot that Dakotah dead. The four Dakotahs who had been smoking got on their horses and ran. They ran well. Maybe they are running yet. But the man I shot did not run. He was dead. I killed him. I have heard that his name was Running Hawk."

Lillie turned on Joe, her eyes burning. "Get that, you lousy Dakotah?" she triumphed. "The Crows are not so dumb."

Lone Bear sat with hanging head, and sang a sad song.

Joe glared at Lillie. He was breathing hard through his nostrils. "Running Hawk was a relative of mine," he said, sternly.

"Joe! Is that true?" Lillie turned to him, her face stricken. "Oh, Big Boy, I'm so sorry. Look here, Joe. The old folks know we are watching them. I bet they are trying us out. That's what. If we can't take it, they don't want us to marry."

Joe stared at her. He looked quickly at the group in the arbor. "Kid, you're smart. You've said a mouthful. That's it, all right. It's just like them old-time peace treaties Granddad tells about. They got together and insulted each other—to make sure the peace would stick!"

Lillie nodded.

Joe got up. "Look here, Lil. This has gone far enough. If they keep on, they'll make saps of us. We got to stop it. Come on. I don't give a damn if he was my relative. That was ages ago. It's got nothing to do with us."

The old women were weeping. The old men beamed at each other. "A Dakotah and a Crow will always be fighting," Hard-tack declared, with satisfaction.

"True," Lone Bear assented, with gusto. "They are like two mean dogs. If they fight, you can pull them apart. But if you turn them loose, they will go right back to fighting again."

But Joe and Lillie were in the arbor, each talking as fast as possible—the one in Crow, the other in Dakotah, and both in the sign language. "The past is rubbed out. All this talk is no good. We want to get married. We ain't old-time Indians. We got to forget the past, and think about the future."

The old folks sat still, astonished at the outburst. One by one they subsided. They sat staring at the ground, with disappointed faces. The women wiped their tears with the corners of their blankets. The old men hung their heads. The happy game of bluff and brag was over.

When the young folks stopped talking, they stood there, a little frightened at their own rashness. But after a time, Lone Bear took the floor. He was the oldest man—a man of experience. His face lighted with a smile. He stood up, and began to move his hands in his best oratorical manner.

"My grandson is right. The trail behind is lost. The rains and snows of many winters have filled in with mud. It is covered with grass. Here and there it has been plowed under. When I was young, I used to come upon the bones of a man lying on the prairie. Sometimes they were the bones of a Crow, sometimes of a Dakotah. But now I never find bones lying on the prairie. The old trail is lost. The young men cannot find it.

"Yet it is good to remember the old ways. Ours was a good trail. Once I had a Crow woman in my lodge. She was my fifth wife. I stole her. She was a fine woman, and we were happy. It is true, I made her very jealous. I never knew when she would whip out her knife and try to stab me. She used to hide my clothes to keep me at home. But now she is dead, and these grandchildren of ours want to get married. That is good. I am willing, we are all willing. It is time to forget the past and think of the days ahead. It is time for us to do something for our grandchildren. They will marry, and set up a lodge of their own, and have a son. That boy must have a good name. What shall we call him?"

"Yes. A good name," Mrs. Lone Bear assented.

"The name of some friendly animal," Mrs. Hardtack insisted, firmly.

Chief Hardtack sat up grandly. "Above all, a famous name."

"The child will be a Dakotah, like his father. He should be called Sitting Bull," Lone Bear advised.

"No," Hardtack objected. "The husband lives with his wife's folks. That is the custom. The child will be Crow. He ought to have a Crow name."

"My woman goes with me," Joe gestured, positively. "She does not like it here."

Lillie turned on him. "Oh, yeah? That's what you think. What's the matter with Crow country, I'd like to know?"

"Why, Lil, you told me yourself—"

"You're crazy. Anyhow, if we did marry and have a kid, like as not it would be a girl."

"My kid a girl?" he protested, grappling with the new idea.

"Sure. Why not? What's wrong with a girl? I thought you was modern."

"But Lillie—"

"I say it's a girl, Joe. That's flat. And you bet I won't have no girl named Sitting Bull!"

"Skip it, Lil. Call her Prairie Flower, Milkweed, Sagebrush, Cactus, or Hollers All Night. We got plenty of time to name the kid. Let's get married. Come on. We can find the missionary in town in ten minutes."

"Don't get tough, Big Boy. We got to make the old folks like it, or the kid won't have no grandparents to look after it."

"Lucky kid," Joe groaned.

Lillie's eyes blazed. "You think I'm going to stay home all day with that baby? I ain't no squaw. I want some fun out of life."

"Fun!" Joe barked. "They'll be plenty of fun, if you don't take care of my kid. Let's get going. All this fuss makes me sick. Come on." Joe took her by the arm.

Stung by the shame of having him touch her in the presence of her relatives, Lillie struggled to wrench herself free. "Let go of me," she raged. "Where do you think you are anyhow?" She slapped him hard across the cheek. Joe let go.

Breathless, she stood poised, with open mouth, watching his

face. She whirled and ran. The moment she moved, Joe was after her. Two strides brought him close. Lillie heard him coming, stepped to one side quickly, and stuck out her foot. She tripped him. Joe hit the grass on his face.

Lillie laughed at him. "Don't you try to boss me, Big Boy. You ain't big enough." She ran into the shack and slammed the door.

Joe got up. The old folks were laughing. Joe hitched up his jeans and stalked off to his car. He was still trying to start it when Lillie Fineweather passed by on her way to the gate. She sailed past in her new sneakers, blue dungarees, and a clean white shirt. Her shining bob swung free. Joe thought she looked swell. She was headin' for town, sure. Joe tried to catch her eye. "Where you goin', Lillie?"

"Nowhere with you," she replied. "And don't you follow me neither—if you ever do get that thing started. You damn Dakotah, I'm through."

Joe stamped on the starter furiously, and held his foot down. Lil went on, and he saw her halt at the gate. A truck was rolling down the road in a cloud of dust. Lillie raised her thumb and waggled it in the air above her head. Joe saw the truck slow to pick her up.

"No you don't," Joe muttered, and jumped from his seat. He sprinted to the gate. The truck had stopped. The driver was a big red-faced bruiser, thick in the neck and wide in the shoulders. Fat, though. Automatically, Joe judged the man outweighed him twenty pounds.

The big roughneck looked Lillie up and down. "Goin' to town? Hop in, Sister."

Lillie grasped the handbar and set foot on the board. Joe jerked her back to earth with a single movement, shoved her to one side. He did not hear her protests. "Get going, you big ape," Joe commanded, "or I'll knock you cold."

The driver appraised Joe, and laughed. "You and how many more, you damned Indian!"

Joe swung himself up, hanging to the truck with one hand,

· 82 ·

jabbing with the other. The driver raised his feet suddenly, pivoted to face Joe, planted his boots with a violent shove on Joe's middle, then let drive with all his force. As the man's legs straightened, Joe shot backward into the ditch. He did not get up. He lay there, both hands on his belt, gasping for breath.

The driver jumped down. "Just a minute, Sister, till I tromp him." He sprang towards Joe.

Lillie said nothing. She stuck out her foot. She tripped him. The driver was a heavy man; when he hit the ground, he grunted.

But he was soon up, and whirling on the girl to strike her. His first blow barely reached her shoulder, but it sent her staggering.

Joe got up then, stumbling across the ruts to slug the big hick scientifically and hard, first on one jaw, then on the other, in spite of the clutching pain at his midriff. The driver put up a fight. But as Joe's wind came back, the other's left him. A final clip on the chin sent the driver back to collapse against the front fender of the truck. He got up blinking, warded off Joe's fists with open hands, and crawled back into his cab.

As the engine roared to a start, the driver yelled some words at Lillie Fineweather. She could not make them out, but she saw his face. She made a gesture, as if she were throwing dirt at it. The truck lurched away.

Joe stood panting, looking admiringly at the girl. "Gee, Lil. You sure pack a wicked foot."

Lillie's eyes showed fire. "Nobody's going to call you names while I'm around," she declared. "Say, Big Boy, will your old bus start? This dump is getting me. Folks around here do nothing but fight. You got some cash, I guess. Tomorrow the rodeo starts at Sheridan. You promised me we could see it."

"Boy howdy. You sure can—after we see the missionary. But what'll I do with my old folks?"

"Park them here," Lillie advised sagely. "It's a cinch they can't pull out till you get back. They'll love it; they ain't had a good fight for fifty years. Two-three days here will get it out of their system. Then they'll kiss and make up."

Together they walked to the car. Joe got in and fiddled with things on the dash, while Lillie waited to see whether it would go or not. At last, by some method which Joe pretended to understand, but did not, he managed to start the engine.

"Hop in, Lillie," he commanded.

She stood looking back at the arbor. She seemed troubled. "Hold on, Joe. We forgot the name for the kid. We've got to settle that now, or we'll never have peace in the family."

Joe laughed. "That's easy. I already done it. You looked so cute and friendly back there, when you tripped that big bozo, it come to me all at once. I got it."

"No soft-soap, Joe. My name won't do. You heard the old folks. All Crow and Dakotah names are out." She remained standing beside the car.

"Sure," he answered. "I got it. A good name, an animal name, above all a famous name. Hop in. We'll call the kid Mickie Mouse!"

Lillie Fineweather stood open-mouthed at the dazzling wisdom of his idea. She climbed in obediently, and snuggled close to Joe. "Big Boy," she whispered, "you're wonderful!"

Joe Lone Bear made himself look even bigger than he was. He threw in the clutch, the car sailed off, cutting a wide circle through the grass on its way back to the gate. Joe felt like a champion.

But by the time that circle was completed, Lillie Fineweather was herself again. She sat up straight beside Joe, and her face was set. When she spoke, she spoke firmly.

"Listen, Joe. We're going to call her *Minnie Mouse!*"

# THE PIMIENTA PANCAKES

*by* O. HENRY (WILLIAM SYDNEY PORTER)

William Sydney Porter ("O. Henry") was the father of the American short story as it was written, almost exclusively, up to the first World War. The stories in most of the popular magazines still owe much to his influence.

O. Henry was jugged in Austin, on charges which may or may not have been warranted. He also performed certain journalistic chores in this city, where incidentally he found the social mannerisms of the local upper crust worthy material for an occasional farce. He also worked a while on the Houston *Post* before he gravitated to New York. He also spent some time on a Texas ranch. A report of this rustication, garnished with many excellent quotes, will be found in the "Biography" section of this book, as set down by Dora Neill Raymond in her *Captain Lee Hall of Texas*.

---

WHILE WE WERE ROUNDING UP A BUNCH OF THE TRIANGLE-O cattle in the Frio bottoms, a projecting branch of a dead mesquite caught my wooden stirrup and gave my ankle a wrench that laid me up in camp for a week.

On the third day of my compulsory idleness I crawled out near the grub wagon, and reclined helpless under the conversational fire of Judson Odom, the camp cook. Jud was a monologist by nature, whom Destiny, with customary blundering, had set in a profession wherein he was bereaved, for the greater portion of his time, of an audience.

Therefore, I was manna in the desert of Jud's obmutescence.

Betimes I was stirred by invalid longings for something to eat that did not come under the caption of "grub." I had visions of the maternal pantry "deep as first love, and wild with all regret," and then I asked:

"Jud, can you make pancakes?"

Jud laid down his six-shooter, with which he was preparing to pound an antelope steak, and stood over me in what I felt to be a menacing attitude. He further indorsed my impression that his pose was resentful by fixing upon me with his light-blue eyes a look of cold suspicion.

"Say, you," he said, with candid, though not excessive, choler, "did you mean that straight, or was you trying to throw the gaff into me? Some of the boys been telling you about me and that pancake racket?"

"No, Jud," I said, sincerely, "I meant it. It seems to me I'd swap my pony and saddle for a stack of buttered brown pancakes with some first crop, open kettle, New Orleans sweetening. Was there a story about pancakes?"

Jud was mollified at once when he saw that I had not been dealing in allusions. He brought some mysterious bags and tin boxes from the grub wagon and set them in the shade of the hackberry where I lay reclined. I watched him as he began to arrange them leisurely and untie their many strings.

"No, not a story," said Jud, as he worked, "but just the logical disclosures in the case of me and that pink-eyed snoozer from Mired Mule Cañada and Miss Willella Learight. I don't mind telling you.

"I was punching then for old Bill Toomey, on the San Miguel. One day I gets all ensnared up in aspirations for to eat some canned grub that hasn't ever mooed or baaed or grunted or been in peck measures. So, I gets on my bronc and pushes the wind for Uncle Emsley Telfair's store at the Pimienta Crossing on the Nueces.

"About three in the afternoon I threw my bridle rein over a mesquite limb and walked the last twenty yards into Uncle Emsley's store. I got up on the counter and told Uncle Emsley that the signs pointed to the devastation of the fruit crop of the world. In a minute I had a bag of crackers and a long-handled spoon, with an open can each of apricots and pineapples and cherries and greengages beside of me with Uncle Emsley busy chopping away with the hatchet at the yellow clings. I was feeling like Adam before the apple stampede, and was digging my spurs into the side of the counter and working with my twenty-four-inch spoon when I happened to look out of the window into the yard of Uncle Emsley's house, which was next to the store.

"There was a girl standing there—an imported girl with fixings on—philandering with a croquet maul and amusing herself by watching my style of encouraging the fruit canning industry.

"I slid off the counter and delivered up my shovel to Uncle Emsley.

"'That's my niece,' says he; 'Miss Willella Learight, down from Palestine on a visit. Do you want that I should make you acquainted?'

"'The Holy Land,' I says to myself, my thoughts milling some as I tried to run 'em into the corral. 'Why not? There was sure angels in Pales—Why yes, Uncle Emsley,' I says out loud, 'I'd be awful edified to meet Miss Learight.'

"So Uncle Emsley took me out in the yard and gave us each other's entitlements.

"I never was shy about women. I never could understand why some men who can break a mustang before breakfast and shave in the dark, get all left-handed and full of perspiration and excuses when they see a bolt of calico draped around what belongs in it. Inside of eight minutes me and Miss Willella was aggravating the croquet balls around as amiable as second cousins. She gave me a dig about the quantity of canned fruit I had eaten, and I got back at her, flat-footed, about how a certain lady named Eve started the fruit trouble in the first free-grass pasture—'Over in Palestine, wasn' it?' says I, as easy and pat as roping a one-year-old.

"That was how I acquired cordiality for the proximities of Miss Willella Learight; and the disposition grew larger as time passed. She was stopping at Pimienta Crossing for her health, which was very good, and for the climate, which was forty per cent hotter than Palestine. I rode over to see her once every week for a while; and then I figured it out that if I doubled the number of trips I would see her twice as often.

"One week I slipped in a third trip; and that's where the pancakes and the pink-eyed snoozer busted into the game.

"That evening, while I set on the counter with a peach and two damsons in my mouth, I asked Uncle Emsley how Miss Willella was.

"'Why,' says Uncle Emsley, 'she's gone riding with Jackson Bird, the sheep man from over at Mired Mule Cañada.'

"I swallowed the peach seed and the two damson seeds. I guess somebody held the counter by the bridle while I got off; and then I walked out straight ahead till I butted against the mesquite where my roan was tied.

"'She's gone riding,' I whisper in my bronc's ear, 'with Birdstone Jack, the hired mule from Sheep Man's Cañada. Did you get that, old Leather-and-Gallops?'

"That bronc of mine wept, in his way. He'd been raised a cow pony and he didn't care for snoozers.

"I went back and said to Uncle Emsley: 'Did you say a sheep man?'

"'I said a sheep man,' says Uncle again. 'You must have heard tell of Jackson Bird. He's got eight sections of grazing and four thousand head of the finest Merinos south of the Arctic Circle.'

"I went out and sat on the ground in the shade of the store and leaned against a prickly pear. I sifted sand into my boots with my unthinking hands while I soliloquized a quantity about this bird with the Jackson plumage to his name.

"I never had believed in harming sheep men. I see one, one day, reading a Latin grammar on hossback, and I never touched him! They never irritated me like they do most cow men. You wouldn't go to work now, and impair and disfigure snoozers, would you, that eat on tables and wear little shoes and speak to you on subjects? I had always let 'em pass, just as you would a jack-rabbit; with a polite word and a guess about the weather, but no stopping to swap canteens. I never thought it was worth while to be hostile with a snoozer. And because I'd been lenient, and let 'em live, here was one going around riding with Miss Willella Learight!

"An hour by sun they come loping back, and stopped at Uncle Emsley's gate. The sheep person helped her off; and they stood throwing each other sentences all sprightful and sagacious for a while. And then this feathered Jackson flies up in his saddle and raises his little stewpot of a hat, and trots off in the direction of his mutton ranch. By this time I had turned the sand out of my boots and unpinned myself from the prickly pear; and by the time he gets half a mile out of Pimienta, I single-foots up beside him on my bronc.

"I said that snoozer was pink-eyed, but he wasn't. His seeing arrangement was gray enough, but his eyelashes was pink and his hair was sandy, and that gave you the idea. Sheep man? He wasn't more than a lamb man, anyhow—a little thing with his neck involved in a yellow silk handkerchief, and shoes tied up in bowknots.

"'Afternoon!' says I to him. 'You now ride with a equestrian who is commonly called Dead-Moral-Certainty Judson, on account of the way I shoot. When I want a stranger to know me I always introduce myself before the draw, for I never did like to shake hands with ghosts.'

"'Ah,' says he, just like that. 'Ah, I'm glad to know you, Mr. Judson. I'm Jackson Bird, from over at Mired Mule Ranch.'

"Just then one of my eyes saw a roadrunner skipping down the hill with a young tarantula in his bill, and the other eye noticed a rabbit-hawk sitting on a dead limb in a water-elm. I popped over one after the other with my forty-five, just to show him. 'Two out of three,' says I. 'Birds just naturally seem to draw my fire wherever I go.'

"'Nice shooting,' says the sheep man, without a flutter. 'But don't you sometimes ever miss the third shot? Elegant fine rain that was last week for the young grass, Mr. Judson?' says he.

"'Willie,' says I, riding over close to his palfrey, 'your infatuated parents may have denounced you by the name of

Jackson, but you sure moulted into a twittering Willie—let us slough off this here analysis of rain and the elements, and get down to talk that is outside the vocabulary of parrots. That is a bad habit you have got of riding with young ladies over at Pimienta. I've known birds,' says I, 'to be served on toast for less than that. Miss Willella,' says I, 'don't ever want any nest made out of sheep's wool by a tomtit of the Jacksonian branch or ornithology. Now, are you going to quit, or do you wish for to gallop up against this Dead-Moral-Certainty attachment to my name, which is good for two hyphens and at least one set of funeral obsequies?'

"Jackson Bird flushed up some, and then he laughed.

"'Why, Mr. Judson,' says he, 'you've got the wrong idea. I've called on Miss Learight a few times; but not for the purpose you imagine. My object is purely a gastronomical one.'

"I reached for my gun.

"'Any coyote,' says I, 'that would boast of dishonourable—'

"'Wait a minute,' says this Bird, 'till I explain. What would I do with a wife? If you ever saw that ranch of mine! I do my own cooking and mending. Eating—that's all the pleasure I get out of sheep raising. Mr. Judson, did you ever taste the pancakes that Miss Learight makes?'

"'Me? No,' I told him. 'I never was advised that she was up to any culinary maneuvers.'

"'They're golden sunshine,' says he, 'honey-browned by the ambrosial fires of Epicurus. I'd give two years of my life to get the recipe for making them pancakes. That's what I went to see Miss Learight for,' says Jackson Bird, 'but I haven't been able to get it from her. It's an old recipe that's been in the family for seventy-five years. They hand it down from one generation to another, but they don't give it away to outsiders. If I could get that recipe, so I could make them pancakes for myself on my ranch, I'd be a happy man,' says Bird.

"'Are you sure,' I says to him, 'that it ain't the hand that mixes the pancakes that you're after?'

"'Sure,' says Jackson. 'Miss Learight is a mighty nice girl,

· 90 ·

but I can assure you my intentions go no further than the gastro—' but he seen my hand going down to my holster and he changed his similitude— 'than the desire to procure a copy of the pancake recipe,' he finishes.

" 'You ain't such a bad little man,' says I, trying to be fair. 'I was thinking some of making orphans of your sheep, but I'll let you fly away this time. But you stick to pancakes,' says I, 'as close as the middle one of a stack; and don't go and mistake sentiments for syrup, or there'll be singing at your ranch, and you won't hear it.'

" 'To convince you that I am sincere,' says the sheep man, 'I'll ask you to help me. Miss Learight and you being closer friends, maybe she would do for you what she wouldn't for me. If you will get me a copy of that pancake recipe, I give you my word that I'll never call upon her again.'

" 'That's fair,' I says, and I shook hands with Jackson Bird. 'I'll get it for you if I can, and glad to oblige.' And he turned off down the big pear flat on the Piedra, in the direction of Mired Mule; and I steered northwest for old Bill Toomey's ranch.

"It was five days afterward when I got another chance to ride over to Pimienta. Miss Willella and me passed a gratifying evening at Uncle Emsley's. She sang some, and exasperated the piano quite a lot with quotations from the operas. I gave imitations of a rattlesnake, and told her about Snaky McFee's new way of skinning cows, and described the trip I made to St. Louis once. We was getting along in one another's estimations fine. Thinks I, if Jackson Bird can now be persuaded to migrate, I win. I recollect his promise about the pancake receipt, and I thinks I will persuade it from Miss Willella and give it to him; and then if I catches Birdie off of Mired Mule again, I'll make him hop the twig.

"So, along about ten o'clock, I put on a wheedling smile and says to Miss Willella: 'Now, if there's anything I do like better than the sight of a red steer on green grass it's the taste of a nice hot pancake smothered in sugar-house molasses.'

"Miss Willella gives a little jump on the piano stool, and looked at me curious.

" 'Yes,' says she, 'they're real nice. What did you say was the name of that street in St. Louis, Mr. Odom, where you lost your hat?'

" 'Pancake Avenue,' says I, with a wink, to show her that I was on about the family receipt, and couldn't be side-corralled off of the subject. 'Come, now, Miss Willella,' I says, 'let's hear how you make 'em. Pancakes is just whirling in my head like wagon wheels. Start her off, now—pound of flour, eight dozen eggs, and so on. How does the catalogue of constituents run?'

" 'Excuse me for a moment, please,' says Miss Willella, and she gives me a quick kind of sideways look, and slides off the stool. She ambled out into the other room, and directly Uncle Emsley comes in in his shirt sleeves, with a pitcher of water. He turns around to get a glass on the table, and I see a forty-five in his hip pocket. 'Great post-holes!' thinks I, 'but here's a family thinks a heap of cooking receipts, protecting it with fire-arms. I've known outfits that wouldn't do that much by a family feud.'

" 'Drink this here down,' says Uncle Emsley, handing me the glass of water. 'You've rid too far today, Jud, and got yourself over-excited. Try to think about something else now.'

" 'Do you know how to make them pancakes, Uncle Emsley?' I asked.

" 'Well, I'm not as apprised in the anatomy of them as some,' says Uncle Emsley, 'but I reckon you take a sifter of plaster of paris and a little dough and saleratus and corn meal, and mix 'em with eggs and buttermilk as usual. Is old Bill going to ship beeves to Kansas City again this spring, Jud?'

"That was all the pancake specifications I could get that night. I didn't wonder that Jackson Bird found it uphill work. So I dropped the subject and talked with Uncle Emsley a while about hollow-horn and cyclones. And then Miss Willella came and said 'Goodnight,' and I hit the breeze for the ranch.

"About a week afterward I met Jackson Bird riding out of

Pimienta as I rode in, and we stopped in the road for a few frivolous remarks.

" 'Got the bill of particulars for them flapjacks yet?' I asked him.

" 'Well, no,' says Jackson. 'I don't seem to have any success in getting hold of it. Did you try?'

" 'I did,' says I, 'and 'twas like trying to dig a prairie dog out of his hole with a peanut hull. That pancake receipt must be a jookalorum, the way they hold on to it.'

" 'I'm most ready to give it up,' says Jackson, so discouraged in his pronunciations that I felt sorry for him; 'but I did want to know how to make them pancakes to eat on my lonely ranch,' says he. 'I lie awake at nights thinking how good they are.'

" 'You keep on trying for it,' I tells him, 'and I'll do the same. One of us is bound to get a rope over its horns before long. Well, so-long, Jacksy.'

"You see, by this time we was on the peacefullest of terms. When I saw that he wasn't after Miss Willella I had more endurable contemplations of that sandy-haired snoozer. In order to help out the ambitions of his appetite I kept on trying to get that receipt from Miss Willella. But every time I would say 'pancakes' she would get sort of remote and fidgety about the eye, and try to change the subject. If I held her to it she would slide out and round up Uncle Emsley with his pitcher of water and hip-pocket howitzer.

"One day I galloped over to the store with a fine bunch of blue verbenas that I cut out of a herd of wild flowers over on Poisoned Dog Prairie. Uncle Emsley looked at 'em with one eye shut and says:

" 'Haven't ye heard the news?'

" 'Cattle up?' I asks.

" 'Willella and Jackson Bird was married in Palestine yesterday,' says he. 'Just got a letter this morning.'

"I dropped them flowers in a cracker-barrel, and let the news trickle in my ears and down toward my upper left-hand shirt pocket until it got to my feet.

" 'Would you mind saying that over again once more, Uncle Emsley?' says I. 'Maybe my hearing has got wrong, and you only said that prime heifers was 4.80 on the hoof, or something like that.'

" 'Married yesterday,' says Uncle Emsley, 'and gone to Waco and Niagara Falls on a wedding tour. Why, didn't you see none of the signs all along? Jackson Bird has been courting Willella ever since that day he took her out riding.'

" 'Then,' says I, in a kind of yell, 'what was all this zizzaparoola he gives me about pancakes? Tell me *that*.'

"When I said 'pancakes' Uncle Emsley sort of dodged and stepped back.

" 'Somebody's been dealing me pancakes from the bottom of the deck,' I says, 'and I'll find out. I believe you know. Talk up,' says I, 'or we'll mix a panful of batter right here.'

"I slid over the counter after Uncle Emsley. He grabbed at his gun, but it was in a drawer, and he missed it two inches. I got him by the front of his shirt and shoved him in a corner.

" 'Talk pancakes,' says I, 'or be made into one. Does Miss Willella make 'em?'

" 'She never made one in her life and I never saw one,' says Uncle Emsley, soothing. 'Calm down now, Jud—calm down. You've got excited, and that wound in your head is contaminating your senses of intelligence. Try not to think about pancakes.'

" 'Uncle Emsley,' says I, 'I'm not wounded in the head except so far as my natural cogitative instincts run to runts. Jackson Bird told me he was calling on Miss Willella for the purpose of finding out her system of producing pancakes, and he asked me to help him get the bill of lading of the ingredients. I done so, with the results as you see. Have I been sodded down with Johnson grass by a pink-eyed snoozer, or what?'

" 'Slack up your grip on my dress shirt,' says Uncle Emsley, 'and I'll tell you. Yes, it looks like Jackson Bird has gone and humbugged you some. The day after he went riding with Willella he came back and told me and her to watch out for you whenever you got to talking about pancakes. He said you was in camp once where they was cooking flapjacks, and one of the fellows cut you over the head with a frying pan. Jackson said that whenever you got overhot or excited that wound hurt you and made you kind of crazy, and you went raving about pancakes. He told us to just get you worked off of the subject and soothed down, and you wouldn't be dangerous. So, me and Willella done the best by you we knew how. Well, well,' says Uncle Emsley, 'that Jackson Bird is sure a seldom kind of a snoozer.' "

During the progress of Jud's story he had been slowly but deftly combining certain portions of the contents of his sacks and cans. Toward the close of it he set before me the finished product —a pair of red-hot, rich-hued pancakes on a tin plate. From some secret hoarding place he also brought a lump of excellent butter and a bottle of golden syrup.

"How long ago did these things happen?" I asked him.

"Three years," said Jud. "They're living on the Mired Mule Ranch now. But I haven't seen either of 'em since. They say Jackson Bird was fixing his ranch up fine with rocking chairs and window curtains all the time he was putting me up the pancake tree. Oh, I got over it after a while. But the boys kept the racket up."

"Did you make these cakes by the famous recipe?" I asked.

"Didn't I tell you there wasn't no receipt?" said Jud. "The boys hollered pancakes till they got pancake hungry, and I cut this receipt out of a newspaper. How does the truck taste?"

"They're delicious," I answered. "Why don't you have some, too, Jud?"

I was sure I heard a sigh.

"Me?" said Jud. "I don't never eat 'em."

# A NAME AND A FLAG

*by* JOHN W. THOMASON, JR.

John W. Thomason is a distinguished soldier and writer who was born in Huntsville, Texas. He is the author of many fine short stories, all notable for their style—a style that has in it something of the colonnaded verandas of the Old South, plus a kind of military influence. His attitude, generally speaking, is more or less a Texas version of Confederate mannerisms and attitudes. (Much the same could be said of the character of Huntsville as a town.) He has done biographical work on Davy Crockett and a celebrated biography of J. E. B. Stuart. Among his books of fiction are *Gone to Texas* and *Lone Star Preacher*, from which the following story is taken. The "Lone Star Preacher" is, of course, Praxiteles Swan, who is perhaps Colonel Thomason's most successful and widely known character.

IT IS ONE OF THE LAST STORIES THEY TELL OF PRAXITELES SWAN, and of the Texas Brigade in the Army of Northern Virginia— how he went with Major Howdy Martin to beard Mr. Jefferson Davis in his private cabinet over a matter that was important to them, in the last dark winter of the Confederate war. If you are diligent in business, Praxiteles used to remark, you stand before kings; you do not stand before mean men. And Jefferson Davis was as near a king as the Confederacy could afford.

Praxiteles used to comment, when the old folks talked of the war and why we lost it, that he felt Jeff Davis did the best he could—as well as anybody, and better than most. Certainly, on the one occasion he, Praxiteles, had reason to confer with the president, Mr. Davis was remarkably sensible in his judgments.

For it fell out, a little before Christmastime of '64, that a rumor not of Yankee issue came to vex the shrunken gray regiments that stood between Grant and Richmond. Longstreet's

Corps held the north side of the James; A. P. Hill covered Petersburg, and the Second Corps was distributed, some with Gordon in the lines, others toward the Valley under Jubal Early.

There were many indications that the war was running down, but the men in the miserable, sodden trenches and in the bleak hutments behind them took very little interest in such matters. They were preoccupied with professional military details and with the problem of keeping alive. They maintained a desultory bickering with equally uncomfortable blue formations over against them, and foraged desperately to supplement their slender rations, and remained tough-minded and generally cheerful throughout. Let the politicians worry about the rest of it, was their word.

An astonishingly large number of private letters from the front, that last bleak winter, shine with a persistent hopefulness; indicate, also, oyster roasts and occasional turkeys. They did not starve and they did not despair. The Yankee excursions in the West, deep thinkers among them asserted, had overextended the Federal resources. Come spring, they'd better look to themselves! It is always that way in war; the people at the point of contact take the most cheerful view. The people behind the lines are the first to cry havoc and the first to cry for peace. Of course, there were desertions—an appalling number of desertions. Some pretty good men were quitting, and the folks back home—even the preachers and the women—appeared to have the blues. But on the line, the word the Texas troops were really grieved to hear dealt with a projected reorganization of the army.

The basis of the Provisional Army of the Confederate States was the old militia structure. From this came most of the volunteer regiments and brigades which fought the opening actions. The orders of battle about the time of First Manassas listed brigades and divisions by number, and regiments after their state designations. But the Confederate soldier was an individual, distrustful of anything that smacked of regimentation, jealous and ardent for his sectional ties, and peculiarly susceptible to leadership. Thus, by the end of 1861, brigades were generally known by the names of their brigadiers and their states; and divisions, then and afterward, were named for their generals; and this applied even to corps. The names of their armies were officially regional. The Confederate service was a personal service. The First Virginia Brigade, for instance, glorious at First Manassas and on other fields, was never anything but the Stonewall Brigade. There were Benning's Georgians and Law's Alabamians; and Pickett's Division was so designated; and the First Corps was Longstreet's Corps, and your old men always said, "Lee's Army." After the formation of the permanent Confederate government and the adoption of a consistent military policy, in 1862, with conscription as its leading feature, the Provisional Army created very few new regiments or brigades. Late volunteers and conscripts alike went into existing formations, and this was the principal source of Confederate excellence in battle. Each regiment of soldiers had a solid core of veterans, with traditions and *esprit* to match. The pride they had in themselves was something fierce and alive, unflagging to the end.

But as the old stock was ground away between the millstones of war, and as the replacement material in the depots dwindled and failed, the numbers and strengths in the units under arms faded also. Regiments, that bleak winter of '64, fell to one hundred men or so—three or four hundred rifles made an unusually strong brigade. A division order of battle might, and usually did, list five brigades, yet muster no more in actual fighting strength than two Northern regiments. Operations officers and clerks alike made moan, and the War Department, dreamily pondering academic details, busied itself with the drafting of an order that would abolish at once the annoying sectional and personal designations, do away with these high-stomached corporals' guards masquerading as combat units, and regroup officers and men into actual, rather than skeleton, organizations.

It was the rumor of this impending anonymity which struck fire in the camps of the four-hundred-odd veterans of Hood's old Texas Brigade. They had every proper sentiment of respect and affection for their companions in arms out of Virginia, the

Carolinas, Tennessee and the Gulf States. But Texas was something else again. Officers and men took counsel together over a score of smoky campfires, and determined on measures. They would make a protest. It was felt that their spokesmen should be persons of loud voice and imposing presence, worthy of the brigade in bearing as well as in combat background. It was felt that they should have enough rank to brush aside slick young aides-de-camp and doorkeepers, yet not enough seniority to make them timid before higher authority. It was decided, in brief, that Maj. Howdy Martin and Capt. Praxiteles Swan, veterans of every battle from Elthan's Landing to the Darbytown Road, both of them humble before God and brash in every other relation, were ideal representatives. The two officers said they'd take the job. They made ready to go to Richmond and present the matter to the Secretary of War, and, if necessary, to the President.

The old men who told this tale a lifetime afterward still chuckled when they described the grooming and titivating which the major and the Elder underwent for the occasion. Uniforms had become mighty shabby on the Northside lines, and the Richmond merchants had no stocks to replenish a man's outfit. Howdy Martin went unabashed in a skin-tight pair of Yankee-blue trousers, taken from a miraculous Yankee quartermaster who had been in life almost as big as the major. Some large officer loaned a uniform coat which, after a little stretching at the shoulder seams, would serve. It was simple to sew a major's star on the collar, and Howdy's winter beard made a shirt quite unnecessary. His boots were a difficulty; they were cracked and broken, so that his toes showed, but nothing could be done about boots, and his feet were too big for any Yankee's they captured— a fact regretfully conceded and accepted—although the pickets went out after dark two nights and brought in specimens. His hat, a slant-brimmed Kilpatrick, was on the small side, but his brass-mounted dragoon revolvers, one on each hip, and his long cavalry saber were sufficiently imposing; and once a man saw his adventurous nose jutting from his great beard, and his bright hard eyes, deep-set under bushy brows, and the whole confident frontier strut of the man, the details didn't matter.

Praxiteles, who wore a good coat all his life, and good boots, was in better case, but not much better. The crude darning showed painfully over his right hip and inside his right sleeve, where his pistol holster had worn away the cloth, and low on his left hip where saber slings had chafed. His breeches were frankly patched at knee and seat; good, weather-tight patches, but unsightly. However, his leather and his weapons were fine and bright, and you had to look close to see that his beaver was broken about the crown. Somebody loaned him a clean paper collar, and, as regimental officers went in that army, he considered himself well turned out. Secretly, he conceded that this was important to him. Old Howdy didn't care, but Praxiteles Swan cared, and made himself as smart as he could in any company.

The brigade commander, who was the senior colonel—John Gregg, dead on the Darbytown Road, not having been replaced, and never would be—said, dubiously, he reckoned they could go, and sent them on to division headquarters. Major General Field, a meticulous administrator, disapproved, but forwarded the request to Longstreet at First Corps.

Longstreet, the old regular, said, "No, not by a damn sight." No officer or man from his corps was going to a higher echelon with a complaint against orders, actual or impending. Orders were orders, he told them severely. The Articles of War were explicit on the circulation of petitions. Such procedures smacked of mutiny. Longstreet could be mighty severe on subjects like that.

But Longstreet knew his Texans, and he had not forgotten how meanly his couriers were treated by the Richmond war lords; the chosen valiant men in whose hands he sent the captured battle flags of Chickamauga to the President, after that hard battle. The story was, not even an adjutant met them at the depot; Winder's military police harassed them; the Yankee standards were carried through the streets of the capital in a dray, behind a Negro and a mule, and slung into the corner of an office. The War Department found no time for Longstreet's orphans at all. This the general considered briefly, then held up a hand to check the outburst he saw gathering in Praxiteles Swan's angry eye and behind Major Howdy Martin's purpled face.

"Of course," he added, "if you two gentlemen wish a brief season of refreshment in Richmond after labor—why, the front's right quiet now. Your services are very well known to me. Why don't you take a little furlough in town? And if you should chance to meet Mr. Secretary of War—whoever he is at the moment—in the Ballard House bar, or encounter Mr. President Davis in a social way—why, any Southern officer has the right to state his private views in any company. And if you choose to discuss professional matters, your blood be on your own shirt fronts! . . . Colonel Latrobe, see about their passes, and before they go out into this weather, remember, colonel, it's confoundedly cold."

There was a warm humanity about old Longstreet, Praxiteles always said. They mounted their horses and rode some miles to Richmond, in time for a latish dinner, for which Howdy Martin paid with a hundred-dollar Confederate bill, and gave the waiter the change. Money was mighty low; the more you had, the less it seemed to be worth. Their coattail pockets were full of it.

Encouraged by what Howdy Martin described as ample vittles, they discussed ways and means. They could go to the office of the adviser to the President, General Bragg, but they didn't like what they knew of Bragg; no nourishment there, Praxiteles thought. They could go to the adjutant general, Cooper, but he was a terrible fellow for orders, everybody said. And the Secretary of War, of course. But the President was over them all; and when you came right down to it, he ran the army. Everybody knew that.

"Why bother with the spoon vittles?" asked Howdy Martin. "Elder, let's go right for the meat. Minnows air safe; we air out after whales!"

Praxiteles agreed that this was horse sense. They walked the few blocks to the gloomy house where the President had his offices. The streets were empty, and the December sky was low and dark. Nobody was outside who didn't have to be. It was coming on to sleet, and the short winter day was drawing in. At the Confederate White House, the sentry, tramping the sidewalk briskly to avoid freezing on his beat, kept his hands in his armpits and his piece under his arm; a length of old shawl was tied around his ears and his wrists were blue with cold.

He started to unjoint himself for ceremony, but Praxiteles stopped him, "Ne' mind, son. We'll just go in."

A mournful Negro doorman in white gloves and a swallowtail admitted them. A smart young staff officer, passing through the hall, raised his brows at them and would have let it go at that, but they loomed enormous in the dim light and their eyes held him.

"Well, gentlemen? . . . Major Martin? Captain Swan? Texas Brigade? Oh, yes, those Cotton States fellows. . . . See the President? See Mr. Jefferson Davis? You have—haven't an appointment?" The staff officer said he'd never heard of such a thing. He leaned against the wall, shaken. He managed to convey that Mr. Jefferson Davis was mighty busy—a mighty busy man these days. Only saw folks by appointment.

"He'll see us," Howdy Martin. "We've come in from Northside in all this weather ———"

"We're grieved to discommode him," began Praxiteles Swan, "but there's a little matter ———" His voice began to rise.

"Whar's his room?" demanded Howdy Martin, at his battle pitch.

The officer was visibly distressed. "Not so loud, please, gentlemen! I'll speak to Colonel ———"

"You'll speak to nobody! Whar's his room?"

"If you'll just be patient, gentlemen! I'll arrange ——— Here; this way."

He led them upstairs to the second floor. There was a hall, and chairs and sofas along it; men in fine civilian broadcloth, with papers in green-baize bags, and neat men in uniform, half a dozen or so, occupied the seats. They eyed the two rough soldiers with distaste. The young aide slipped away. The Texans looked at each other. Which door, Howdy insisted, but there were four doors, and all of them closed.

Praxiteles Swan took thought, and his temper abated. He had waited in the anterooms of the great, in that other existence of his, more than Major Howdy Martin had waited.

"No sense," he said reasonably, "in bulling into this. I reckon Mr. Davis has a lot on his mind. We can wait a spell."

"Don't want to wait," said Howdy. "I'm riled up now. I cain express myself now the way the boys would like me to. Did I sit here in this crib, an' all these nice folks around with little shoes on their feet an' clean paper collars—why, Elder, the strength will go right out of me. I tell you, I'm ————"

A door opened—the door facing them. A medium-sized general with a bluish, bilious face, bushy eyebrows and bad-tempered dark eyes came out, stuffing papers into his pockets. He looked at them without seeing them or the other people who got to their feet for him.

"General Bragg," said Praxiteles. "Saw him after Chickamauga."

Howdy Martin, his saber clanking loudly, was across the hall in three long strides, and through the door. Praxiteles followed him, as duty bound, but he didn't like it. He didn't like it. There was this matter of the fitness of things. He closed the door gently behind him.

There were three men around a desk. Lamps bathed the room in yellow light. Already the day was gone outside the windows. Behind the desk, erect, slender, and with a dignity that made you forget his medium stature—he could have stood up straight under Praxiteles' arm—Mr. Jefferson Davis, President of the Confederate States, looked coldly upon these intruders. A dapper civilian—that would be Burton Harrison—straightened up from some papers and gave them quizzical regard, his head tilted to one side. A tall officer with the yellow collar and cuffs of the cavalry, a handsome, bearded man with a bearing haunt-ingly familiar, took a step toward them.

Praxiteles Swan, watching the President's austere, high-nosed face, tried to recall a thing remembered from long ago.

Spring of 1861. The sandy road through the pines and the sweet gums from Huntsville to Montgomery. Riding down that road to join the war—riding with old Gen. Sam Houston. And the general saying, in that blunt voice of his, "I'll tell you about Jeff Davis. Cold-blooded as a lizard, proud as Lucifer—what he touches will not prosper."

Sam Houston knew his man. The war wasn't prospering; the maps on the desk were maps of Wilmington, last open port of the Confederacy, of Cape Fear River and Fort Fisher. But, Praxiteles conceded, this man was not defeated. There were plenty of officials in high places who were beaten now. But not Mr. Jefferson Davis. The man was tempered steel, whether you ad-mired his judgment or not. You could kill such people; you couldn't defeat them. Months afterward, when Praxiteles heard that Davis had been captured in flight, he needed nobody to tell him that Davis was going West in the hope that he would find enough men of his own hard fiber to keep on fighting.

All this went through Praxiteles' head while Mr. Davis spoke. His voice was thin and keen, and cold as the wind outside. "Of-ficers having business here are usually announced," he informed them. "To what urgency do I owe this honor?"

The timbre of the voice raised the hackles on Praxiteles' neck.

Howdy Martin planted his feet, squared his great shoulders and inflated his chest. "Mr. President, I'll make myself known. I'm Major Martin, of Hood's Texas Brigade. This here is Elder—Captain Swan, of that same command. Mr. President, I'll make a long story short, as the fellow says. The boys out on the Northside, in the lines, hev been told a tale that they don't understand. They hev heard tell of something that bothers them. Mr. President, they hev kind of deputized me an' the Elder—captain, there—me not bein' a man of smooth speech, as the Good Book puts it—to come in here and find out about it."

· 104 ·

A faint shadow of expression, gone as quickly as it showed, flicked across the President's face. Behind his icy front, he had a certain feeling for combat soldiers—wanted, he said always, to serve in the field himself.

"What is it, major," he inquired, "that has thus upset my Texans? If it is properly a matter for my attention—"

"Mr. President, I'll tell you. If it ain't for your attention, I don't know whose attention it's for. They tell us, seh, in ouah camp, that the War Department is gettin' ready to issue an order to take away our state names—to break us up and mix us around, and to number us, by regiments an' brigades an' divisions, like any bunch of conscripts brought in by a posse!

"Mr. President, the Texas Brigade come up here in the summer of 1861! Right after Manassas! We popped our first caps at Elthan's Landing! We was the boys that broke the line at Gaines's Mill. Second Manassas, Mr. President!" The windows rattled and the lamps flickered. "Sharpsburg! . . . You slick civilian there, did you ever hear tell of the cornfield at Sharpsburg? Fredericksburg! Gettysburg! Chickamauga! The Wilderness! An' Spottsylvania! Cold Harbor! An' the Darbytown Road! I tell you, Mr. President, we have left our dead on every field this army has fought, from the James River up into Pennsylvania an' as far west as North Georgia! And outside of a few boys who straggled too far forward at Gettysburg, we have buried our dead ourselves!" This was important to soldiers; it meant you held your ground. "We have our battle flags that our women gave us! Mr. President"—he was terribly passionate—"they air Texas flags! Texas ladies made them! Texas boys have fought under them! Those names I named you, they air on those flags! Will you take 'em away from us an' give us a number in place of them? And a number in place of our Texas name?

"Mr. President, we Texicans have obeyed orders. We aim to keep on fighting while the war lasts. But, Mr. President, we air the Texas Brigade, an' so we will remain."

He stopped talking and the silence fairly thundered. Then Praxiteles added mildly, "That's what the boys wanted you to

· 105 ·

know, Mr. President. Our minds air made up." It was like the still small voice after the hurricane.

Jefferson Davis was moved—only his aides knew how much. He was not a man who showed emotion.

Now he said, "Major Martin. Captain Swan. The details of army administration would not interest you. It is your good fortune, sirs, that you need take the soldier's view only. But you may return to your men out there, and tell them for me: So long as there are enough of them alive to carry their state colors, they will be known as Texans, of the Texas regiments, of Hood's Texas Brigade.

"Now, Major Martin, Captain Swan, it has been a pleasure to receive you here. But I am not master of my own time." He took their hands, first the major's, then the captain's. He bowed formally; his hand was thin and cold, with a nervous strength. And the tall cavalry general, who said his name was Custis Lee, showed them to the door.

The two, in the sleety night, found nothing to say to each other. They thought they might as well go on back to the command. They got their horses from the livery stable. The sleet had changed to a wet snow, driven on a bitter wind. The widely spaced street lights were blanketed, and made luminous yellow spheres of radiance that gave no light at all. The horses' hoofs were muffled on the road. They seemed, to themselves, riding with their heads bent against the wind, the last lonely souls in a world of cold and sleep. They came to a crossroads where all directions looked the same.

"Which road, Elder, which road?" asked Major Martin impatiently. "I'm kind of turned around."

Praxiteles lifted his beard from his chest and answered out of a dark dream, "Either road will take us where we're going. It don't matter now. Same distance and no choice."

Off to the west and south, the rain was falling through the naked boughs of tall trees that stood gaunt around a place called Appomattox.

# SOME FAST CHICKENS

*by* ARCHIE STEAGALL

At the time Archie Steagall wrote "Some Fast Chickens," he was a student in Sam Houston Teachers College, in Huntsville, Texas. It is plain that he had great fun writing this story, which was published in the *Southwest Review*. His control over his medium and the material is firm, and causes one to suspect he had been up to such tricks before. Yet it is the only published story by Archie Steagall which the editor could find. If there are others, they are just as elusive and uncapturable as are biographical notes on the author. When last heard from he was aboard the *S.S. Java Arrow*, headed for points unknown. That is all, unfortunately, that I know about Archie Steagall. I hope he had a good trip on the *Java Arrow*.

---

I DON'T MEAN TO BE BRAGGIN'," THE BIG RED-FACED IRISHMAN SAID, "but I don't know the man who can handle a gamecock as good as me. Last season I got plenty fat fightin' chickens."

A sweater had come into the pool hall and had taken his stand behind the Irishman's chair. On the green plastered wall between two pictures, one of Jack Dempsey and the other of Joe DiMaggio, was a sign: SWEATERS KEEP OUT OF THE GAME.

"I win my chicken fights," the sweater said, "with speed. Last season I win nine and lose one. I lose that fight to the smartest gambler in the chicken business, a man from New Awlins named Razz Bailey."

The Irishman's partner, a Syrian, was shuffling the dominoes.

"How come you take duh count wit duh blank-five? How come you don't lay in duh double? Dis ain't no chicken fight. Dis is dominoes. What duh hal?"

"Quit bleedin', Abie," the bald-headed man on the Syrian's right said. "You always bleed. You win three straights and cry."

"Gimme some help," the bald-headed man's partner, an owl-faced fat man, said. "Show me sump'n. I lose three straights."

"I don't mean to be braggin'," the big Irishman said, "but the way I skin a man in New Awlins last season was a joke. I went down to New Awlins every week-end just to fight a gambler named Razz Bailey."

"I'm afraid you're mistaken," the sweater said. "You never beat Razz Bailey. Razz Bailey is the smartest chicken man in New Awlins. He owns his own chicken house."

"The first time I fight Razz Bailey last season," the Irishman said, "I stand a chance to lose over two hundred dollars. Razz Bailey had a Whitehackle single-stroker and I had a Pure Snyder Warhorse. I'd seen the single-stroker fight before, and he was the cleverest boxer in New Awlins. He wouldn't shuffle a lick. He did all his boxin' in the air. If he didn't put his steel through the neck, he'd put it in the gizzard, a hard punch to land. It goes straight in and chickens can't throw it to do any good.

"When Razz dropped the single-stroker on the scales I told him I'd take two to one. We settled at three to two. He put up three hundred and I put up two hundred. The stands was offerin' high as three to one I can't win.

"Now don't get me wrong. Razz Bailey is a smart handler. I wouldn't be surprised if before that fight started he wasn't the smartest handler them New Awlins people ever saw.

"On the first pittin', Razz Bailey's bird missed the neck and hit the comb and sunk a heel clean through to my chicken's brain.

"I was worried. When a chicken's brain is exposed to the air it gets addled. Air addles a chicken's brain. Durin' the thirty seconds I turned my back on Razz and he thought I was blowin' down my Warhorse's throat to clear off the blood. I was chewin' gum, so I took my chicken's comb in my mouth and filled up the gaff hole. Then I smeared some dirt on it so the referee couldn't see the gum. The gum shut off the air and my cock came out shufflin' and talkin', and two pittin's later he took off a leg and finished the single-stroker in a buckle."

"Last season," the sweater said, "I win nine cock fights with speed. I can thump a chicken's comb so fast you can't tell I did it. I addled a chicken's brain in Port Arthur last month and win—"

"Gimme some help, partner," the owl-faced fat man said; "you're gettin' heavy."

"I had the case ace last hand," the bald-headed man said, "and you cut me off. Who does that make heavy?"

"Not to be braggin'," the big Irishman said, "but I don't know the man who can handle chickens as fast as me. I beat Razz Bailey last season by mashin' his chicken's oil sack. A chicken can't stand you mashin' his oil sack, and he'll run. Razz Bailey showed an ace Meadowlark-Dangerfoot, but he couldn't get started. My Nigger Roundhead ruined him in the first pittin'."

"Dis is dominoes," the Syrian said; "dis ain't chicken. Le's see some dominoes."

"That was fast chickens," the sweater said, "but did you see me fight my Blinsky Roundhead in Houston last season? Did you see—"

"The fastest handlin' I ever saw," the Irishman said, "was the way I handled Razz Bailey's Claiborne-Jap in New Awlins last season. I had to handle fast because I was fightin' a dung-hill. First pittin' the Claiborne-Jap threw a pair of two-inch twisters at my chicken and knocked about half his feathers off, and I kissed my four hundred and sixty-five dollars goodbye. Them New Awlins people was offerin' ten and twenty to one I ain't got a chance.

"The second pittin', the Claiborne-Jap hung his steel up in my chicken's feathers and I was all over the tangle. When I handled I gave my chicken a quick twist and snapped the Claiborne-Jap's leg like it was a matchstick."

"That's fast chickens," the sweater said, "but did you see me whip the Mexican in San Tone two seasons ago? I did it cryin'! I'd holler foul and I'd get the referee's eye on the Mexican. He was a dumb referee and he'd warn the Mexican. While he was warnin' him I was in there sluggin'. If my chicken needed handlin', and the referee hadn't said handle, I'd run in and pull my chicken out of the hole. I saw my chance when my chicken hung his steel under the wings, and when I handled I hit my chicken's jaggers and made 'em sink in deeper. I win with a deep rattle in the second pittin'."

"Come on, partner," the owl-faced fat man said. "Show me sump'n. I can't afford to carry you much longer. Can't you see we're a string and a half behind? Don't get too fast with that chalk, Irish. Knock off that last five. No wonder I lose three straights."

"I never see a pair of scissors," the big Irishman said, "without I think of the five or six hundred dollars I win in New Awlins last season. I had me a ten-times winner, a big blue shake, and I decided to pit him in New Awlins against a gambler named Razz Bailey.

"But there was a hitch. I'd been winnin' so much cash money durin' the first part of the season that everybody in New Awlins was afraid of me. On top of that my big blue shake could knock a hole through a two-by-four, and he looked it.

"Well, I got me a big pair of scissors and made such a mess of my shake that he looked like the dogs had been runnin' him. When them New Awlins people saw me step in the pit with my blue in one hand and plenty of green men in the other, they tried to mob me. They thought I had a turkey. They offered me as high as five to three I can't win, and in two pittin's I win five hundred and eighty-seven dollars.

"The next week Razz Bailey sent me a telegram tellin' me to get the best stag I could find and rush down to New Awlins for some hack fights. Right behind that first telegram he sent me a second one tellin' me not to forget my pocketbook and a good big handkerchief to cry in when he win all my money. He never mentioned the monkey he intended to put on my back.

"Razz got him a two-year-old cock, a good Red Horse, and

scraped his legs smooth with a razor blade and trimmed down his spurs with a pencil sharpener. He looked just like a stag. When I approached him with between five and six hundred dollars, he begged me to make it seven fifty. I—"

"We're losin' dis game, pahtner," the Syrian said. "We ain't but ten ahead. Dey ketchin' us queek. Drop duh chicken and play some domino."

"Come on, partner," the owl-faced fat man said, "we ain't but ten behind. Take all your counts and don't try to star."

"I wouldn't play that seed," the sweater said to the bald-headed man.

"Sweaters stay out o' duh game!" the Syrian shouted. "What duh hal dis is! What duh hal!"

"Razz Bailey," the Irishman said, taking a ten count with the ace-six, "had a two-year-old cock all varnished up so he looked just like a stag. I—"

"What dis is, pahtner?" the Syrian said. "Is dis chicken? We ain't but twenty ahead. Watch out duh domino."

The Irishman took a fifteen count off the spinner and said, "I called over seven hundred and fifty dollars' worth before we pit. I had my Blue Falcon so full of Indian hemp I couldn't turn him loose without gettin' hurt. I had to throw him loose. The Red Horse came out slow and lazy and my cock shot at the breast and they tangled. When we handled, the Red Horse couldn't get up. He was squatted down like he was hatchin' off eggs. My Blue Falcon shuffled in fast and threw his regulations at—"

"Dey almost tied us!" the Syrian shouted, slapping the table with the palm of his hand. "Dey almost tied up duh score! What duh hal!"

"That chicken fight," the sweater said, "reminds me of a fight I—"

"Sweaters stay out o' duh game! See dat sign? Sweaters keep out!"

The big Irishman took a ten count and said, "Razz Bailey picked up his cock and looked at his legs and they was all right.

He tried his back and he wasn't coupled. He pulled his tongue out like a rubber band and turned it loose, and no blood showed.

"In the next pittin' my Blue Falcon topped the Red Horse and finished him with a deep rattle."

The Irishman marked down a twenty count the Syrian had made.

"After I win the fight," he said, "I got out a big handkerchief and offered it to Razz Bailey to cry in."

"That chicken fight," the sweater said, "reminds me of a fight I was in last season. What ailed that Red Horse?"

"Before the fight," the Irishman said, winning the game with a five count, "I put a forty-five bullet in his—"

"Vent!" roared the sweater. "Razz Bailey did that to me. He did that to me! He—"

The Irishman collected fifty cents from the bald-headed man and the Syrian collected fifty cents from the owl-faced fat man. Then they started another game of dominoes.

*Novels* &

LAUGHING BOY—*Oliver La Farge*

QUINCIE BOLLIVER—*Mary King*

MR. GEORGE'S JOINT—*Elizabeth Lee Wheaton*

THE GRAPES OF WRATH—*John Steinbeck*

THE INHERITORS—*Philip Atlee (Jim Phillips)*

THE RIVER OF BLOOD—*Edwin Lanham*

HOLD AUTUMN IN YOUR HAND—*George Sessions Perry*

# from LAUGHING BOY

*by* OLIVER LA FARGE

Oliver La Farge won the Pulitzer prize for fiction in 1929 with his novel of Indian life, *Laughing Boy*. The opening pages of that novel are reprinted here.

His interests are equally divided between writing and ethnology. Few persons are better informed on Indian matters than Mr. La Farge. He has recently edited a symposium on Indian affairs, *The Changing Indian*, for the University of Oklahoma Press, and has personally had a decisive part in the formation of the Government's Indian policy. Mr. La Farge makes his home alternately in New York and Santa Fé.

---

HE WAS RIDING THE HUNDRED MILES FROM T'O TLAKAI TO Tsé Lani to attend a dance, or rather, for the horse-racing that would come afterwards. The sun was hot and his belly was empty, but life moved in rhythm with his pony loping steadily as an engine down the miles. He was lax in the saddle, leaning back, arm swinging the rope's end in time to the horse's lope. His new red headband was a bright color among the embers of the sun-struck desert, undulating like a moving graph of the pony's lope, or the music of his song—

> "*Nashdui bik'é dinni, eya-a, eyo-o* . . .
> Wildcat's feet hurt, *eya-a, eyo-o* . . . "

Rope's end, shoulders, song, all moved together, and life flowed in one stream. He threw his head back to sing louder, and listened to the echo from the cliffs on his right. He was thinking about a bracelet he should make, with four smooth bars running together, and a turquoise in the middle—if he could get the silver. He wished he could work while riding; everything was so perfect then, like the prayers, *hozoji nashad*, travelling

· 115 ·

in beauty. His hands, his feet, his head, his insides all were *hozoji*, all were very much alive. He whooped and struck up the Magpie Song till the empty desert resounded—

> *"A-a-iné, a-a-a-iné,*
> *Ya-a-iné-ainé, ko-ya-ainé . . . "*

He was lean, slender, tall, and handsome, Laughing Boy, with a new cheap headband and a borrowed silver belt to make ragged clothes look fine.

At noon, having no money, he begged coffee from a trader at Chinlee and went on, treasuring his hunger because of the feasting to come. Now he began to meet Navajos of all ages, riding to the dance. The young men bunched together—a line of jingling bridles, dark, excited faces, flashing silver, turquoise, velveteen shirts, dirty, ragged overalls, a pair of plaid calico leggins, a pair of turkey-red ones. Some of them were heavy with jewelry; Horse Giver's Son wore over four hundred dollars in silver alone; most of them had more than Laughing Boy. They stopped to look at his bow-guard, which he himself had made.

"I am a good jeweller," he said, elated; "I make silver run like a song."

"You should make a song about yourself," they told him, "and teach the burros to sing it."

"Have you had any rain up by T'o Tlakai?"

"No, it is just like last year. It is the devil. The grass is all dried up and the sheep are dying."

"They had a cloudburst over by T'isya Lani. It washed out the dam."

"It washed out the missionary's house, they say. His wife ran out in something thin and got wet, they say."

"*Ei-yei!*"

Tall Hunter and his wife drove past in a brand-new buckboard behind two fast-trotting, grey mules. He owned over five hundred head of horses, and his wife had thick strings of turquoise and coral around her neck.

"His brother is in jail for stealing cattle, they say."

"What is jail?" asked Laughing Boy.

Slender Hair explained: "It is something the American Chief does to you. He puts you in a room of stone, like a Moqui house, only it is dark and you can't get out. People die there, they say. They haven't any room; they can't see anything, they say. I do not like to talk about it."

Laughing Boy thought, I should rather die. He wanted to ask more, but was ashamed to show his ignorance before these southern Navajos, many of whom wore hats like Americans, and who knew so much of Americans' ways.

They raced. His horse was tired, but it won by a nose, which was just as well, since he had bet his bow-guard. Now he had six dollars. He hoped there would be gambling.

Tsé Lani showed a distant bonfire in the dusk, with mounted Indians moving in on it like spokes of a wheel. About two hundred young men came together half a mile away, making their ponies prance, exchanging greetings. Crooked Ear carried the ceremonial wand. Now they all lined up, with the dull, red sunset behind their black figures. They started going like getting off to a race, right into a gallop, yelling. Over by the fire was shouting, and another line tearing towards them. The world was full of a roar of hooves and two walls of noise rushing together, the men leaning forward over their horses' necks, mouths wide. "*E-e-e-e-e!*" They met in a great swirl of plunging, dodging horses, and swept on all together, whooping for dear life, with the staff in front of them, almost onto the fire, then dissolved with jingling of bits, laughter, and casual jokes as they unsaddled by the pool.

The steady motion of excitement was slowed then, in the last of the day, by the rocks and the piñons, by the reflection of the sky in the pool where flat, vague silhouettes of horses stooped to drink. The voices of many people, the twinkling of fires continued the motif, joining the time of quiet with elation past and to come; a little feeling of expectation in Laughing Boy's chest, a joyful emptiness, part hunger and part excitement.

He tended his pony minutely. The little mare had had two

days of loping; shortly he wanted to race her; three days of rest would not be too much. She was his only horse; he had traded two others for her. She was tough, as a horse had to be to live at all in the north country. He ran his hands down her withers, feeling the lean, decisive muscles. In all that section, from Dennihuitso to Biltabito, from T'o Tlikahn to T'o Baka, where he knew every horse by sight, she was the best, but she would meet some competition here. He felt as if she were his own creation, like the bow-guard; at least he had selected her, as he had chosen the soft blue turquoise in the ornament. Little, compact, all black save for the tiny white spot on her forehead, she had the ugly Roman nose of character. She was like an arrow notched to a taut bowstring—a movement of the hand would release level flight swiftly to a mark.

He was thinking some of these things, half hearing the noises of the people. Just like the prayer, "travelling in beauty." It would be good to be a singer as well, to express all these things through the prayers. He would like to know many of them, to learn to conduct the Mountain Chant, and know all the beautiful stories behind the songs and ceremonies inside the Dark Circle of Branches. That would be really on the trail of beauty; to work in silver and turquoise, own soft-moving ponies, and lead the Mountain Chant. Just thinking about it was good. It made him feel cool inside.

> "*Hozho hogahn ladin nasha woyen* . . .
> In the house of happiness there I wander . . . "

All the time he was passing his hand along the pony's neck, along her back, feeling the lines of tough muscles.

"*E-ya*, Grandfather, are you going to dance with the horse?" Jesting Squaw's Son called over to him, "Food is ready."

"*Hakone!*" He returned abruptly to the quick-moving life of the dance. "I can eat it. I did not know you were coming."

"I came when I heard you were to race your mare. I think there is money to be made, then, and I want to see her race."

They went up arm in arm into the crowd, pushing their way

into the circle around one of the fires. Busy housewives gave them coffee, the big pot of meat was passed over, and a flat, round loaf of rubbery, filling bread. The meat was the backbone of a yearling calf, boiled with corn. It was good. He munched joyfully, feeling his empty stomach fill, wadding himself with bread, washing it down with bitter coffee. A couple of Americans carrying their own plates dipped in gingerly. A Hopi, having collected everything he could possibly eat, sat down officiously beside them to air his school English and his bourgeois superiority.

## II

A small drum beating rapidly concentrated the mixed noises into a staccato unison. Young men gathered about the drummer. Laughing Boy might have eaten more, but he left the fire immediately with Jesting Squaw's Son. Some one led off high-pitched at full voice,

"*Yo-o galeana, yo-o galeana, yo-o galeana . . .*"

By the end of the second word the crowd was with him; more young men hurried up to join the diapason,

"*Galeana ena, galeana eno, yo-o ay-e hena ena . . .*"

They put their arms over each other's shoulders, swaying in time to the one drum that ran like a dull, glowing thread through the singing, four hundred young men turning loose everything they had.

A bonfire twenty feet long flared to the left of them. Opposite, and to the right, the older people sat wrapped in their blankets. Behind them, men crouched in their saddles, heads and shoulders against the night sky, nodding time to the rhythm, silent, with here and there a reflection of firelight on a bit of silver, a dark face, or a horse's eye.

Twelve girls in single file stole into the open space, moving quietly and aloof as though the uproar of singing were petrified into a protective wall before it reached them. Only the pulse of the drum showed in their steps. They prowled back and forth before the line of young men, considering them with predatory judgment.

Laughing Boy at the back of the crowd looked at them with mild interest; he liked to watch their suave movements and the rich display of blankets and jewelry. One caught his attention; he thought she had on more silver, coral, turquoise, and white shell than he had ever seen on any one person. He speculated on its value—horses—she must have a very rich mother, or uncles. She was too slender, seeming frail to dance in all that rich, heavy ornamentation. He wished she would move more into the firelight. She was well dressed to show off what she wore; silver and stones with soft highlights and deep shadows glowed against the night-blue velveteen of her blouse; oval plaques of silver were at her waist, and ceremonial jewels in the fringe of her sash. Her blue skirt swung with her short, calculated steps, ankle-length, above the dull red leggins and moccasins with silver buttons. The dark clothing, matching the night, was in contrast to the other dancers, even her blanket was mainly blue. He felt animosity towards her, dark and slight, like a wisp of grass—only part of a woman. Her gaze, examining the singers, was too coolly appraising. Now she was looking at him. He threw his head back, losing himself in the singing. He wished he, too, had an American hat.

Her mincing steps took her out of sight. Jesting Squaw's Son's arm was over his shoulder, and on the other side another Indian, unknown, but young. Their life flowed together with all those others, complete to themselves, merged in one body of song, with the drumbeats for a heart,

"*Yo-o galeana, yo-o galeana . . .* "

Song followed song with a rush; when one ended, the next took up, as though the whole night would never suffice to pour out all that was in them.

Some one plucked at his blanket; then with another, stronger pull it was snatched from his shoulder. He whirled about. The

· 120 ·

men near him snickered. The frail girl held his blanket up toward him, mockingly.

"*Ahalani!*" she greeted him.

He stood for a moment in feigned stupidity. He did not want to dance. The devil! Then with a sudden lunge he snatched the blanket. It was no use. She hung on with unexpected strength, digging her heels into the sand, laughing. The men on either side were watching over their shoulders with open joy.

"What's the matter? I think your feet hurt, perhaps. I think you are bandy-legged, perhaps."

Girls didn't usually say these things. He was shocked. Her clear, low voice turned the insults into music, bringing out to the full the rise and fall of a Navajo woman's intonation. All the time they tugged against each other, her long eyes were talking. He had seen girls' eyes talk before as they pulled at the blanket, but these were clear as words. He wanted desperately to be back among the men. He nearly pulled her over, but she hung on, and her eyes seemed to be making a fool of him.

Suddenly he gave up. She led him around behind the men, not speaking to him, uninterested. He pulled his end of the blanket over his shoulders, assuming the conventional pose of resistance, setting each foot before the other reluctantly, in response to her dragging. He watched her closely, but her grip did not slacken. Out in the clear space she transferred her hands to his belt. He pulled his blanket to his chin, masking enjoyment in a pose of contemptuous tolerance, like the other men dancing there.

The solemn turning of the couples contrasted with the free release of the singers: this was a religious ceremony and a rustic, simple pleasure, the happiness of a natural people to whom but few things happen. They were traditional and grave in their revelry.

According to the etiquette, whenever there is a rest, the man asks what forfeit he must pay; by the length of time taken by the girl to get down to a reasonable figure, he gauges her liking for his company. The music paused an instant for the singers to catch their breath. He made a feeble attempt to get away, then asked,

"How much?"

"Ten cents."

The prompt answer astonished him. He paid the forfeit, still staring at her, chagrined, and furious at the blank, correct impassiveness of her face, at the same time noting delicately chiselled features, set of firm lips, long eyes that in their lack of expression were making fun of him. Ten cents! Already! With a splendid gesture he swept his blanket round him, stalking back to the singers.

He was set to lose himself in the songs, but he watched the girl drag out a man nearly as tall as himself. Instead of dancing in the usual way, they held each other face to face and close to, each with one hand on the other's shoulder. It was shocking; and why had she not done it with him? But she had let him go the first time he had asked. She had insulted him, she was too thin, and probably ill-behaved.

### III

Jesting Squaw's Son's arm was over his shoulder, his ears were full of the beat and uproar of music. He was a man among men, swinging with them, marking the rhythm, releasing his joy of living in ordered song.

*"Nashdui bik'é dinni, eya-a, eyo-o . . . "*

A late moon rose, cool and remote, dissociated. They brought another tree up to the bonfire, standing it on end a moment so that the hot light played on its dead branches; then they let it topple over and fall, sending up in its place a tree of moving sparks into the blackness.

Night passed its middle and stood towards day. The girls moved off together in single file, blankets drawn over heads, worn out by the night of unremitting dancing. The older people fell rapidly away. Inert forms like mummies stretched out in their blankets by the embers of the feast fires. Most of the young

· 122 ·

men gave in, leaving about a hundred knotted in a mass, still hard at it. They surrounded the drummer, an older man, intently serious over drawing forth from a bit of hide stretched across the mouth of a jar rapidly succeeding beats that entered the veins and moved in the blood. He played with rhythm as some men play with design; now a quick succession of what seemed meaningless strokes hurried forward, now the beat stumbled, paused, caught up again and whirled away. Devotedly intent over his work, his long experience, his strength and skill expended themselves in quick, wise movements of the wrist, calling forth a summation of life from a piece of goatskin and a handful of baked clay, while younger men about him swayed and rocked in recurrent crescendos.

Night stood towards morning, now night grew old. Now the first white line was traced across the east far away, outlining distant cliffs. Now it was first light, and Dawn Boy was upon them. The drumming stopped; suddenly the desert was empty and vast. Young men, whose bodies felt like empty shells and whose heads still buzzed with songs, moved down to drink at the pool.

*"Hayotlcatl Ashki, Natahni . . . "*

Laughing Boy breathed his prayer to himself, feeling a moment of loneliness,

"Dawn Boy, Chief . . . "

He rolled up in his blanket. When he rode his horse in the races, people would see; he would ride past the people, back to T'o Tlakai, with all his winnings. That girl was strong for one who looked so slight. He would make a bracelet about her, thin silver, with stars surrounded by stone-knife-edge. His horse came to stand by him. He roused himself to look at it, struggled awake, and dragged out the corn from under his saddle.

He pulled his blanket over his head. All different things melted together into one conception of a night not like any other.

# *from* QUINCIE BOLLIVER

*by* MARY KING

Mary King is unquestionably one of the most promising of young Southwestern writers. Her excellent novel, *Quincie Bolliver*, which deals with the lives of some of the people who followed the oil field booms, was written on a Houghton Mifflin Literary Fellowship. The portion of the book reprinted here is the very opening of the book. It is hoped that this sample will tempt the reader to read the story in its entirety.

———————————

WHILE SHE HAD BEEN ASLEEP, NIGHT HAD FALLEN. SHE awoke to find the sky clotted with stars. At first she did not know where she was, and then she smelled the strong fragrance of crude oil, and remembered. The odor came from the floor boards under her head. She was lying in a truck, with her head on a croker sack, and the truck was running along through the night. She stirred, felt a sharp pain under her, and lay still again.

Her father's head slid along the skyline, his mouth framed by the glow from his cigarette. He leaned forward, loose and shadowy, speaking to the driver through the open back of the cab.

Here and there in the shouted sentences whipped away by the wind, words she knew well spiraled down to her—work . . . youngun . . . far . . . sleep . . . where . . . . Mournful and questioning, like a dove's voice in a deep wood, the sound of her father's words fell upon her as from a great height, and were snatched away instantly into the past.

They were running through a tunnel of trees, the headlights flashing over gnarled trunks that printed shadows darker than the common blackness of the night, the sky shut away by heavy branches looped with moss. With senses made acute by long night travel upon highways, she sniffed the air and named the trees. "Them's live oaks, and there's a spot of elder. It'd be easy to find wood here, wood for a big fire, and places you could hide if anybody come to look." But the grove was passing; now it lay behind. Projecting herself far down the road, she spoke of the grove to herself. "A place I passed through, a sheltering place back yonder somewhere. I wouldn't know where. Just some place."

The stars were thick again overhead. The wind rushed by. The truck slowed for a curve, and turned off the asphalt highway onto a dirt road that ran straight between barbed-wire fences. Along this road the timber had been cut back to make way for cotton and corn fields, but in places it had sprung again in shaggy second growth interspersed with humped thickets of Cherokee rose. The farmhouses were poor and small, each lonely from its neighbor. Curtin Bolliver saw all this in the brief flash of headlights as the truck sped forward.

"What direction now?" he shouted.

"West," answered the driver. "Couple miles farther on we swing southwest, and you can see the field lights."

"How far?"

"Seven, eight miles."

"These dirt roads 'll be bad in rainy weather. How do they haul?"

"I mean black mud a foot deep, like pig slop, but most get through. You drive a truck?"

"Never tried it."

"Well, if you can handle mules like you say I wouldn't worry. You'll get a job. Is the kid still asleep?"

"Sound asleep. Tired out. We must've walked twelve mile today before you picked us up."

"I'm not asleep, either," said Quincie. "I run a splinter in me."

"Did you have a nice nap, honey?" asked her father, patting her stomach.

"A splinter's jabbing me, right through my dress!"

"Get up and pull it out."

Quincie kneeled, and felt behind her. Curtin steadied her with a hand on her leg. "I can't get a-holt of it!" she said.

The truck swung southwest. The flat prairie lay open before them, peppered with lights. Some of the lights moved, and others stood still. Above the lights the sky was pale; below them the dark land seemed to heave and fall like the chest of a giant sleeper, the slow breath coming and going. The child in the truck forgot the splinter. Pointing, she said: "It's moving! Look, daddy, the land is moving!"

"Looks like a sizable city," Curtin said.

The truck-driver laughed. "Half of them lights is lightning-bugs," he said, "and the other half is derrick lights. The rest is town lights. Name of Good Union."

"Sounds like a right nice place."

"Judith Paradise, she'll feed you. Got a boarding-house a little piece down from the post office."

"Rooms?"

"Can't say. You ask."

They turned into the long main street of the town and stopped under a light to wait for a load of pipe to cross. Quincie whispered to Curtin.

"Turn up," he said. "I'll get it out." She whispered again in his ear.

"Nobody'll see! It'll be over in a minute."

Sitting on the bottom of the truck, he turned her over his lap. "However you done this without knowing, I don't see. You must 've been sleeping hard."

"It don't hurt much, only jags me when I move."

"Well, out she comes!"

"Ouch!"

"Now I wouldn't set on it for a spell if I was you."

The driver let them out and went on. They stood on the dusty street, Quincie clinging to Curtin's hand, her legs unsteady.

"Now where?" said Curtin.

"A little piece down from the post office, he said."

"Judith Paradise the name was, I remember."

"There it is!" said Quincie, pointing to a large white house with a sign swung between the peeling columns over the front step.

"Paradise House. Rooms and Board If You Have Cash." Curtin spelled out the sign, and said: "Well, let's go see. Watch out where you step. No stock law in this town, looks like."

They crossed the street, walked up the steps, and knocked on the door. Receiving no answer, they opened the door and entered. As they stood indecisively in the bare bright hall, a tall woman with a big bosom came from the back of the house and faced them. Although the night was hot, she wore a corset. Quincie could tell when women wore corsets, because their bodies always looked smooth and stiff and angry.

The tall woman thrust a hand into the front of her dress, snapped out a balled handkerchief, and wiped the sweat from her face. "Well?" she said.

Quincie blinked in the light, and with one hand rubbed the place where the splinter had been. She smelled food. Through an open door on the right of the hall sounded the clamor of many people eating: the sounds of steel and glass and crockery, and now and then the rumble of a man's voice choked with food.

"Are you Mrs. Paradise?" Curtin said.

"That's my name."

"Me and my youngun here, they said you could feed us. A man on the road said you might be able to put us up for the night."

"I've got nothing for beggars. You go on away."

"We ain't beggars!" said Quincie hotly.

"Lady, we got money. What we want is supper, and maybe a place to sleep. I come here to get a job. My little girl's tired out."

Quincie rubbed one aching leg with the back of the other bare foot. "I ain't very tired," she said.

"If you've got money, let me see it. Terms are cash here. If you've got money I can feed you, but I can't sleep you. My rooms are all taken."

"How much?"

"Supper is six-bits apiece."

Curtin slipped a weathered billfold from his hip pocket, and put silver in the woman's hand. She counted the money, and led the way into the dining-room.

The room was long, with a high ceiling. Lighter squares and oblongs, areas once occupied by pictures, patched the brown wallpaper. Above the mantel hung a large fly-specked calendar, lettered in red and black. Pine boards laid upon trestles made the table. The table was crowded with eating men.

"Bring two plates!" Mrs. Paradise shouted to a Negro girl who put her head through the swinging door at the end of the room.

Curtin filled both plates and began to eat. Quincie looked once at the table, and then sat still with her head bowed and her hands folded in her lap. The rough bench upon which she sat was pushed a man's distance back from the table. She could not reach her plate without leaning forward, and she could not move with so many eyes upon her. She felt elbows: those of her father on one side, and on the other, the strange arm bones of a man at whom she dared not look. She smelled sweat, and mixed with the sweat another smell, the raw heavy fragrance of crude oil. The men's clothes were splattered with oil.

She was very hungry. She leaned forward, picked up her fork, and thrust it into a mound of potatoes. The man beside her was watching; she could feel his eyes.

"Here, sissy," he said, "too long a reach for a little girl. Hey, you, let's shove up a bit, the little lady missed her mouth, or mighty near it."

Laughing, the men dragged the bench closer to the table.

"Say 'Much oblige,'" said Curtin, with his mouth full.

"Much oblige," whispered Quincie.

"Sure, that's all right. Now you go ahead and eat."

"Pretty little girl you got there," said a dark young man across the table.

· 128 ·

"Aw, Tip, leave her alone," said another.

"Only she got the fidgets. What makes you wiggle around like that? We won't eat you. We don't eat little girls, only big girls. What's your name, sweetheart?"

"Answer him," said Curtin.

"Quincie Bolliver."

"Yeah," said Curtin. "She just run a splinter in her backside. How's it feel now, honey?"

Quincie bowed her head before the wave of laughter. Only the man beside her did not laugh. He said: "You better get busy and eat, sissy, or they won't be nothing left. These men is hogs, but don't you mind. Here, try some coffee."

His hand pushed a cup toward her. The back of the hand glittered with gray hairs; its broken nails looked enormous. The first joint of the forefinger was missing.

Quincie picked up the cup. It was heavy and hot, and it slipped from her shaking fingers and crashed to the floor.

"Who did that?" The landlady was coming.

Quincie flashed one agonized look at the kitchen door, and throwing her legs over the bench, fled from the room, through the bright, empty hall, and down the steps of Judith Paradise's house. Under the dusty leaves of a Cape jasmine bush by the steps she crouched in darkness, and listened for pursuit. Laughter rolled through the door.

"She run like a scared cat!"

"It's a shame, the kid ain't had a bite!"

"Go find her, Judy. It was you scared her."

"Judith won't let nobody else break her cups—only herself."

"Mister, you better go find your little girl before she crosses the county, the way she was running!"

Quincie flattened herself on the ground and gripped the bush with both hands. Curtin had come out on the porch and was looking up and down the street. She was close enough to touch his foot, but she did not answer when he called. Judith Paradise joined him. Curtin called again.

Inside, she heard the bench pushed back and the sound of

feet in the hall. The men were coming to look for her; they were all coming! She began to tremble. The men tramped down the steps and disappeared in groups of clotted shadow under the deeper shadow of the oak trees along the dusty street.

"Likely she's around the house somewhere," said the woman's voice. "I didn't mean to scare her. I thought it was Tip Morgan dropped that cup. Sometimes he does it just to make me mad."

"Come on in and eat your supper, honey!"

"Look yonder!" Although there was no wind, the top of the jasmine bush was shaking violently.

It was Mrs. Paradise who loosened her fingers and brushed the dirt from her torn dress. Brought into the light, she ceased crying.

"Ain't you ashamed, acting such a baby?" Curtin said gently. "The lady wasn't mad. You oughtn't always run away like that. You ought to say 'Excuse me, please,' and act like a lady."

"You sit on a splinter, little girl?"

Quincie hung her head, sniffling.

"Answer the lady!"

"Yes, ma'am."

"You better let me have a look at it before you go."

"It don't hurt."

"Go along with the lady when she asks you," said Curtin.

Prisoning the child's small hard hand in a firm grip, Judith walked down the hall and rapped on a door under the stairs.

"Justa minute!" called a woman's voice. Quincie looked at the floor. The boards were rough and splintery, holding gray lint from the mop. A gurgle of water came from behind the closed door; a glass clinked. She heard heel-taps, sharp and nervous, and then the bolt clicked from the latch, and the door opened on a lavender kimono and a pungent odor of carnations.

"You, Fern!" said Judith angrily, "what's wrong with the bathroom upstairs? A hundred times I tell you, use your own bathroom, don't come down here! I didn't put a bathroom on the second floor for a place to wash bottles!"

The woman jerked the kimono tighter about her hips. Her hip bones were thrust forward, and the top of her body swayed backward from her hips so that she seemed to be made in two sections, the joinder casual. "Just go look!" she said. "Go look, go see for yourself! Oil on the tub, oily pants on the floor, drop a match and *whoosh!*"

"You might try cleaning it. Some people do things like that sometimes, I've heard. There's a can of kerosene and a rag on the window sill."

"Not me, any more, not after them roughnecks. Who's the kid?"

"You come in here," said Judith to Quincie, ignoring the question.

The child hung back. The woman drew her impatiently over the threshold and shut the door. She rummaged among the bottles of hair oil and toothpowder on the shelf, and found a bottle of iodine. "Pull down your drawers," she said.

"Look, the lady forgot her powder." Quincie pointed to the can of talcum left on the washbasin. *Lovme Talc*, read the label. The box was purple, with fat pink flowers. The air of the bathroom was close and sour-sweet, the smell of carnations fighting the smell of wet towels. Her eyes, avoiding the woman, circled the cubbyhole desperately and came to rest on the tub. "Look the nice bathtub," she said in a small voice.

"I said unbutton your drawers . . . no, it wasn't your leg you stuck the splinter in. It was your behind, your daddy said."

Backed against the wall, Quincie moved to obey.

"Over here, under the light, where I can see!"

There was no help for her. She stumbled under the light and began to unbutton her drawers. They were the only pair she had; a kindly woman at a road camp had made them from a flour sack. The bold pink and green lettering of the label had not worn off: *Cream of the Pantry*.

She unfastened them all the way around, stepped quickly out of them and kicked them aside, disowning them savagely. They fell seat up, the label plain to see.

The woman looked at the child's red face and did not laugh. She turned up the ragged dress, disclosing the knobby spine and the soft brown flesh of the skinny buttocks, one side marked by the angry purple wound of the splinter. "Don't your daddy ever feed you?" she asked.

"Ol' drawers, ol' ugly things! I got a nice pair back home, back where I come from."

Stinging with iodine, she followed the woman again into the dining-room. The room was clean and swept now, empty save for one man who sprawled asleep with his head on the table.

"Daddy!" She ran to him and shook his shoulder.

"Wake up, man, you can't sleep here!" Together they tried to rouse him. He sighed and muttered sleepily. The unshaded light above him bored deep holes in his temples.

"Get up, get out of here! Come on, wake up!"

He lifted his head and fixed them with a wide stare. "If it's mules, why, fine. . . . I never driven a truck." His head drooped and settled upon the table. He was asleep again.

"I can sleep anywhere," Quincie said. "One time I slept on the ground in the woods."

"Feel in his pockets and see if he has two dollars."

"Yes, ma'am." Quincie eased the wallet from her father's overalls and gave the landlady two one-dollar bills. She returned the wallet to the pocket. Her father was beginning to snore.

"Well, leave him be. I'll bring you a quilt, little girl, and you can sleep under the table, but mind out you're here in the morning and nothing missing."

"Yes, ma'am."

The woman went away and returned with a quilt. A few minutes later the table, swinging in a wide arc above Quincie's heavy eyes, tipped over completely, shutting out the hard white light from the hall, and she was asleep.

Judith Paradise, coming downstairs at daybreak, saw the man's blond head on the table, his long body slacked on the bench, and stepped forward angrily. Then her eyes fell upon the

· 132 ·

sleeping child under the table. She had completely forgotten the two. They must be waked and sent on their way. The town had been full of their kind, the kind who lived in tents and flung their wash water through the open fly without bothering to step outside. They had come in wagons, in trucks, and on foot: whole families and broken pieces of families. In the first boom days of the Good Union field they had poured into the town like a swarm of bees settling over a honey pot. With the field two years old now, and the town more or less stabilized, the most of them had departed to other newer and more prosperous fields. Enough, however, still remained. This blond man and his dark little girl did not look like prospective roomers; they looked like tramps. The man's blue-denim overalls were caked with sweat and dust; the little girl's calico dress was spotted and torn. They must be waked, she thought, and yet she stood indecisively in the doorway, a tall, big-boned woman, awkwardly, emphatically alive, regarding the sleepers. Father and daughter slept like the dead, their oblivion lending them a curious dignity and weight of ownership in the room. "You'd think they owned the place, and I ought to knock and wait," she thought wryly.

She tiptoed around the end of the table to the window, un-latched the screen, and, leaning far out, looked up and down the street.

This was the one quiet hour of the twenty-four. Out in the oil field the graveyard shift waited to be relieved, and the men who would relieve them were not yet awake. Under the great live oaks that shaded the street, drops of dew falling from leaf and twig had pitted the ankle-deep dust with small black holes. The smell of crude oil lay thick upon the air.

Judith looked again at the sleepers. The man's cheek lay on his hand, his breath moving the thick blond fur on his knuckles. Where the pale hair grew to a point, the nape of his neck was curiously smooth and tender compared with his lined and weatherbeaten face. His open mouth was a round black cave. "Another to fill," she thought, "and this one empty clean to his toes. Even his bones look hollow."

Quincie sighed and sat up, leaning on her elbows. She might be anywhere between nine and twelve; she was so thin it would be hard to say. The sun had burned her skin the color of coffee, and bleached her hair to an indeterminate shade neither dark nor light. It hung lank and straight to her shoulders, the long bangs swept to one side. Her face was small and smooth in its outline, but an observer noticed chiefly her eyes. These eyes were long and narrow, pale gray, startlingly light in her dark face. They were grave and watchful eyes. They swept the room slowly, and came to rest upon the woman by the window.

"Go to the kitchen and wash your face, little girl. The privy's out back."

Quincie crept from under the table, and stumbled sleepily in the direction Judith pointed out to her. The door slammed behind her. Curtin stirred and came awake, stretching. Judith watched him sardonically. He looked about the room bewilderedly, knotting his brows.

"Well?" she said.

He studied her silently for a minute, rubbing his hand over his face, and then he got to his feet and hitched up his pants.

"I reckon I went to sleep. It's early, ain't it?"

"Past five o'clock."

"Where's the kid?"

"Out back."

"Much oblige, lady, for letting us sleep here."

"You paid for it."

Curtin put his hand to his pocket. Judith had already turned toward the kitchen. "Breakfast is four-bits," she said over her shoulder. "Dinner's four-bits, and supper six-bits, the same as last night, or you can pay me a dollar-fifty for the day. Rooms all taken now, but you might come back when you get a job, and I'll see what I can do."

"You taken too much, didn't you? That was all the money I had. Only two-bits left here, not enough for breakfast."

"That's your lookout."

"But lady—"

· 134 ·

"I should run a boarding-house for the fun of it!"

"Well, listen. Could I maybe leave the kid here, and you could let her help around, pay for her breakfast thataway, and then I'd come back for her later?"

Judith looked at him considering. The father's eyes were pale, like the daughter's; they were slow and impudent.

He said, "You're hard, ain't you?"

"Read my sign. Cash. That's the way I do business."

"Not even for a man that might come in handy for odd jobs sometimes?" He came close to her. She moved away.

"Not for any liar on an empty belly!"

Quincie came through the kitchen door and saw the two looking angrily at each other. "Here I am!" she called.

"Listen, honey," said Curtin hurriedly, patting her shoulder. "You stay here with the lady, and she'll give you breakfast. Just help out with whatever she says do, and I'll be back soon as I can. I got to go see for a job."

"Well!" said Judith.

Before Quincie could reply, her father was gone, and she was left alone with the strange woman in the strange woman's house.

"My daddy can run fast," she said, her lips quivering.

"Which way?"

"Oh, fast—any way."

"I expect so. He looks like it. Can you lay a table without breaking any more dishes?"

The smoothness of steel and crockery as she spaced them down each side of the long table pleased Quincie in spite of the trouble she felt at her father's desertion. At first she moved diffidently, not knowing who might appear and ask her business. Upstairs, she heard footsteps; twice the front door slammed. The woman called Fern, still wearing the lavender kimono, her bare feet thrust into run-down, high-heeled slippers, sagged sleepily down the hall carrying a chamber-pot to empty at the privy. A cigarette hung from a corner of her mouth. Her eyes were squinted against the smoke.

Did the house belong to Mrs. Paradise? Where was Mrs.

Paradise's husband? Did she have any children? Why did she wear a corset so early in the morning? Ladies wore corsets on Sundays or for funerals. Where was the Negro girl who had waited on table last night? Mrs. Paradise asked no questions, so she wasn't the sort to answer them.

A dozen trips made between dining-room and kitchen, and Quincie began to feel more at home. As she came and went between the two rooms, she talked to herself as she often did. "I been here a long time. There's two windows on one side and three on the other, with a door to the hall. In the kitchen there's two doors, one to the hall and one to the back porch. I been out there. I could get away easy if anybody chased me. There's a grease spot by that chair. That spot on that window screen looks like a goose stretching up his neck for corn. Somebody throwed something at somebody through the window, I reckon. Will she feed me? I got no money."

When the table was set she looked with pride at her handiwork. She had never set a table before, but often she had seen it done. With her head on one side she looked at the plates. She turned them bottom side up and crossed the knives and forks on top. They were prettier that way. The pepper-sauce bottle, the vinegar cruet, the sugar bowl and the spoon-holder she grouped together in the middle of the table. To the spoon-holder she announced in a whisper: "I'm Quincie Bolliver, and my daddy is the best mule-skinner in Texas, Mis'ippi, and Louisiana, and we come from I don't know whereall, and sometimes we sell things and sometimes we buy things, and I never seen a mountain, just flat land or little-bitsy hills. The Hills of Zion, she said, and I said where? and she said up in the sky. Politely thank-youma'am, but you're a liar, and you can go to hell."

She tiptoed to the fireplace and looked up at the calendar. It was an Oil Center Supply Company calendar. She did not know the day, but the month was June. Above June, a little derrick spouted black oil. Above each day in June was a gadget: big wheels and little wheels, valves and couplings, sprockets and wrenches. They looked like funny-shaped metal bugs.

At the sound of feet in the hall she fled to the kitchen. There she found that the Negro girl had come and was flinging food onto platters. Saliva jumped into her mouth. She swallowed, and her stomach growled. A small girl with red hair looked at her curiously, and began to giggle. Quincie shrank against the wall. The structure of familiarity she had taken such pains to erect crumbled about her ears. The house was again menacing with newness.

"Wheah did that git in?" asked the Negro girl.

"It's the child that broke the cup last night. Her father's gone to look for work, and she'll have to stay here till he gets back. I don't know what else to do with her. What's your name, little girl? I forget."

"Quincie Bolliver."

"Ellie," Judith said to the red-headed child, "fill two plates, one for you and one for Quincie, and take 'em out on the back porch to eat. We're busy here."

Ham and eggs, hot biscuits and pear preserves Quincie ate, the first good meal she had eaten since noon of the day before. When she had scraped her plate, she leaned back and patted her stomach. The food on Ellie's plate was hardly touched.

"Ain't you hungry?" she asked.

"Not very," said Ellie.

"I'll eat it for you."

"No."

"How old are you?"

"Twelve."

"I'm nearly thirteen. What makes your skin so white? Are you all over white like that? Does your mama wash you every day? Le's see the insides of your hands!"

Ellie put her hands behind her back. Quincie grabbed one of them and spread it open. "Gee!" she said. Ellie looked at her with frightened eyes, her small pink mouth pulled down at the corners.

"Open your mouth," said Quincie.

"I won't!"

"Please, I just want to look inside."

"My mama has a iron dog," said Ellie, pulling away.

"Where?"

"In the side yard."

They left the porch and went around the house to the side yard. Under the live oak in the fence corner an iron dog with mossy ears stood on three feet and bayed silently at passers-by.

"We had him a long time, since before I was born," said Ellie mysteriously.

"What kind of a dog is he?"

"A iron dog, like I said."

"Well, he ain't a very big dog, and the birds have dripped all over him."

"Mama says it's a owl does that, and she hears him sometimes at night. She gets mad. She's going to kill him."

"Huh!"

Ellie looked up into the somber tree. She said: "It scares me to look up at high things. Does it scare you?"

"No, I ain't scared. You just take a-holt of my hand, and we'll look up together."

Holding hands they gazed again into the tree. Quincie whirled, caught Ellie's jaws between strong thumb and forefinger, and pried them apart. The inside of the wide mouth was as pink as a watermelon. Ellie squirmed free and ran screaming the the house. "Mama, she hurt me!"

"Honest, I didn't mean to! She's so white on the outside I just wanted to see what color her insides was. I just looked in her mouth. Honest, that's all!"

# *from* MR. GEORGE'S JOINT

*by* ELIZABETH LEE WHEATON

To the people of Texas City, where Elizabeth Lee Wheaton lives,
and where she set her Negro novel, *Mr. George's Joint,* she is known as
Mrs. Grant W. Wheaton. Though *Mr. George's Joint* is Mrs. Wheaton's
first novel, it nevertheless won the Thomas Jefferson Southern Award.
The hub of the story, its center of gravity, is the joint itself—the com-
ings and goings, the antics, disappointments, and pleasures of the
people who come to it. To this story the joint is what the Grand
Hotel was to Vicki Baum's story of that name. It has for that reason
seemed fitting to present here the gala opening of the joint.

---

BY DUSK ON THE HOT JULY EVENING, THE BIG SPOON WAS OPEN
for business. In contrast to the feeble oil lamps glowing
through the windows of the neighboring houses, George's
place was ablaze with light. Yellow light streamed from each
window on the first floor, unrestrained by any sort of curtain or
shade; only the upstairs windows were discreetly masked to a
soft luminance, by wrapping paper tacked over each sash. The
latticed-in front porch half concealed, half revealed the interior,
giving an illusion of privacy without unduly impeding glimpses
into regions of delight, even as veils serve a burlesque dancer.
The nickel-in-the-slot phonograph, fed by slugs, blared forth
tantalizingly rhythmic dance tunes.

The two downstairs rooms were festooned with strips of red
crepe paper tacked to the walls and caught up on the cords by
which naked light bulbs dangled from the dingy ceiling. In
one corner of the larger room, where George intended eventually
to build a bar, cans and bottles of beer and soda water cooled
in tubs of cracked ice. The tubs were flanked on either side by
empty cases from which the cooling bottles and cans had been

· 139 ·

taken. On a near-by table stood the keg to be raffled, festively girded by a wide band of rapidly dampening crepe paper tied in a large, lopsided bow.

Through the open, unscreened windows and doors came myriads of small bugs and mosquitoes, attracted by the light or fleeing from the smudges smoldering in the yards across the street. The smell of burning rags and whatnot in the smudges almost overcame the heavenly aroma of fried fish that permeated the atmosphere after May Lou had cooked a few of the less choice pieces for the family's evening meal.

The staff of the Big Spoon, as well as the house itself, seemed to be in a state of breathless expectancy. George, attired in his best, was all but polished. His teeth were white as pearls, and his small mustache was curled at the points. He posed and swaggered about with grandiose dignity. Only in hovering near the door, nervously readjusting his tie and fingering his mustache, did he betray apprehension.

"With all them tickets Ah sol' on that kaig uh beer," he remarked loudly, to reassure himself, "the folks is boun' to clustah in soon."

"Sho they is, honey," Annie agreed, smoothing her red silk dress around her large hips.

She had spent a considerable sum on the red dress, but Annie was the type of person who looks the same in silk or cotton. Her hair had been straightened and carefully curled, but her face was as dull and uninteresting as discarded coffee grounds, except for her eyes, which were black and shone with a light of suspicion, combined with greed. She felt under her arms to see if she was perspiring. Discovering that she was, she held her arms out from her body to let the breeze dry the damp spots.

"Ah wist we'd uh put mo' papah strips 'roun' when we deckrated," George fretted, glancing up at the red paper canopy gently fluttering overhead.

"Reckon will the pop an' beer be col'?"

"It oughta be," George snorted. "It been coolin' ovah a nouah."

Flo's trim figure, in crisp pink taffeta, swayed to the music of the phonograph. May Lou, whose face seldom showed anything save a good-natured bewilderment, smiled as she clapped her hands to the rhythm of the selection to which Flo danced.

"You bettah not swing 'roun' too much 'fo' the folks ma'ches in," Annie warned Flo. "This a th'ee-payday night, an' we oughta have lots uh folks, with all them tickets Jawge sol' on that beer."

"Ah ain't nevah been too give out to dance *yit*," Flo answered tartly.

"You bettah set down an' res' yo'se'f, any-how. Ain't no call fuh you to sweat yo' dress dancin' by yo'se'f."

Flo continued to sway to the music. Irritated, Annie stalked out to the kitchen. George strolled out on the porch to peer expectantly up the street in search of possible patrons.

"Mistah Jawge an' dem sho nerved up 'bout dis openin'," May Lou giggled.

"They rightly is," Flo agreed, "an' they ain't no call fuh 'em to be. Payday is payday, an' with all this music an' feesh in the win', folks is boun' to flock in."

George wandered back indoors and looked critically about.

"Is this 'S' wrote out right?" he asked Flo, pointing to a reversed letter on the blackboard menu.

"They sumpn funny 'bout it," Flo admitted, looking at it fixedly, "but all them 'S's' is wrote out the same way. Ah reckon efn folks can't make 'em out, they kin ast."

"Hit look gran' to me," May Lou volunteered.

"Any kin' uh writin' look good to you, Lou," Flo grinned good-naturedly, "sense you ain't able to read no-way."

It was not long until customers began to drift in. George greeted each effusively, sold more chances on the keg of beer, and helped Annie and Flo take orders. He even served those he thought might be worthy of his personal attention, meanwhile trying to keep mental account of the money Annie and Flo were taking in.

The Big Spoon had no cash register or money drawer. Each of the staff dropped the money received into his or her own pocket. When a customer tipped one of the women, she dropped the tip into her pocket with George's money. When she estimated the accumulated tips amounted to a dollar, the woman would extract a dollar bill and slip it into her shoe. George suspected that some of his money was augmenting the sum of the tips to the proportions of bills.

Out of the corner of his eye, George noted the arrival of two men in soiled work clothes. They sidled over to one corner, as befitted the improperly dressed. George hurried to receive them.

"Evenin', boys!" he greeted cheerfully. "Is y'all got a chanct on the kaig uh beer we is rufflin' off? Jes tin cints, an' y'all gits a chanct on a whole kaig uh beer!"

The two accepted the proffered tickets dubiously, but paid for them from sizable rolls of bills.

"Us wants two bottles uh beer," one said.

"Yeah," the other confirmed.

"Two bottles uh beer, comin' up!" George responded, withdrawing two dripping bottles from the tub and opening them dexterously. "Heah y'all is, boys!"

He took their money and gave them change from his pocket.

"Ah thanks y'all. Now jes step out onto the back po'ch an' sip y'all's beer by y'all's se'ves. Ain't 'low nobody daity as y'all is to set an' sip stuff in ma jinte."

"Y'all sho deckrated up fuh a pahty," the first observed, as they moved slowly toward the back porch.

"Whyn't y'all go 'head on home an' git dress up an' come back an' pleasure y'all's se'ves, soon's y'all gits y'all's beer drank up?" George suggested; then, more loudly, for the benefit of his other patrons sitting in an interested hush, "This gonna be a high-class jinte, an' Ah ain't want nobody to come in an' set 'roun' an' sip nothin' onless they dress *right*."

"Us all do dat, jes soon's us drinks up dis bottle," the dirtier promised.

"Dat right," the other grinned, and they retired to the back porch, no whit chagrined.

In a moment after their departure, chatter and light-hearted laughter of happy Negroes again filled the room. The blaring phonograph, scraping of dancers' feet, and the clatter from the kitchen formed a background for snatches of conversation which soared above the uproar:

"Ain't y'all pass out no napkins wid dis sumpn t'eat?" and Annie's soothing, "Ah'll pack y'all in papah napkins when y'all's finish an' needs 'em. Ain't no call to put 'em out when you fust stahts; they jes blows onto the flo'."

"Kin Ah offah you a bottle uh pop, Miss Lucy?"

"Don't keer efn you does!"

"Ah say to ma boss-man, 'Ah be *too* proud to do it, efn it was lef' wid me, but de Union ain't 'low me to."

"She a good-lookin' gal, but she done gone fum heah."

"Heah come Buckey Boy an' Shawty! Ain't nevah look to see them come to no Gran' Openin', tight as they is!"

The subjects of the last remark were just entering. George shepherded them to a table and beckoned Flo to serve them.

"Y'all keer fuh sumpn to eat an' drink?" she inquired.

"Pack us in a bottle uh beer, an' two glasses," the big black Buckey Boy ordered.

"Ain't y'all wanna can uh beer?" Flo suggested politely.

"No, us wanna bottle an' two glasses," Buckey Boy repeated. "Ain't dat right, Shawty?"

The small brown Shorty nodded his simian head.

"We mos'ly ain't se've glasses to mens," Flo argued, "lessen they awdahs a can, what hol' mo'n a bottle."

"Ya'll gots glasses, ain't you?" Buckey Boy asked softly.

"Yeah, we got glasses, but we mos'ly ain't se've 'em to mens."

"Mens kin git 'em efn dey awdahs 'em, can't dey?"

"Yeah, but we mos'ly—"

"Well, Ah's awdahin' 'em!" Buckey Boy barked. "Pack us in a bottle uh beer an' two glasses!"

Shrugging disdainfully, Flo gave up.

Two couples came in and sat down at a table. They ordered sandwiches and beer; then one of the girls asked, "Is y'all got cig'rettes?"

"Yeah, we got cig'rettes," Flo replied.

"How much is they?"

"We got 'em eithah a pack uh mos' any kin' you kin name fuh twenny cints, an' you kin git 'em one by one fuh two cints apiece, too."

"Y'all makes on 'em efn we buys 'em fuh two cints apiece, don't y'all?"

"You gits twenny in a pack fuh twenny cints," Flo shrugged, "but efn you jes wants one, you saves eighteen cints, sense you ain't got to pass 'em out to the gimme folks what flocks at you when you gits a whole pack."

"Ah sho hates to give two cints apiece fuh 'em," the girl demurred.

"It lef' with you efn you does uh efn you don't," Flo responded indifferently.

"Y'all got any gum?" the other girl inquired while the first hesitated.

"Yeah, we got it by the package an' the piece," Flo replied. "The packages is fi' cints, an' the sticks is a penny, but they's fi' sticks in a package, so they costes the same."

"Tote us in a pack uh Lestahfiel's an' a package uh Mintchew," one of the men ordered. "Ah's gittin' rightly give out wid all dat 'how much' static!"

"Yassuh," Flo smiled.

When she returned with the cigarettes and the chewing-gum, the man opened the gum package and handed a stick to each of his companions and kept one stick.

"Heah the odd stick fuh you, purty gal," he said, giving Flo the remaining piece.

He opened the package of cigarettes and gave each of his companions five, keeping five for himself.

"Now don't y'all gals nevah git into no mo' ahgymint 'bout how much do sumpn cos' when y'all's out wid me!" he instructed them. "Ah tinks it's pure common to ahgy 'bout prices when you steps into a jinte."

In a surprisingly short time, George found he was almost out of beverages. Hastily checking the kitchen supplies, he learned that the pork chops, link sausage, fish, and barbecue were nearly gone. Grateful that there was yet time to get more from the near-by market, George collected the money Annie and Flo had taken in during the evening; then, commandeering a light truck belonging to a guest, he and the guest dashed out to replenish the supplies.

By the time they returned, the place was so full of people that there was hardly room to turn around. Some of the younger couples were dancing, threading jostling courses through the crowded rooms. George clapped his hands smartly for attention.

"Listen, folks!" he cried; "the folks is flock in so numerous to the gran' openin' that the jinte done ovahflow with folks. The music loud an' strong, an' some uh y'all got the itchin' feets to dance. Them what wanna dance go upstai's an' dance. The music rise to'a'ds Gawd's heavens, an' y'all'll heah it bettah'n efn y'all's 'long side it. When y'all wants 'freshmints, y'all kin step on back down an' y'all'll be se'ved. Come on, who gonna push a nickel into the music machine? This music so fah's been funnish by the managemint; that's me, Mistah Jawge. This Mistah Jawge's jinte! Now who gonna pacify the needs uh the music monstah?"

A young fellow swaggered up to Flo, standing by the phonograph. He gave her a handful of nickels.

"You feed the music monstah, Sweet Stuff," he said. "An' whin that money gone, they's mo' wheah it come fum."

Several other men, anxious to impress the attractive new girl, followed his example. In a moment Flo had more money than she could hold in both hands. She dropped the coins into the pocket of her dress, then put a few into the machine.

Laughing couples filed up the stairs into the unfurnished room above. Soon the sound of their dancing could be heard below.

The din was terrific, with the blatant music, the rhythmic thudding of the dancers' feet on the bare floor above, and the ribald remarks called back and forth among those gradually becoming exhilarated by the mild intoxicant.

Flo now found time to join in the merrymaking. Even May Lou deserted her kitchen from time to time, to dance or accept a proffered bottle of soda water or beer.

When the music stopped, no one else offering, Flo would drop into the phonograph one of the coins that had been entrusted to her; but two or three found their way into her shoe for every one she fed into the machine.

She was easily the belle of the evening. Her clear, light skin glowed and her brown eyes sparkled as she realized her popularity.

She patted her elaborately coiffed, straightened hair as she set a bottle of beer before a large black man.

"Heah yo' awdah, Mistah," she smiled.

"How 'bout me'n you sippin' a lil drink togethah?" he mumbled tipsily.

"Don't keer efn Ah does," Flo answered companionably. "Ah'll pick pop."

"Naw. Ah's sippin' beer, an' Ah wants ma comp'ny to sip beer, too."

"What kin' uh frien' is you?" Flo chided. "Offah me a drink, an' then won't let me pick it!"

"Go git you a bottle uh beer," he insisted stubbornly, "an' pack hit back an' sip hit whilst Ah sips mines."

Giggling, Flo complied, although she had already had too many drinks for comfort.

Despite a disadvantage because of her age and weight, Annie strove to be entertaining. She tried to make up in unabashed friendliness what she lacked in looks. After watching and listening as best she could to a quarrel between a man and his girl at one of the tables, she saw the girl leave the table abruptly, then walk alone out of the Big Spoon. The man sat on, morosely drinking.

Annie, deserting her domino games, strolled over to him and inquired sociably, "How 'bout me takin' the place uh yo' ustah-was comp'ny?" as she settled herself comfortably in the chair the girl had vacated.

The man barely glanced at her before grunting, "Ah's lakin' dat black gul ovah in dat cawnah what ain't sayin' nothin' to nobody." He indicated the girl with a nod of his woolly head.

"What you wants with that gul?" Annie asked sarcastically. "She Bootsie Mason. She the mos' unsociablest somebody they is. She ain't gonna make no good drinkin' compn'y."

"Go git huh fuh me," he ordered, "an' carry huh ovah heah an' make me 'quainted wid huh."

Flo had moved to a table with two men. They were more considerate than the big black man, who had quietly folded his arms on the table, to pillow his head, and lapsed into slumber. Flo's two new companions did not insist that she drink with them. Each of them put a five-cent piece at her place with every round of drinks.

Serving a sandwich to a light brown boy, Annie inquired coyly, "What'll you pick to drink?"

"Ah'll pick beer. Could Ah offah you some?"

"Ah'll take the dime," Annie simpered. "Ah gotta git back to the domino games."

"Not fum me, you won't!" the man contradicted bluntly. "Efn you sets an' sips the beer, Ah'll pay fuh it, but Ah ain't intrusted in givin' you a dime to switch off fas' as you kin. Ah'll let you swing me fuh a drink, but you sho can't swing me fuh no dime."

"O. K., Ah'll drink with you," Annie capitulated with a silly grin, starting for the beer.

At midnight George took his place in the center of the large room, and clapped his hands to gain attention.

"Flo," he instructed importantly, "step upstai's an' tell the folks to come down fuh the drawin'."

"Yassuh," Flo answered, leaving quickly.

George stood smiling jovially as those outdoors sidled in and the dancers arranged themselves on the stairs or anywhere where they would be able to hear the number called. When he had the undivided and breathless attention of the crowd, he began unctuously:

"Ma frien's, we is now gonna draw the lucky numbah uh the lucky somebody what git the free kaig uh beer. Free, fuh only tin cints he done pay fur the ruffle ticket. Who wanna do the drawin'?"

"Lilly a good one to draw!" someone called, and a girl in a bright-blue dress was pushed forward.

"That suit me," George agreed genially, rubbing his hands together. "Come heah, Miss Lilly, an' draw out the lucky numbah uh the lucky somebody."

Lilly drew a slip of paper from the box George held toward her. She offered it to him, but George shook his head.

"This gotta be puhfeckly faiah," he said. "Ast that man beside you to read the numbah uh the lucky somebody what you jes drawed."

"He can't read."

"Then you read the numbah, Miss Lilly," George requested.

"Numbah fo'teen," she read carefully.

"Me! Dat ma numbah!" shouted a small black man excitedly.

"Rally 'roun' an' we opens it fuh you!" George offered, twirling his mustache.

"Sho!" the winner urged; "rally 'roun' evahbody, an' Ah treats y'all to ma ice col' beer!"

There ensued a mad scramble for glasses, empty bottles or anything that would hold beer. Then, amid squeals and giggles, pushing and shoving and many coarse jokes, the containers were filled with beer from the keg, while the owner stood politely by, grinning with pleasure, waiting for all to be served.

Suddenly the keg was empty! Too late, the lucky winner realized that a keg of beer is not inexhaustible.

· 148 ·

# *from* THE GRAPES OF WRATH

*by* JOHN STEINBECK

John Steinbeck has had one of the most spectacular literary careers of any living American. His first few books were largely ignored by the public. Not until he wrote his delightful *Tortilla Flat* did the word begin to get round that here was a remarkable talent. By the time *Of Mice and Men* appeared, both in book form and on Broadway, many of the critics had begun to wonder if "talent" were not much too mild a word. Then came *The Grapes of Wrath*. Its sale was astronomical and its influence on American thinking probably greater than any book since Harriet Beecher Stowe's *Uncle Tom's Cabin*. The following passage from *The Grapes of Wrath* finds the Joad family, like so many of their depression-hit neighbors, preparing to move, lock, stock, and barrel, from their Oklahoma farm to California.

---

THE SKY GRAYED AMONG THE STARS, AND THE PALE, LATE quartermoon was insubstantial and thin. Tom Joad and the preacher walked quickly along a road that was only wheel tracks and beaten caterpillar tracks through a cotton field. Only the unbalanced sky showed the approach of dawn, no horizon to the west, and a line to the east. The two men walked in silence and smelled the dust their feet kicked into the air.

"I hope you're dead sure of the way," Jim Casy said. "I'd hate to have the dawn come and us be way to hell an' gone somewhere." The cotton field scurried with waking life, the quick flutter of morning birds feeding on the ground, the scamper over the clods of disturbed rabbits. The quiet thudding of the men's feet in the dust, the squeak of crushed clods under their shoes, sounded against the secret noises of the dawn.

Tom said, "I could shut my eyes an' walk right there. On'y

way I can go wrong is think about her. Jus' forget about her, an' I'll go right there. Hell, man, I was born right aroun' in here. I run aroun' here when I was a kid. They's a tree over there— look, you can jus' make it out. Well, once my old man hung up a dead coyote in that tree. Hung there till it was all sort of melted, an' then dropped off. Dried up, like. Jesus, I hope Ma's cookin' somepin. My belly's caved."

"Me too," said Casy. "Like a little eatin' tobacca? Keeps ya from gettin' too hungry. Been better if we didn' start so damn early. Better if it was light." He paused to gnaw off a piece of plug. "I was sleepin' nice."

"That crazy Muley done it," said Tom. "He got me clear jumpy. Wakes me up an' says, ''By, Tom. I'm goin' on. I got places to go.' An' he says, 'Better get goin' too, so's you'll be offa this lan' when the light comes.' He's gettin' screwy as a gopher, livin' like he does. You'd think Injuns was after him. Think he's nuts?"

"Well, I dunno. You seen that car come las' night when we had a little fire. You seen how the house was smashed. They's somepin purty mean goin' on. 'Course Muley's crazy, all right. Creepin' aroun' like a coyote; that's boun' to make him crazy. He'll kill somebody purty soon an' they'll run him down with dogs. I can see it like a prophecy. He'll get worse an' worse. Wouldn' come along with us, you say?"

"No," said Joad. "I think he's scared to see people now. Wonder he come up to us. We'll be at Uncle John's place by sunrise." They walked along in silence for a time, and the late owls flew over toward the barns, the hollow trees, the tank houses, where they hid from daylight. The eastern sky grew fairer and it was possible to see the cotton plants and the graying earth. "Damn' if I know how they're all sleepin' at Uncle John's. He on'y got one room an' a cookin' leanto, an' a little bit of a barn. Must be a mob there now."

The preacher said, "I don't recollect that John had a fambly. Just a lone man, ain't he? I don't recollect much about him."

"Lonest goddamn man in the world," said Joad. "Crazy

· 150 ·

kind of son-of-a-bitch, too—somepin like Muley, on'y worse in some ways. Might see 'im anywheres—at Shawnee, drunk, or visitin' a widow twenty miles away, or workin' his place with a lantern. Crazy. Ever'body thought he wouldn't live long. A lone man like that don't live long. But Uncle John's older'n Pa. Jus' gets stringier an' meaner ever' year. Meaner'n Grampa."

"Look a the light comin'," said the preacher. "Silvery-like. Didn' John never have no fambly?"

"Well, yes, he did, an' that'll show you the kind a fella he is—set in his ways. Pa tells about it. Uncle John, he had a young wife. Married four months. She was in a family way, too, an' one night she gets a pain in her stomick, an' she says, 'You better go for a doctor.' Well, John, he's settin' there, an' he says, 'You just got a stomickache. You et too much. Take a dose a pain killer. You crowd up ya stomick an' ya get a stomick-ache,' he says. Nex' noon she's outa her head, an' she dies at about four in the afternoon."

"What was it?" Casy asked. "Poisoned from somepin she et?"

"No, somepin jus' bust in her. Ap—appendick or somepin. Well, Uncle John, he's always been a easy-goin' fella, an' he takes it hard. Takes it for a sin. For a long time he won't have nothin' to say to nobody. Just walks aroun' like he don't see nothin', an' he prays some. Took 'im two years to come out of it, an' then he ain't the same. Sort of wild. Made a damn nuisance of hisself. Ever' time one of us kids got worms or a gutache Uncle John brings a doctor out. Pa finally tol' him he got to stop. Kids all the time gettin' a gutache. He figures it's his fault his woman died. Funny fella. He's all the time makin' it up to somebody—givin' kids stuff, droppin' a sack a meal on somebody's porch. Give away about ever'thing he got, an' still he ain't very happy. Gets walkin' around alone at night sometimes. He's a good farmer, though. Keeps his lan' nice."

"Poor fella," said the preacher. "Poor lonely fella. Did he go to church much when his woman died?"

"No, he didn'. Never wanted to get close to folks. Wanted

to be off alone. I never seen a kid that wasn't crazy about him. He'd come to our house in the night sometimes, an' we knowed he come 'cause jus' as sure as he come there'd be a pack a gum in the bed right beside ever' one of us. We thought he was Jesus Christ Awmighty."

The preacher walked along, head down. He didn't answer. And the light of the coming morning made his forehead seem to shine, and his hands, swinging beside him, flicked into the light and out again.

Tom was silent too, as though he had said too intimate a thing and was ashamed. He quickened his pace and the preacher kept step. They could see a little into gray distance ahead now. A snake wriggled slowly from the cotton rows into the road. Tom stopped short of it and peered. "Gopher snake," he said. "Let him go." They walked around the snake and went on their way. A little color came into the eastern sky, and almost immediately the lonely dawn light crept over the land. Green appeared on the cotton plants and the earth was gray-brown. The faces of the men lost their grayish shine. Joad's face seemed to darken with the growing light. "This is the good time," Joad said softly. "When I was a kid I used to get up an' walk around by myself when it was like this. What's that ahead?"

A committee of dogs had met in the road, in honor of a bitch. Five males, shepherd mongrels, collie mongrels, dogs whose breeds had been blurred by a freedom of social life, were engaged in complimenting the bitch. For each dog sniffed daintily and then stalked to a cotton plant on stiff legs, raised a hind foot ceremoniously and wetted, then went back to smell. Joad and the preacher stopped to watch, and suddenly Joad laughed joyously. "By God!" he said. "By God!" Now all dogs met and hackles rose, and they all growled and stood stiffly, each waiting for the others to start a fight. One dog mounted and, now that it was accomplished, the others gave way and watched with interest, and their tongues were out, and their tongues dripped. The two men walked on. "By God!" Joad said. "I think that up-dog is our Flash. I thought he'd be dead. Come, Flash!" He laughed again. "What the hell, if somebody called me, I wouldn't hear him neither. 'Minds me of a story they tell about Willy Feeley when he was a young fella. Willy was bashful, awful bashful. Well, one day he takes a heifer over to Graves' bull. Ever'body was out but Elsie Graves, and Elsie wasn't bashful at all. Willy, he stood there turnin' red an' he couldn't even talk. Elsie says, 'I know what you come for; the bull's out in back a the barn.' Well, they took the heifer out there an' Willy an' Elsie sat on the fence to watch. Purty soon Willy got feelin' purty fly. Elsie looks over an' says, like she don't know, 'What's a matter, Willy?' Willy's so randy he can't hardly set still. 'By God,' he says, 'by God, I wisht I was a-doin' that!' Elsie says, 'Why not, Willy? It's your heifer.' "

The preacher laughed softly. "You know," he said, "it's a nice thing not bein' a preacher no more. Nobody use' ta tell stories when I was there, or if they did I couldn' laugh. An' I couldn' cuss. Now I cuss all I want, any time I want, an' it does a fella good to cuss if he wants to."

A redness grew up out of the eastern horizon, and on the ground birds began to chirp, sharply. "Look!" said Joad. "Right ahead. That's Uncle John's tank. Can't see the win'mill, but there's his tank. See it against the sky?" He speeded his walk. "I wonder if all the folks are there." The hulk of the tank stood above a rise. Joad, hurrying, raised a cloud of dust about his knees. "I wonder if Ma—" They saw the tank legs now, and the house, a square little box, unpainted and bare, and the barn, low-roofed and huddled. Smoke was rising from the tin chimney of the house. In the yard was a litter, piled furniture, the blades and motor of the windmill, bedsteads, chairs, tables. "Holy Christ, they're fixin' to go!" Joad said. A truck stood in the yard, a truck with high sides, but a strange truck, for while the front of it was a sedan, the top had been cut off in the middle and the truck bed fitted on. And as they drew near, the men could hear pounding from the yard, and as the rim of the blinding sun came up over the horizon, it fell on the truck, and they saw a man and the flash of his hammer as it rose and fell. And the

· 153 ·

sun flashed on the windows of the house. The weathered boards were bright. Two red chickens on the ground flamed with reflected light.

"Don't yell," said Tom. "Let's creep up on 'em, like," and he walked so fast that the dust rose as high as his waist. And then he came to the edge of the cotton field. Now they were in the yard proper, earth beaten hard, shiny hard, and a few dusty crawling weeds on the ground. And Joad slowed as though he feared to go on. The preacher, watching him, slowed to match his step. Tom sauntered forward, sidled embarrassedly toward the truck. It was a Hudson Super-Six sedan, and the top had been ripped in two with a cold chisel. Old Tom Joad stood in the truck bed and he was nailing on the top rails of the truck sides. His grizzled, bearded face was low over his work, and a bunch of six-penny nails stuck out of his mouth. He set a nail and his hammer thundered it in. From the house came the clash of a lid on the stove and the wail of a child. Joad sidled up to the truck bed and leaned against it. And his father looked at him and did not see him. His father set another nail and drove it in. A flock of pigeons started from the deck of the tank house and flew around and settled again and strutted to the edge to look over; white pigeons and blue pigeons and grays, with iridescent wings.

Joad hooked his fingers over the lowest bar of the truck side. He looked up at the aging, graying man on the truck. He wet his thick lips with his tongue, and he said softly, "Pa."

"What do you want?" old Tom mumbled around his mouthful of nails. He wore a black, dirty slouch hat and a blue work shirt over which was a buttonless vest; his jeans were held up by a wide harness-leather belt with a big square brass buckle, leather and metal polished from years of wearing; and his shoes were cracked and the soles swollen and boat-shaped from years of sun and wet and dust. The sleeves of his shirt were tight on his forearms, held down by the bulging powerful muscles. Stomach and hips were lean, and legs, short, heavy, and strong. His face, squared by a bristling pepper and salt beard, was all drawn down to the forceful chin, a chin thrust out and built out by the stubble beard which was not so grayed on the chin, and gave weight and force to its thrust. Over old Tom's unwhiskered cheek bones the skin was as brown as meerschaum, and wrinkled in rays around his eye-corners from squinting. His eyes were brown, black-coffee brown, and he thrust his head forward when he looked at a thing, for his bright dark eyes were failing. His lips, from which the big nails protruded, were thin and red.

He held his hammer suspended in the air, about to drive a set nail, and he looked over the truck side at Tom, looked resentful at being interrupted. And then his chin drove forward and his eyes looked at Tom's face, and then gradually his brain became aware of what he saw. The hammer dropped slowly to his side, and with his left hand he took the nails from his mouth. And he said wonderingly, as though he told himself the fact, "It's Tommy—" And then, still informing himself, "It's Tommy come home." His mouth opened again, and a look of fear came into his eyes. "Tommy," he said softly, "you ain't busted out? You ain't got to hide?" He listened tensely.

"Naw," said Tom. "I'm paroled. I'm free. I got my papers." He gripped the lower bars of the truck side and looked up.

Old Tom laid his hammer gently on the floor and put his nails in his pocket. He swung his leg over the side and dropped lithely to the ground, but once beside his son he seemed embarrassed and strange. "Tommy," he said, "we are goin' to California. But we was gonna write you a letter an' tell you." And he said, incredulously, "But you're back. You can go with us. You can go!" The lid of a coffee pot slammed in the house. Old Tom looked over his shoulder. "Le's supprise 'em," he said, and his eyes shone with excitement. "Your ma got a bad feelin' she ain't never gonna see you no more. She got that quiet look like when somebody died. Almost she don't want to go to California, fear she'll never see you no more." A stove lid clashed in the house again. "Le's supprise 'em," old Tom repeated. "Le's go in like you never been away. Le's jus' see what your ma says." At last he touched Tom, but touched him on the shoulder, timidly, and instantly took his hand away. He looked at Jim Casy.

Tom said, "You remember the preacher, Pa. He come along with me."

"He been in prison too?"

"No, I met 'im on the road. He been away."

Pa shook hands gravely. "You're welcome here, sir."

Casy said, "Glad to be here. It's a thing to see when a boy comes home. It's a thing to see."

"Home," Pa said.

"To his folks," the preacher amended quickly. "We stayed at the other place last night."

Pa's chin thrust out, and he looked back down the road for a moment. Then he turned to Tom. "How'll we do her?" he began excitedly. "S'pose I go in an' say, 'Here's some fellas want some breakfast,' or how'd it be if you jus' come in an' stood there till she seen you? How'd that be?" His face was alive with excitement.

"Don't le's give her no shock," said Tom. "Don't le's scare her none."

Two rangy shepherd dogs trotted up pleasantly, until they caught the scent of strangers, and then they backed cautiously away, watchful, their tails moving slowly and tentatively in the air, but their eyes and noses quick for animosity or danger. One of them, stretching his neck, edged forward, ready to run, and little by little he approached Tom's legs and sniffed loudly at them. Then he backed away and watched Pa for some kind of signal. The other pup was not so brave. He looked about for something that could honorably divert his attention, saw a red chicken go mincing by, and ran at it. There was the squawk of an outraged hen, a burst of red feathers, and the hen ran off, flapping stubby wings for speed. The pup looked proudly back at the men, and then flopped down in the dust and beat its tail contentedly on the ground.

"Come on," said Pa, "come on in now. She got to see you. I got to see her face when she sees you. Come on. She'll yell

· 156 ·

breakfast in a minute. I heard her slap the salt pork in the pan a good time ago." He led the way across the fine-dusted ground. There was no porch on this house, just a step and then the door; a chopping block beside the door, its surface matted and soft from years of chopping. The graining in the sheathing wood was high, for the dust had cut down the softer wood. The smell of burning willow was in the air, and, as the three men neared the door, the smell of frying side-meat and the smell of high brown biscuits and the sharp smell of coffee rolling in the pot. Pa stepped up into the open doorway and stood there blocking it with his wide short body. He said, "Ma, there's a coupla fellas jus' come along the road, an' they wonder if we could spare a bite."

Tom heard his mother's voice, the remembered cool, calm drawl, friendly and humble. "Let 'em come," she said. "We got a'plenty. Tell 'em they got to wash their han's. The bread is done. I'm jus' takin' up the side-meat now." And the sizzle of the angry grease came from the stove.

Pa stepped inside, clearing the door, and Tom looked in at his mother. She was lifting the curling slices of pork from the frying pan. The oven door was open, and a great pan of high brown biscuits stood waiting there. She looked out the door, but the sun was behind Tom, and she saw only a dark figure outlined by the bright yellow sunlight. She nodded pleasantly. "Come in," she said. "Jus' lucky I made plenty bread this morning."

Tom stood looking in. Ma was heavy, but not fat; thick with child-bearing and work. She wore a loose Mother Hubbard of gray cloth in which there had once been colored flowers, but the color was washed out now, so that the small flowered pattern was only a little lighter gray than the background. The dress came down to her ankles, and her strong, broad, bare feet moved quickly and deftly over the floor. Her thin, steel-gray hair was gathered in a sparse wispy knot at the back of her head. Strong, freckled arms were bare to the elbow, and her hands were chubby and delicate, like those of a plump little girl. She looked out into the sunshine. Her full face was not soft; it was controlled, kindly. Her hazel eyes seemed to have experienced all possible tragedy and to have mounted pain and suffering like steps into a high calm and a superhuman understanding. She seemed to know, to accept, to welcome her position, the citadel of the family, the strong place that could not be taken. And since old Tom and the children could not know hurt or fear unless she acknowledged hurt and fear, she had practiced denying them in herself. And since, when a joyful thing happened, they looked to see whether joy was on her, it was her habit to build up laughter out of inadequate materials. But better than joy was calm. Imperturbability could be depended upon. And from her great and humble position in the family she had taken dignity and a clean calm beauty. From her position as healer, her hands had grown sure and cool and quiet; from her position as arbiter she had become as remote and faultless in judgment as a goddess. She seemed to know that if she swayed the family shook, and if she ever really deeply wavered or despaired the family would fall, the family will to function would be gone.

She looked out into the sunny yard, at the dark figure of a man. Pa stood near by, shaking with excitement. "Come in," he cried. "Come right in, mister." And Tom a little shamefacedly stepped over the doorsill.

She looked up pleasantly from the frying pan. And then her hand sank slowly to her side and the fork clattered to the wooden floor. Her eyes opened wide, and the pupils dilated. She breathed heavily through her open mouth. She closed her eyes. "Thank God," she said. "Oh, thank God!" And suddenly her face was worried. "Tommy, you ain't wanted? You didn' bust loose?"

"No, Ma. Parole. I got the papers here." He touched his breast.

She moved toward him lithely, soundlessly in her bare feet, and her face was full of wonder. Her small hand felt his arm, felt the soundness of his muscles. And then her fingers went up to his cheek as a blind man's fingers might. And her joy was nearly like sorrow. Tom pulled his underlip between his teeth and bit it. Her eyes went wonderingly to his bitten lip, and she saw the little line of blood against his teeth and the trickle of blood down his lip. Then she knew, and her control came back, and her hand dropped. Her breath came out explosively. "Well!" she cried. "We come mighty near to goin' without ya. An' we was wonderin' how in the worl' you could ever find us." She picked up the fork and combed the boiling grease and brought out a dark curl of crisp pork. And she set the pot of tumbling coffee on the back of the stove.

Old Tom giggled, "Fooled ya, huh, Ma? We aimed to fool ya, and we done it. Jus' stood there like a hammered sheep. Wisht Grampa'd been here to see. Looked like somebody'd beat ya between the eyes with a sledge. Grampa would a whacked 'imself so hard he'd a throwed his hip out—like he done when he seen Al take a shot at that grea' big airship the Army got. Tommy, it come over one day, half a mile big, an' Al gets the thirty-thirty and blazes away at her. Grampa yells, 'Don't shoot no fledglin's, Al; wait till a growed-up one goes over,' an' then he whacked 'imself an' throwed his hip out."

Ma chuckled and took down a heap of tin plates from a shelf.

Tom asked, "Where is Grampa? I ain't seen the ol' devil."

Ma stacked the plates on the kitchen table and piled cups beside them. She said confidentially, "Oh, him an' Granma sleeps in the barn. They got to get up so much in the night. They was stumblin' over the little fellas."

Pa broke in, "Yeah, ever' night Grampa'd get mad. Tumble over Winfield, an' Winfield'd yell, an' Grampa'd get mad an' wet his drawers, an' that'd make him madder, an' purty soon ever'body in the house'd be yellin' their head off." His words tumbled out between chuckles. "Oh, we had lively times. One night when ever'body was yellin' an' a-cussin', your brother Al, he's a smart aleck now, he says, 'Goddamn it, Grampa, why don't you run off an' be a pirate?' Well that made Grampa so goddamn mad he went for his gun. Al had ta sleep out in the fiel' that night. But now Granma an' Grampa both sleeps in the barn."

Ma said, "They can jus' get up an' step outside when they

· 159 ·

feel like it. Pa, run on out an' tell 'em Tommy's home. Grampa's a favorite of him."

"A course," said Pa. "I should of did it before." He went out the door and crossed the yard, swinging his hands high.

Tom watched him go, and then his mother's voice called his attention. She was pouring coffee. She did not look at him. "Tommy," she said hesitantly, timidly.

"Yeah?" His timidity was set off by hers, a curious embarrassment. Each one knew the other was shy, and became more shy in the knowledge.

"Tommy, I got to ask you—you ain't mad?"

"Mad, Ma?"

"You ain't poisoned mad? You don't hate nobody? They didn' do nothin' in that jail to rot you out with crazy mad?"

He looked sidewise at her, studied her, and his eyes seemed to ask how she could know such things. "No-o-o," he said. "I was for a little while. But I ain't proud like some fellas. I let stuff run off'n me. What's a matter, Ma?"

Now she was looking at him, her mouth open, as though to hear better, her eyes digging to know better. Her face looked for the answer that is always concealed in language. She said in confusion, "I knowed Purty Boy Floyd. I knowed his ma. They was good folks. He was full a hell, sure, like a good boy oughta be." She paused and then her words poured out. "I don' know all like this—but I know it. He done a little bad thing a' they hurt 'im, caught 'im an' hurt him so he was mad, an' the nex' bad thing he done was mad, an' they hurt 'im again. An' purty soon he was mean-mad. They shot at him like a varmint, an' he shot back, an' then they run him like a coyote, an' him a-snappin, an' a-snarlin', mean as a lobo. An' he was mad. He wasn't no boy or no man no more, he was jus' a walkin' chunk a mean-mad. But the folks that knowed him didn' hurt 'im. He wasn' mad at them. Finally they run him down an' killed 'im. No matter how they say it in the paper how he was bad—that's how it was." She paused and she licked her dry lips, and her whole face was

· 160 ·

an aching question. "I got to know. Tommy. Did they hurt you so much? Did they make you mad like that?"

Tom's heavy lips were pulled tight over his teeth. He looked down at his big flat hands. "No," he said. "I ain't like that." He paused and studied the broken nails, which were ridged like clam shells. "All the time in stir I kep' away from stuff like that. I ain' so mad."

She sighed, "Thank God!" under her breath.

He looked up quickly. "Ma, when I seen what they done to our house—"

She came near to him then, and stood close; and she said passionately, "Tommy, don't you go fightin' 'em alone. They'll hunt you down like a coyote. Tommy, I got to thinkin' an' dreamin' an' wonderin'. They say there's a hun'erd thousand of us shoved out. If we was all mad the same way, Tommy—they wouldn't hunt nobody down—" She stopped.

Tommy, looking at her, gradually dropped his eyelids, until just a short glitter showed through his lashes. "Many folks feel that way?" he demanded.

"I don' know. They're jus' kinda stunned. Walk aroun' like they was half asleep."

From outside and across the yard came an ancient creaking bleat. "Pu-raise Gawd fur vittory! Pu-raise Gawd fur vittory!"

Tom turned his head and grinned. "Granma finally heard I'm home. Ma," he said, "you never was like this before!"

Her face hardened and her eyes grew cold. "I never had my house pushed over," she said. "I never had my fambly stuck out on the road. I never had to sell—ever'thing— Here they come now." She moved back to the stove and dumped the big pan of bulbous biscuits on two tin plates. She shook flour into the deep grease to make gravy, and her hand was white with flour. For a moment Tom watched her, and then he went to the door.

Across the yard came four people. Grampa was ahead, a lean, ragged, quick old man, jumping with quick steps and favoring his right leg—the side that came out of joint. He was buttoning his fly as he came, and his old hands were having trouble finding the buttons, for he had buttoned the top button into the second buttonhole, and that threw the whole sequence off. He wore dark ragged pants and a torn blue shirt, open all the way down, and showing long gray underwear, also unbuttoned. His lean white chest, fuzzed with white hair, was visible through the opening in his underwear. He gave up the fly and left it open and fumbled with the underwear buttons, then gave the whole thing up and hitched his brown suspenders. His was a lean excitable face with little bright eyes as evil as a frantic child's eyes. A cantankerous, complaining, mischievous, laughing face. He fought and argued, told dirty stories. He was as lecherous as always. Vicious and cruel and impatient, like a frantic child, and the whole structure overlaid with amusement. He drank too much when he could get it, ate too much when it was there, talked too much all the time.

Behind him hobbled Granma, who had survived only because she was as mean as her husband. She had held her own with a shrill ferocious religiosity that was as lecherous and as savage as anything Grampa could offer. Once, after a meeting, while she was still speaking in tongues, she fired both barrels of a shotgun at her husband, ripping one of his buttocks nearly off, and after that he admired her and did not try to torture her as children torture bugs. As she walked she hiked her Mother Hubbard up to her knees, and she bleated her shrill terrible war cry: "Pu-raise Gawd fur vittory."

Granma and Grampa raced each other to get across the broad yard. They fought over everything, and loved and needed the fighting.

Behind them, moving slowly and evenly, but keeping up, came Pa and Noah—Noah the first-born, tall and strange, walking always with a wondering look on his face, calm and puzzled. He had never been angry in his life. He looked in wonder at angry people, wonder and uneasiness, as normal people look at the insane. Noah moved slowly, spoke seldom, and then so slowly that people who did not know him often thought him stupid. He was not stupid, but he was strange. He had little pride, no sexual urges. He worked and slept in a curious rhythm that nevertheless sufficed him. He was fond of his folks, but never showed it in any way. Although an observer could not have told why, Noah left the impression of being misshapen, his head or his body or his legs or his mind; but no misshapen member could be recalled. Pa thought he knew why Noah was strange, but Pa was ashamed, and never told. For on the night when Noah was born, Pa, frightened at the spreading thighs, alone in the house, and horrified at the screaming wretch his wife had become, went mad with apprehension. Using his hands, his strong fingers for forceps, he had pulled and twisted the baby. The midwife, arriving late, had found the baby's head pulled out of shape, its neck stretched, its body warped; and she had pushed the head back and molded the body with her hands. But Pa always remembered, and was ashamed. And he was kinder to Noah than to the others. In Noah's broad face, eyes too far apart, and long fragile jaw, Pa thought he saw the twisted, warped skull of the baby. Noah could do all that was required of him, could read and write, could work and figure, but he didn't seem to care; there was a listlessness in him toward things people wanted and needed. He lived in a strange silent house and looked out of it through calm eyes. He was a stranger to all the world, but he was not lonely.

The four came across the yard, and Grampa demanded, "Where is he? Goddamn it, where is he?" And his fingers fumbled for his pants button, and forgot and strayed into his pocket. And then he saw Tom standing in the door. Grampa stopped and he stopped the others. His little eyes glittered with malice. "Lookut him," he said. "A jailbird. Ain't been no Joads in jail for a hell of a time." His mind jumped. "Got no right to put 'im in jail. He done just what I'd do. Sons-a-bitches got no right." His mind jumped again. "An' ol' Turnbull, stinkin' skunk, braggin' how he'll shoot ya when ya come out. Says he got Hatfield blood. Well, I sent word to him. I says, 'Don't mess around with no Joad. Maybe I got McCoy blood for all I know.' I says, 'You lay your sights anywheres near Tommy an' I'll take it an' I'll ram it up your ass,' I says. Scairt 'im, too."

Granma, not following the conversation, bleated, "Pu-raise Gawd fur vittory."

Grampa walked up and slapped Tom on the chest, and his eyes grinned with affection and pride. "How are ya, Tommy?"

"O.K." said Tom. "How ya keepin' yaself?"

"Full a piss an' vinegar," said Grampa. His mind jumped. "Jus' like I said, they ain't a gonna keep no Joad in jail. I says, 'Tommy'll come a-bustin' outa that jail like a bull through a corral fence.' An' you done it. Get outa my way, I'm hungry." He crowded past, sat down, loaded his plate with pork and two big biscuits and poured the thick gravy over the whole mess, and before the others could get in, Grampa's mouth was full.

Tom grinned affectionately at him. "Ain't he a heller?" he said. And Grampa's mouth was so full he couldn't even splutter, but his mean little eyes smiled, and he nodded his head violently.

Granma said proudly. "A wicketer, cussin'er man never lived. He's goin' to hell on a poker, praise Gawd! Wants to drive the truck!" she said spitefully. "Well, he ain't goin' ta."

Grampa choked, and a mouthful of paste sprayed into his lap, and he coughed weakly.

Granma smiled up at Tom. "Messy, ain't he?" she observed brightly.

Noah stood on the step, and he faced Tom, and his wide-set eyes seemed to look around him. His face had little expression. Tom said, "How ya, Noah?"

"Fine," said Noah. "How a' you?" That was all, but it was a comfortable thing.

Ma waved the flies away from the bowl of gravy. "We ain't got room to set down," she said. "Jus' get yaself a plate an' set down wherever ya can. Out in the yard or someplace."

Suddenly Tom said, "Hey! Where's the preacher? He was right here. Where'd he go?"

Pa said, "I seen him, but he's gone."

And Granma raised a shrill voice, "Preacher? You got a

preacher? Go git him. We'll have a grace." She pointed at Grampa. "Too late for him—he's et. Go git the preacher."

Tom stepped out on the porch. "Hey, Jim! Jim Casy!" he called. He walked out in the yard. "Oh, Casy!" The preacher emerged from under the tank, sat up, and then stood up and moved toward the house. Tom asked, "What was you doin', hidin'?"

"Well, no. But a fella shouldn' butt his head in where a fambly got fambly stuff. I was jus' settin' a-thinkin'."

"Come on in an' eat," said Tom. "Granma wants a grace."

"But I ain't a preacher no more," Casy protested.

"Aw, come on. Give her a grace. Don't do you no harm, an' she likes 'em." They walked into the kitchen together.

Ma said quietly, "You're welcome."

And Pa said, "You're welcome. Have some breakfast."

"Grace fust," Granma clamored. "Grace fust."

Grampa focused his eyes fiercely until he recognized Casy. "Oh, that preacher," he said. "Oh, he's all right. I always liked him—" He winked so lecherously that Granma thought he had spoken and retorted, "Shut up, you sinful ol' goat."

Casy ran his fingers through his hair nervously. "I got to tell you, I ain't a preacher no more. If me jus' bein' glad to be here an' bein' thankful for people that's kind and generous, if that's enough—why, I'll say that kinda grace. But I ain't a preacher no more."

"Say her," said Granma. "An' get in a word about us goin' to California." The preacher bowed his head, and the others bowed their heads. Ma folded her hands over her stomach and bowed her head. Granma bowed so low that her nose was nearly in her plate of biscuit and gravy. Tom, leaning against the wall, a plate in his hand, bowed stiffly, and Grampa bowed his head sidewise, so that he could keep one mean and merry eye on the preacher. And on the preacher's face there was a look not of prayer, but of thought; and in his tone not supplication, but conjecture.

"I been thinkin'," he said. "I been in the hills, thinkin',

almost you might say like Jesus went into the wilderness to think His way out of a mess of troubles."

"Pu-raise Gawd!" Granma said, and the preacher glanced over at her in surprise.

"Seems like Jesus got all messed up with troubles, and He couldn't figure nothin' out, an' He got to feelin' what the hell good is it all, an' what's the use fightin' an figurin'. Got tired, got good an' tired, an' His sperit all wore out. Jus' about come to the conclusion, the hell with it. An' so He went off into the wilderness."

"A-men," Granma bleated. So many years she had timed her responses to the pauses. And it was so many years since she had listened to or wondered at the words used.

"I ain't sayin' I'm like Jesus," the preacher went on. "But I got tired like Him, an' I got mixed up like Him, an' I went into the wilderness like Him, without no campin' stuff. Nighttime I'd lay on my back an' look up at the stars; morning I'd set an' watch the sun come up; midday I'd look out from a hill at the rollin' dry country; evenin' I'd foller the sun down. Sometimes I'd pray like I always done. On'y I couldn' figure what I was prayin' to or for. There was the hills, an' there was me, an' we wasn't separate no more. We was one thing. An' that one thing was holy."

"Hallelujah," said Granma, and she rocked a little, back and forth, trying to catch hold of an ecstasy.

"An' I got thinkin', on'y it wasn't thinkin', it was deeper down than thinkin'. I got thinkin' how we was holy when we was one thing, an' mankin' was holy when it was one thing. An' it on'y got unholy when one mis'able little fella got the bit in his teeth an' run off his own way, kickin' an' draggin' an' fightin'. Fella like that bust the holiness. But when they're all workin' together, not one fella for another fella, but one fella kind of harnessed to the whole shebang—that's right, that's holy. An' I got thinkin' I don't even know what I mean by holy." He paused, but the bowed heads stayed down, for they had been trained like dogs to rise at the "amen" signal. "I can't say no grace like I use' ta say. I'm glad of the holiness of breakfast. I'm glad there's love here. That's all." The heads stayed down. The preacher looked around. "I've got your breakfast cold," he said; and then he remembered. "Amen," he said, and all the heads rose up.

"A-men," said Granma, and she fell to her breakfast, and broke down the soggy biscuits with her hard old toothless gums. Tom ate quickly, and Pa crammed his mouth. There was no talk until the food was gone, the coffee drunk; only the crunch of chewed food and the slup of coffee cooled in transit to the tongue. Ma watched the preacher as he ate, and her eyes were questioning, probing and understanding. She watched him as though he were suddenly a spirit, not human any more, a voice out of the ground.

The men finished and put down their plates, and drained the last of their coffee; and then the men went out, Pa and the preacher and Noah and Grampa and Tom, and they walked over to the truck, avoiding the litter of furniture, the wooden bedsteads, the windmill machinery, the old plow. They walked to the truck and stood beside it. They touched the new pine side-boards.

Tom opened the hood and looked at the big greasy engine. And Pa came up beside him. He said, "Your Brother Al looked her over before we bought her. He says she's all right."

"What's he know? He's just a squirt," said Tom.

"He worked for a company. Drove truck last year. He knows quite a little. Smart aleck like he is. He knows. He can tinker an engine, Al can."

Tom asked, "Where's he now?"

"Well," said Pa, "he's a billygoatin' aroun' the country. Tom-cattin' hisself to death. Smart-aleck sixteen-year-older, an' his nuts is just a-eggin' him on. He don't think of nothin' but girls an engines. A plain smart aleck. Ain't been in nights for a week."

Grampa, fumbling with his chest, had succeeded in buttoning the buttons of his blue shirt into the buttonholes of his underwear. His fingers felt something was wrong, but did not care enough to find out. His fingers went down to try to figure out the intricacies of the buttoning of his fly. "I was worse," he said happily. "I was much worse. I was a heller, you might say. Why, they was a camp meetin' right in Sallisaw when I was a young fella a little bit older'n Al. He's just a squirt, an' punkin-soft. But I was older. An' we was to this here camp meetin'. Five hundred folks there, an' a proper sprinklin' of young heifers."

"You look like a heller yet, Grampa," said Tom.

"Well, I am, kinda. But I ain't nowheres near the fella I was. Jus' let me get out to California where I can pick me an orange when I want it. Or grapes. There's a thing I ain't never had enough of. Gonna get me a whole big bunch a grapes off a bush, or whatever, an' I'm gonna squash 'em on my face an' let 'em run offen my chin."

Tom asked, "Where's Uncle John? Where's Rosasharn? Where's Ruthie an' Winfield? Nobody said nothin' about them yet."

Pa said, "Nobody asked. John gone to Sallisaw with a load a stuff to sell: pump, tools, chickens, an' all the stuff we brung over. Took Ruthie an' Winfield with 'im. Went 'fore daylight."

"Funny I never saw him," said Tom.

"Well, you come down from the highway, didn' you? He took the back way, by Cowlington. An' Rosasharn, she's nestin' with Connie's folks. By God! You don't even know Rosasharn's married to Connie Rivers. You 'member Connie. Nice young fella. An' Rosasharn's due 'bout three-four-five months now. Swellin' up right now. Looks fine."

"Jesus!" said Tom. "Rosasharn was just a little kid. An' now she's gonna have a baby. So damn much happens in four years if you're away. When ya think to start out west, Pa?"

"Well, we got to take this stuff in an' sell it. If Al gets back from his squirtin' aroun', I figgered he could load the truck an' take all of it in, an' maybe we could start out tomorra or day after. We ain't got so much money, an' a fella says it's damn near two thousan' miles to California. Quicker we get started, surer it is we get there. Money's a-dribblin' out all the time. You got any money?"

"On'y a couple dollars. How'd you get money?"

"Well," said Pa, "we sol' all the stuff at our place, an' the whole bunch of us chopped cotton, even Grampa."

"Sure did," said Grampa.

"We put ever'thing together—two hundred dollars. We give seventy-five for this here truck, an' me an' Al cut her in two an' built on this here back. Al was gonna grind the valves, but he's too busy messin' aroun' to get down to her. We'll have maybe a hundred an' fifty when we start. Damn ol' tires on this here truck ain't gonna go far. Got a couple of wore out spares. Pick stuff up along the road, I guess."

The sun, driving straight down, stung with its rays. The shadows of the truck bed were dark bars on the ground, and the truck smelled of hot oil and oilcloth and paint. The few chickens had left the yard to hide in the tool shed from the sun. In the sty the pigs lay panting, close to the fence where a thin shadow fell and they complained shrilly now and then. The two dogs were stretched in the red dust under the truck, panting, their dripping tongues covered with dust. Pa pulled his hat low over his eyes and squatted down on his hams. And, as though this were his natural position of thought and observation, he surveyed Tom critically, the new but aging cap, the suit, and the new shoes.

"Did you spen' your money for them clothes?" he asked. "Them clothes are jus' gonna be a nuisance to ya."

"They give 'em to me," said Tom. "When I come out they give 'em to me." He took off his cap and looked at it with some admiration, then wiped his forehead with it and put it on rakishly and pulled at the visor.

Pa observed, "Them's a nice-lookin' pair a shoes they give ya."

"Yeah," Joad agreed. "Purty for nice, but they ain't no shoes to go walkin' aroun' in on a hot day." He squatted beside his father.

Noah said slowly, "Maybe if you got them side-boards all true on, we could load up this stuff. Load her up so maybe if Al comes in—"

"I can drive her, if that's what you want," Tom said. "I drove truck at McAlester."

"Good," said Pa, and then his eyes stared down the road. "If I ain't mistaken, there's a young smart aleck draggin' his tail home right now," he said. "Looks purty wore out, too."

Tom and the preacher looked up the road. And randy Al, seeing he was being noticed, threw back his shoulders, and he came into the yard with a swaying strut like that of a rooster about to crow. Cockily, he walked close before he recognized Tom; and when he did, his boasting face changed, and admiration and veneration shone in his eyes, and his swagger fell away. His stiff jeans, with the bottoms turned up eight inches to show his heeled boots, his three-inch belt with copper figures on it, even the red arm bands on his blue shirt and the rakish angle of his Stetson hat could not build him up to his brother's stature; for his brother had killed a man, and no one would ever forget it. Al knew that even he had inspired some admiration among boys of his own age because his brother had killed a man. He had heard in Sallisaw how he was pointed out: "That's Al Joad. His brother killed a fella with a shovel."

And now Al, moving humbly near, saw that his brother was not a swaggerer as he had supposed. Al saw the dark brooding eyes of his brother, and the prison calm, the smooth hard face trained to indicate nothing to a prison guard, neither resistance nor slavishness. And instantly Al changed. Unconsciously he became like his brother, and his handsome face brooded, and his shoulders relaxed. He hadn't remembered how Tom was.

Tom said, "Hello. Jesus, you're growin' like a bean! I wouldn't of knowed you."

Al, his hand ready if Tom should want to shake it, grinned self-consciously. Tom stuck out his hand and Al's hand jerked out to meet it. And there was liking between these two. "They tell me you're a good hand with a truck," said Tom.

And Al, sensing that his brother would not like a boaster, said, "I don't know nothin' much about it."

Pa said, "Been smart-alecking aroun' the country. You look

wore out. Well, you got to take a load of stuff into Sallisaw to sell."

Al looked at his brother Tom. "Care to ride in?" he said as casually as he could.

"No, I can't," said Tom. "I'll help aroun' here. We'll be— together on the road."

Al tried to control his question. "Did—did you bust out? Of jail?"

"No," said Tom. "I got paroled."

"Oh." And Al was a little disappointed.

# *from* THE INHERITORS

*oroororoororoororoororoororoororoororoororoororooro*

## *by* PHILIP ATLEE (JIM PHILLIPS)

At the age of seventeen Jim Phillips (who sometimes writes under the pen name "Philip Atlee") was a contributor to a literary magazine called *The Calithump*, which was published with more tumult than material success at Georgetown, Texas, in the very shadow of Southwestern University. His novel, *The Inheritors*, from which the following passage is taken, caused a sizable eruption in Fort Worth, where it was presumed by many that any resemblance between the characters in his book and actual human beings was anything but accidental. At last report he was working on another novel, while acting as director of operations at an Air Forces training school in Fort Worth. If you care to know what kind of man writes such prose as that in *The Inheritors*, the answer is: a very angry one, indeed.

---

A DELAYED HANGOVER IS A CRUEL AFFLICTION. I AM NOT familiar with the quantitative theory of alcohol absorption, hence I cannot explain the dogmas involved, but when a man drinks long enough, drinks in vain combat against the inevitable hour of reckoning, he will reach and pass the saturation point and arrive finally at that dismal outpost of intoxication where whiskey rims his eyes, leaves his mouth trembling, and puts vague and tricky wonder in his head. This sensation of wonder is most dangerous of all, for it will lead perilous close to the shadow line where buffoons dance eternally in greenish twilights and the dead are not dead and one can walk upon the water. It is a concomitant of these periods of suspension after extreme drunkenness that newsboys become potential presidents, and one wishes to take them home, clean and clothe them, and send them off to be Rhodes Scholars and great characters in history. But all newsboys do not have presidential calibre, as the grandeurs of hangover fever will lead us to believe, and one must be wary. Then too, moments come that bring a swift descent into the abyss, where life in toto is unadulterated hell.

It was with knowledge of these matters that I awoke in the afternoon after Rick Walton's precipitate departure from town. I came awake without warning and found myself staring at the grim visage of the tarpon hanging on my wall. The supercilious smirk graven on that piscatorial head did not rouse my spirits any, and I thrust my body stiffly along under the sheets, accounting for legs and arms. I was conscious of the crusty feel of my eyelids, as though a fine dust had caked there, and a languorous, almost painful aching threaded through my whole body. A nerve was jerking fitfully in my right cheek, and distaste for the world went hammering through my mind as I heaved up and stared at myself in the long mirror on the closet door.

Reddened eyes stared back at me without enthusiasm. Excess had etched its wavering warnings along my chin, and the sacs of my eyes were dark and puffed. I halfheartedly dodged the fellow in the mirror a few times, but soon gave it up, for he was as fast as I was. Then, for a while, I just sat in the middle of the bed listening to the construction work being carried on in my head. Something big was being built; I could tell that, and when I remembered where the bottle was cached, I tiptoed over to the bookshelf for it.

There was a drink left, but the smell came up out of the bottle and thonged at my stomach. My whole body tightened convulsively and jerked in protest, so I put the bottle down and lighted a cigarette. The first acrid smoke made by head whirl; it forced me to hang on to the bedpost. But things grew better after a few minutes and I took the drink, flopped back on the bed, and waited for the whiskey to build its firm fire.

A pleasant glow spread in the stomach, like water colors running on a blotter, and the glow mantled upward toward the brain. I lay there savoring it and wondering whether or not to go down and get some breakfast. I thought to myself that I would not bother with the stairs, just step right down out of the window and conserve my strength. The idea was faulty, and, after consideration, I realized it, so I put on a robe and inched down the stairs.

Pearl was dusting in the living room, dusting to swing time, and she flirted the oiled rag like a stout black dervish. I jigged into the room with one finger raised.

"Good mornin', good mornin', a brand new day is dawning . . . " I caroled, and Pearl gave the piano a parting slap and took up the chorus.

"A happy, carefree, gay good mornin' to you . . . "

"And to you, Pearl," I said gravely. "Have you seen my brains around here?"

"Brains?" Her bulldog face was puzzled. "Oh, Mr. Jimble, you is foolin'."

"I certainly are not," I said. "I have lost all my brains, Pearl."

She was undecided.

"Land's sake," she murmured.

"Have you seen them in your matutinal peregrinations?"

She smiled broadly and shook her kinky thatch. "Nawsir, but I kin fix you a potion for that achin' head," she announced with the air of one who has cut a Gordian knot. I bowed low.

"Madame, I shall count it no little favor," I said, and she cackled heartily and went waddling back to the kitchen.

Sunlight slanted through the figured lace curtains and dappled the red rug. Through the blinds, I could see some women standing on the fifth tee. As I watched, with my hands thrust into the pockets of the dressing gown, the lady golfers waggled their rumps one after the other, and lunged at the ball. The thought came to me that the object ball should be larger for the girls, say about grapefruit size. Turning the proposition over in my mind, I watched the feminine foursome waver through their stiff arcs and strike out down the fairway. I lighted another cigarette and had taken three drags from it when the telephone rang.

· 174 ·

It was for me. An earnest young lady named Wilkins, calling for the Little Theatre, informed me that the next play was to be "The Road to Rome," and would I play the part of a Carthagenian corporal?

"It is not a large part," gushed Miss Wilkins, "but something really fine could be done with it."

"You mean I could steal the show?" I enquired.

There was a pause on the line.

"Well, as to that I'm not sure," answered Miss Wilkins, finally and crisply. She was a trifle offended. "After all, we have Hightower doing the lead . . . "

"Probably run until the end of time. What does a corporal have to do?"

Miss Wilkins wasn't finding any civic spirit, and it hurt her. She wavered uncertainly, "Oh, I don't know. You just say your lines . . . "

Pearl brought me a large glass of tomato juice, and I took a long pull at it.

"One cannot be chary of sympathy for the smaller parts, Miss Wilkins," I said, "but how about a sergeant stint?"

"I'm very sorry," she said briskly. "The other parts have been filled."

I took another drink of the tomato juice. Spices and tart tastes were in it.

"More's the pity," I said, "but as a matter of fact, I'm under contract now. Otherwise I would be flattered."

"Contract?"

"Yes," I said, "I'm playing the fool."

Miss Wilkins was troubled. "Oh, I didn't know. We had so counted on having you. Bob was saying only yesterday that you were exactly what we needed . . . " I didn't call Bob to mind, but she went on. "This Fool thing, when are you playing it? This month?"

"Yes," I answered. "Undoubtedly this month."

"Next month?"

"In all probability."

Her voice was anguished. "But when will you be through?"

It was a fair question and I considered it gravely, holding the cool glass against my forehead.

"Hard to tell," I said finally. "I have a run of the show contract."

"Oh . . . " She whispered blankly. "But next time maybe?"

"Perhaps," I rejoined, and finished the tomato juice. She said that she wished me luck in "this Fool thing," and I replied that I would undoubtedly need it, and she hung up.

Pearl brought a platter of eggs in and I sat down to them, but without great enthusiasm. I was midway in them, and gazing out over the elms in the back yard when the phone rang again. I took it from the cradle, put it to my ear, and Lucille's voice flowered from the black receiver.

"Good morning!"

"Good morning," I said. "You slept well?"

"Of course. And you?" She was gay. Too gay.

"Exelenté. The pure in heart, you know," I answered, puzzled.

"Ah, but that is bound to be hearsay with you," she said archly, and I laughed moderately, wondering when the badinage would cease. When I did not answer she called out my name in a low tone.

"Yes?"

"About last night?" And she waited again, but I would not help her. There was not a drop of Lochinvar in me. "It was all right, wasn't it?"

I reached for a cigarette and found none, so I dispatched Pearl upstairs for some.

"How do you mean, all right?" I queried. "I thought it was exciting."

It was too blunt but it was also too early in the morning. She said nothing for a minute; she was timid and on unfamiliar ground.

"I mean . . . there's no danger, is there?"

"Danger?" I temporized. "But of course not. No. Everything absolutely okay."

"All right."

The words floated over the line. The morning sunlight slanted through the breakfast room windows, and it felt warm and comfortable on my face and arms, but a tremor shook me. She spoke again and as she did, the hangover lifted its vengeance long enough for memory to go smashing through my head.

"I just wondered," she said.

"Weep no more, my lady," I answered, "and remember that we have a date, come Tuesday, for the Tonto dance."

"All right." Her voice sounded lighter and less troubled. "I'll be looking forward to it," she said, and then hung up.

Pearl was thundering around upstairs, and I opened the hall door and asked her where the family was. When I did, she came to lean over the railing of the stairs and her mountainous breasts spilled over laxly. She dropped me a package of cigarettes, and said that "evvabody" was in town someplace, but she didn't know where. I ripped the cellophane off the cigarettes and lighted one, and then I went back into the living room to rest on the couch and pluck at the cords on a floor lamp. I was thinking of Lucille, wondering whether I had been first with her, and if not, I was considering who the scoundrel might have been. It was not logical, but it is what I was doing. The thought process was so discouraging, however, that I finally gave it up and drove over to the Mirrolite office.

Cavin was lying on the cot regarding the ceiling and Fred was patiently numbering a marker, so I sat down and began to read a magazine. Both of them looked at me, grunted shortly, and went back to what they had been doing. It was not the most heart-warming reception I had ever received, but I ignored it entirely and sat there looking at the cartoons in the magazine. We were like that when Buddy Perry pushed the door open and came inside.

"Notice!" he said, fighting an imaginary bull with an imaginary cape, "Mumford's got a job!"

Jarvis went on doing nothing, and Fred lifted his broad face from the wooden panel. His eyes were abstracted.

"A job?" he asked. "Mumford?" The paint brush was poised up by his ear. "You mean a working job?"

Perry made another deft pass with the invisible cape, and his nostrils dilated as the bull went by.

"Yuss," he hissed. "He is now our Mr. Mumford, neckties, socks, shorts, shirts, and stuff like that, down to Sack's Store."

Jarvis came up on one elbow.

"My God," he said, "how came him to do a thing like that?"

Perry stood silently, one foot in advance of the other, like a matador accepting the plaudits of the crowd. "Money," he said. "People do things like that for money. It's the only reason."

Jarvis was staring at him, twisting his shoulders under a light crew-necked sweater.

"Pure crap. What does he make?"

Perry whirled in a *pas de seul*, and that unseen cape settled gently around him. "Wouldn't tell me in the store's office," he said frankly. "Mumford claims twenty a week and commission."

Jarvis lay back down.

"How do you like that?" he asked us generally. "He could always chisel twice that much any week he ever lived."

Bradley chortled. "Ain't it the truth, though?" He bent back over the Mirrolite he was painting, and his mouth twisted as he put the brush down.

The chickens in the pen outside the office clucked drowsily, and sunlight fell through the window and flung a golden fan across the littered floor. It was a somnolent day, and we sat there in the shadowed room considering the fact of Mumford's employment.

"I don't like it," said Jarvis finally. His tone was dubious. "It just doesn't sound right."

Perry was playing the bull again, playing him too close to his body, and he lunged back suddenly, a squarefaced boy pirouetting in the center of the room.

"Close," I said, turning a page of my magazine. "Too close for comfort, that one."

Perry stared at me, his straw-colored thatch motionless above bright eyes.

"Don't worry," he said. "I'm just tiring him out. He'll never get me."

I was doubtful. "Looks like a tough one to me . . . "

"He won't ever in this world get me," promised Perry, and whirled with both hands up as the bull came snorting back at him from the southeast corner of the room. Jarvis got up and pulled on a tan sport coat. Bradley was finishing the sign; he put a few last swipes on it and held it up. Jarvis cocked his head and looked at it critically.

"The Four is lousy," he announced without enthusiasm, and Fred hung the glistening sign on the wall bracket. I could see his lips compress, but he said nothing.

"Watch!" shouted Perry, and came up on his toes for the kill. He had been stepping silently about the room, and now he was ready for the dénouement. As we watched, he leaned forward with his body arched and thrust out his arm. Then, as we waited, he twisted the sword in the invisible bull's hump and stood there smiling fiercely.

"Viva!" I cried, coming out of my chair. "Viva Perry!"

He bowed gracefully, and I was still cheering and he was still bowing when Fred yawned and stretched. Jarvis was over in the corner, smouldering about something.

"I don't like it," he said. "Mumford getting a job. Bad business, that." He smoothed back his hair carefully, and his eyes were troubled. "Maybe we oughtta go down and see the Hot Horse."

He looked at me and I shrugged my shoulders. Fred was washing his hands in the bathroom, and he started humming, "what about the Hot Horse, tum te tum, how about the Hot Horse . . . " Perry extricated his sword from the dead bull, and we started toward the door.

"It's all because of the money," said Perry, apologetically.

"I have it from him direct that he only did it because of the money."

We climbed into Bradley's brown Buick, and he stomped on the starter and whirled out of the driveway. A truck swerved to avoid hitting us, and the driver cursed fulsomely.

"I don't like it at all," said Jarvis, trailing one hand out of the window.

The store was crowded. Throngs of people were clotted under the high arches of its bastard gothic ceiling, and we pushed through until we came to the Men's Wear section. Mumford was wearing dark glasses, and his slight frame and sharp profile made him look like a growing eaglet. He was behind a counter, fawning on a man in a tweed suit.

The man had three or four neckties in his hand, and we stopped and watched Mumford beam at him. While we watched, with people pushing around us, the Hot Horse kept talking earnestly, and he was in the middle of an oration anent the beauty of those particular pieces of neckwear when he looked up and saw us. After he did, an apprehensive smile flooded his face. He nodded shortly and kept talking, and finally the man put down several dollars. Mumford dropped two ties in a sack, rang the sale up, and we walked over to him.

"Well," he said cheerily, "what goes?"

Jarvis was in front, and he put his hands down on the counter.

"Fine damned thing this is," he said, and started jerking ties out of a box.

Mumford stood in front of us. His smile faded slowly until he was absolutely disconsolate.

"Ain't it a bitch?" he asked.

We agreed that it was, and he stood back of the counter shifting from foot to foot. Jarvis had begun opening more boxes, and Perry was trying on a pair of leather suspenders.

"Now, fellows," pleaded Mumford, "after all, this is my first day."

Jarvis and Perry kept fumbling along the counter, and Mumford kept watching them with a pained look.

"God Almighty," he wailed, "you guys know I'll get stuck for anything you steal." He looked over at me imploringly.

"Silence, clerk," I said. "Fine thing when a few leading citizens can't come into a store like Sack's and not be accused of dishonesty. Call the manager, sirrah!"

The Hot Horse was nervous. He hitched his narrow shoulders and glanced around.

"Jimble," he whispered, "for God's sake don't start that stuff in here." He gazed at me mournfully.

Jarvis and Perry were still rummaging down the counter, and Bradley was across the aisle trying on hats. By the tens and twenties, he was trying hats on his square head.

"I got a little dough," whispered Mumford in my ear. "How about putting a little bet down for me? A fin on Desert Queen in the fifth at Aqueduct. I can't leave here right now, but this baby"—he leaned over the counter—"was fifteen in the morning line. She can win in that company. You can go right down to Massara's and lay it in. Won't take a minute."

"James," I said rebukingly, "not only does Sack's frown upon its employees betting the broomtails, but the horse you speak of has very bad blood lines, and will put up a strenuous snoot for last place. I doubt whether she will be back in the stable by Labor Day."

I had never heard of Desert Queen. Mumford tightened his tie and glanced around.

"It's only two blocks," he said.

"The distance to hell, for you, is shorter than that," I said. "The distance is immaterial. We must consider the principle. Five dollars will buy a little of the old hard, and besides, the horse cannot win."

He was staring at me when a buzzer sounded, and he turned to answer the house phone. He said "Yessir" three times, and hung the phone up.

"I got to go up to the stock room for a minute," he said

stiffly. He was still offended because I wouldn't take the bet over for him. "Don't let these bastards take over the whole place."

Then he slipped out from behind the counter and started toward the elevators. On the way, he stopped to say something to Jarvis, who was at the far end of the counter. As soon as he was out of sight, Cavin and Perry sidled back toward me. Perry was humming *The Music Goes Down and Around* . . . , and through some oversight, he was still wearing the leather suspenders. Cavin stopped in front of me and stared across the store.

"Well," he said, in the abrupt way which meant that his mind was made up, "I guess we better sell some of this stuff."

I looked at him. "What lines would you like to push?"

"Immaterial," he answered, and walked over into the next aisle.

There he gathered up an armload of floor lamp hoods of all patterns and shapes. A buxom saleswoman hurried over to him, and for a moment they conversed. In the course of it, Jarvis gestured at me and I smiled pleasantly. The woman ducked her head and scurried back up the line to some waiting customers.

Jarvis walked over with his bright burdens and crouched down beside me. He was hidden behind the counter, picking through the articles he had brought across the store. I combed my hair carefully, and looked around.

"Get us a prospect," hissed Jarvis from the floor. "Get 'em in! That's the first rule of merchandising. You can't sell 'em till you've got 'em stopped."

I put my hands down on the counter in a clerkly fashion and looked around some more. "What the hell will you do down there? Are they supposed to come around and lie down by you?"

"No, you stupid ass," he whispered. "You just get them in and I'll do the rest."

We didn't have any luck at first. Two men came sauntering down our lane, but when I spoke to them they glanced up and hurried off. Jarvis was beginning to fume and rustle his lamp shades angrily when a woman came up to the counter and stood there warming herself in my smile. She was a dumpy matron with a contented look, and she poised before me with a birdlike smile. Her head was thrust forward demurely, and her shoulders sagged. I suppose the weight of her breasts must have caused that. She tapered at both ends, like a stretched tear drop, and a black toque was on her head. Bundles were in her arms, and an umbrella jutted out from them.

"Madam," I said, leaning forward, "Sack's greets you and wishes you to be welcome. We are glad you came in. We hope that everyone in your family is well, and that you will spend many happy hours with us. Madam, God bless you and make His light to shine upon you, what is your pleasure?"

The little woman bridled. She put her head on one side and eyed me delightedly.

"How terribly nice!" she said. "What a nice young man . . ."

I shuffled one foot, murmured that it was really nothing, and Jarvis bit me on the ankle. It was quite painful, and I heeled him gently as I leaned forward. The woman was still gazing at me admiringly.

"Now what I want," she said coyly, "is something for Herman, my oldest boy. He's only twelve, you know."

"No!" I answered. "I thought Herman must be all of fifteen by now."

She drew her head head back in about fourteen inches and pursed her lips reflectively.

"No." The great breasts heaved sluggishly. "No," she said severely, "Herman could hardly be taken for fifteen." She was trying to be fair to Herman. "Possibly fourteen, or thirteen, but fifteen. . . . No, I hardly think so."

"Well," I said, "it's not as though I had counted on it, now is it?" We both simpered moderately at that, and then I took up the attack again. "Madam, you are in luck. Does the boy ever listen to the Purple Yellowjacket on the radio?"

She waggled her head; she wasn't sure.

"Well," I went on, "the most peachy thing you can imagine. Today, not tomorrow or yesterday, the Purple Yellowjacket is in this store, and he has really got something svelte for that scamp of a Herman."

I stopped and stared down at the dumpy little woman, and she stepped up closer to the counter.

"Oh, fudge," she said. "How stupid of me not to know about the Purple Yellowjacket." She whispered to me. "Who is he?"

I was properly amazed. "Why my admirable woman," I asked incredulously, "do you mean to stand there and tell me that you never heard of that amazing man, that G-guy of the sky, that adventurer of the astral orbits called the Purple Yellowjacket?"

She raised the umbrella and would have stayed me, but I rushed on.

"You mean to say you never heard of Brumble's Buttered Crumblies for Little Stumblebums, in the purple and yellow package?"

She was sulking now, and I nudged Jarvis with my foot.

"Well, I'm sure," she said primly, "that Herman knows all about him."

"At twelve?" I shook my head and sneered.

"Yes, at twelve," she answered, "and where is this monstrosity, this Brumble's jacket person?"

I soothed her, "Madam," I said softly, "he is here, and he has one of the brand new Space hats for Herman. These hats are the result of long years of effort and research by the company's engineers. They are equipped with cross ventilation, pilot light, neon headlights, two-way radio, gyro compass, and a guaranteed death ray. With one of them, Herman can fly like a kite under his own power."

She was staring at me.

"Tush," she said, halfheartedly. "You mean, actually fly?"

My enthusiasm was carrying me away. "Like a damned bluebottle fly, he can fly," I shouted. "Barrel rolls in the kitchen, loops and spins in the parlor, and power dives in the laundry chute!" I flung out one hand. "Madam, allow me to present the master of the ozone, the Purple Yellowjacket!!"

Jarvis bobbed up beside me. A large scarlet lamp shade was riding on the top of his head, and two smaller conical shades were clamped over his ears. His eyes blazed and his cheeks were puffed. He shot up suddenly and stood there with his staring eyes fixed full on the little woman.

"Alla ma fong!" he moaned, and then crumpled as the woman ripped out a raw quivering scream and slugged him across the head with her umbrella. She hit him and stood there in the center of the aisle, her parcels scattered on the floor, and she was still bawling at the top of her lungs, like a woman having both legs cut off.

The umbrella had torn through the light silk of the shade as nothing, and Jarvis was down on the floor with blood gushing from his scalp. The two small shades were still fitted neatly over his ears, and he did look like a space adventurer, albeit one who had come to considerable grief. In fact, as he lay there with his own blood darkening the wrecked fabric of the large shade that was jammed down across his eyes, he looked as though he might have been mangled between two comets.

People began to rush down the aisle toward us as the woman kept up her screaming, and Bradley and Perry came running back from the hat department to kneel beside the stunned Jarvis. With some difficulty, I got the woman to stop her bellowing, although she was still shaking all over. The crowd was banked around us on all sides, and I looked out over their collective heads.

I could see two blue uniforms start across the store, and I called out the information to Bradley. He and Perry lifted Jarvis up, by the arms. His eyes gradually cleared, and he started to push through the crowd. He was a bit unsteady, and the smaller shades were still on his ears, a fact which enchanted the populace. I was kneeling down, picking up the woman's bundles, and I called out to Jarvis.

"Hey, Cavin, why don't you show the woman how the Space Hat works?"

He must not have heard me. He weaved out of sight, and Fred and Von Perry vanished after him. I tried to hand the woman her packages. She was still breathing heavily, and that great bosom was heaving.

"Madam," I said sorrowfully, "you did something nobody on any of the other worlds could do. You made the Purple Yellowjacket cry." I shook my head mournfully. "This will ruin him with the kids. . . . "

She was still watching me like a woman under a spell. She wouldn't take her packages, and she seemed to be paralyzed.

"You shouldn't have done it," I said. "Just wait until Herman hears about it."

And then I went smashing through the crowd to the south doors, and, after leaving the store, doubled around the block to the car.

Jarvis was sitting in the middle of the back seat with a stained handkerchief on his head, and Perry was next to him, howling with laughter. Mumford was sitting in the front seat, and he didn't say anything when I came up, just sat there looking straight ahead. He still had on the dark glasses, and his lean profile didn't turn a fraction of an inch. Bradley started the car, and I got in next to Jarvis. The motor whined and we swung out into traffic.

"It's a terrible thing," I said gravely, panting a little from my dash out of the store. "It's a long, long way to fall. The Purple Yellowjacket, even . . . . Jarvis, this will ruin you with the kids."

Perry was wheezing immensely, Bradley hiccoughed with delight, and Mumford's thin chin began to waggle. I could see his shoulders start to shake, and we all went down the street roaring. All, that is, except Jarvis, who seemed depressed.

# THE RIVER OF BLOOD

*by* EDWIN LANHAM

Though Edwin Lanham is no stranger to Paris, and has played his part of the ping-pong and "Go" at Chumley's restaurant in Greenwich Village, his home, and the setting of some of his finest writing, is the watermelon country around Weatherford, Texas. He comes from pioneer Texas stock which has played an important part in the destiny of the state. (Two of his grandfathers were Governors, and he has an uncle in the United States Congress.) His latest novel, *Thunder in the Earth*, was published in 1941 and deals with the oil business in the Southwest. "The River of Blood" however is reprinted from Mr. Lanham's earlier novel, *The Wind Blew West*.

---

P RAY TO GOD," BOYD COLEMAN SAID. "IT'S A RIVER OF blood."

He stood up in the wagon and gazed down at the turbid stream of water, winding among shelving banks and wide flats of red sand.

"It's the Red River, Boyd," Emma Coleman said in a thin tone. "Set down, please."

Her face was pale and her brown hair straggled from the knot at the back of her head. Her hair was soiled and dry and had lost its luster in the dust of the long journey. She sat on the hard wooden seat of the wagon with a sunbonnet shading her tense face. Her lips were colorless and she had lost the bloom that had lent something of prettiness to her features three weeks before.

"It's the Red River, Boyd," she repeated, looking up at him.

"Where at are we goin' to cross it?"

Coleman got out of the wagon without replying. He moved stiffly, and when he stood upon the ground he stretched, and tautened the muscles of his legs. The wagon was on a sandy knoll, above the river. Behind them across a dismal stretch of sand the ruts left by the broad-tired wheels ran in straight lines to the opening in a clump of scrub oak through which they had come.

"A river of blood," Coleman said slowly, "and over beyond lies Texas. Over beyond is the new Canaan, Emma."

"Boyd, I declare you're touched by the sun," Emma Coleman said. "Go down there and look fer a fordin', do you hear?"

"I reckon we can cross anywheres. It don't look very deep."

The afternoon sun was losing its intensity and he took off his hat, smiling as he watched Reuben on the bay mare. The boy had ridden the mare to the water's edge and was sitting relaxed as the animal drank. The two work horses were pulling at the wagon-tongue, thirsting.

The canvas cover Coleman had constructed over the wagon, bent tight across high arches, was weather-beaten and stained. In one place it had been ripped for about four inches where the canvas was taut over a wagonbow. While fording a rocky creek the wagon had jolted and the canvas had been ripped by the land-slide of the plow, which was roped to the side of the wagon. On the other side the harrow was made fast. Dennis was asleep on the mattress spread on the bottom of the wagon.

"Boyd, I wish we'd git across so's we can camp," Emma Coleman said.

"I don't look for any trouble, Emma. From the looks of it they ain't had much rain in these parts. Look how gray them trees are, and how shoal the water is. It's been that way all through this country. That creek we crossed five miles back was plumb dry and from the looks of the watermark on the bed they had a right smart flow of water there in the spring."

He put on his hat and walked slowly down through sliding sand to the river bank. The water seemed to be painted on the flat sand, which near the bank had dried and hardened and had turned a deeper red than that far out in the river-bed where the stream coursed.

"Are we goin' to cross over tonight, Pop?" Reuben asked. He sat astride the bay mare ten yards away.

Coleman looked across the river. The land opposite was higher and densely covered with trees, but there appeared to be a break in the underbrush at one point, where the bank sloped. Coleman held up one hand to shade his eyes.

"Why it looks like this is a ford right here, Reuben," he said. "What do you think?"

"It ain't more than hub-deep, Pop. I swear it ain't."

"Ride the mare in a ways, boy, and let's see."

Reuben pressed his heels to the flanks of the mare and tightened the flat of one rein across its neck to turn it. Cautiously the bay mare waded out into the river.

"Search out the best way, Reuben," Coleman said. "How does the bottom feel?"

"It's sound bottom, Pop."

"Go on a little further, boy."

Reuben drove the mare halfway across the river. The water did not come to within six inches of the stirrups.

"You're sure right, Reuben," Coleman called. "It ain't more than hub-deep. How does the current look?"

"It's easy, Pop."

"All right. Come on in."

Reuben turned the horse and splashed back to the sand bank where his father stood.

"You stay handy with your rope in case the work stock can't pull it through," Coleman said. "I'll git the wagon down."

He dug his boots sideways into the sand to walk up to the knoll where the wagon was. Standing by it, he looked up and down the river.

"A hundred yards down there is an easy place to git down," he said. "Then we can drive over the sand up to the fordin'. You git out, Emma, and you can ride over on the mare."

"I'll set where I'm at," Emma Coleman said. "I'll ride easier here than horseback—Boyd, it's coming soon."

"In a week or ten days we ought to be in Rutherford

City," Coleman said. "Stay in the wagon if you want, Emma."

He put one foot on the wheel-hub and swung up to the spring seat. He gathered up the reins and gripped the brake handle with his free hand.

"Hee-yi," he cried.

The shout awakened Dennis and he put his tow head through the flap of the canvas.

"Where are we?" he asked. "Mom, where are we at?"

"Hold still, Dennis," Emma said. "This here is the Red River. We're headin' fer the fordin' now."

"Stay back in the wagon," Coleman said. "Don't you bother me, Dennis."

The wheels sank deep in the soft sand as they followed the river bank to the slope Coleman had chosen. With the wagon-tongue reared skyward, the horses gathered their muscular haunches under them and the wagon slid, with brakes locked, down the incline to the level bank of red sand. Emma Coleman, her teeth clenched, clung to the back of the seat and did not relax as the wagon rolled smoothly across the hard sand to where Reuben sat the bay mare at the water's edge. Coleman knotted the reins loosely around the brake handle and got out of the wagon.

"You git your rope handy, Reuben," he said, walking to the edge of the river.

The red sand sloped gradually to the water, which near at hand was a pale sienna color. The current seemed swift in midstream. Near shore it flowed gently along the bank of sand. Halfway across the river the water rippled across a sand-bar which at one point barely emerged above the surface. Coleman squinted across the river.

"We'll make fer that bar, I figure, Reuben," he said. "You ride on ahead."

Reuben untied the leather thongs that fastened the coiled lariat at his saddlebow. He held the lariat in one hand, wide from his body, and drove the bay mare with his heels into the water. Coleman put one foot on the fore hound of the wagon and swung to the seat.

"All ready, Emma," he said.—"Git thar!"

The horses strained at the harness, the singletree surged forward with their effort, and the broad-tired wheels rolled evenly down to the water. Coleman used the whip to force the horses into the river. Standing erect in the wagon, with his legs braced against the seat, he held the reins tightly in one hand and with the other cracked the whip above the horses' ears. Emma Coleman sat silent beside him, her fingers pinching a pleat of her wide calico skirt. Behind them Dennis thrust his head through the wagon-flap.

"Git a-goin' now, git a-goin'," Coleman shouted at the team. "You lead the way, Reuben."

Still standing, he watched the brown water surge around the horses' hocks. The team moved on steadily and soon the wagon-tongue seemed to be floating on the surface of the river.

"Be careful, Boyd," Emma said. "That water's deep."

"Only hub-deep."

"I declare I wish we'd asked somebody about a crossing," Emma said. "I declare."

Reuben was twisted around in the saddle, one foot hanging free of the stirrup. The mare splashed through the river a little to one side and ahead of the wagon team. It was very silent except for the splashing of the team and the gurgling of the center current around the wheel-spokes of tough *bois d'arc*. From the wooded bank opposite came the shrill cry of a crane. A startled curlew ran swiftly along the bank of dry sand across the river and took flight, disappearing into the tall foliage of a live-oak tree.

Halfway across the river they drew abreast of the sand-bar. The horses, walking on hard bottom, forged powerfully ahead and the wagon tilted as one broad rear wheel mounted the sloping bar.

"Hee-yi," Coleman cried, snapping the whip.

One horse slipped and almost fell; the other strained at the collar of plaited cornshucks, which was dried and cracked from exposure.

"Git," Coleman shouted, "git along thar."

The team strained at the harness, but the wagon seemed stuck fast. It moved slowly back and forth with the irregular pulling of the horses.

"What's the matter, Pop?" Reuben asked, riding back on the bay mare.

"What is it, Boyd?" Emma asked. Her sunbonnet was pushed back from her set face. "Are we mired?"

Coleman looked over the side of the wagon at the soft sandbar barely beneath the surface. The high rear wheel was sunk almost to the hub in the sand.

"My God," Coleman said. "That there must be quicksand."

"Quicksand?" Emma echoed.

Coleman leaned forward and brought the full lash of the whip down on the haunches of the near horse. The animal leaped forward. Its team-mate shied and the wagon-tongue sheered off upstream as the horses pivoted.

"Easy," Coleman shouted, tightening the reins, "Easy now."

The wagon had not budged, and the wheel-hub was barely above the sand.

"We're a-sinkin' right in, Pop," Dennis cried, peering through the wagon-flap. "What is that stuff, Pop? It's suckin' the wagon right in."

"Be quiet, Dennis," his mother said.

"Reuben," Coleman called, "git that lasso out and throw me one end of it."

He stepped down to the fore hound and caught the rope that Reuben tossed to him. He made one end fast, and returned to the seat.

"You pull off upstream, Reuben," he said. "Try and git some leverage on it. We want to work fast."

"Is it going to swaller us right up, Boyd?" Emma asked. "Now we ought to looked fer another crossing. You know we ought."

"There ain't no danger. We can git out of the wagon if'n we have to."

"And lose all our things? And my new cook stove?"

"I'll buy you a big new stove to Rutherford City," Coleman said. "Git going now. Start your horse, Reuben."

The team drove forward under the whip and Reuben, with the lariat stretched taut, turned the bay mare to bear upstream. The wagon moved forward a little. The hub of the rear wheel rose clear of the sand and the wagon seemed to hang in balance, then slowly slipped back and the wheel settled in the quicksand. Coleman plied the whip again, and Reuben dug his heels in the mare's flanks. Emma Coleman sat with her hands gripped on the edge of the seat under her. She sucked in her breath through her teeth and her face was drawn with pain.

"It ain't movin' none, Pop," Dennis called from the back of the wagon. "It's stuck in it and it's oozing right up over the hub too."

"Ease off that mare, Reuben," Coleman called. He thrust the butt of the whip into the leather whip-socket and stood up. "We got to lighten the wagon."

On the side of the wagon above the mired wheel the plow was made fast with rope and rawhide. Coleman loosened one end and the heavy share dropped with a splash to the sand-bar. He opened the canvas flap and went to the back of the wagon. Leaning over the side, he took out a wide-bladed knife and slashed the rope holding the handles of the plow. They fell just clear of the wheel into the water.

"Help me here, Dennis," Coleman said. "We can't keep but what we got to have. Give a hand with this here."

He leaned over to pick up the sheet iron stove.

"Boyd," Emma cried. "Don't drop that stove out."

"We got to lighten the wagon."

"But it's all I got to cook on," Emma said, her voice rising. Tears were in her eyes. "It don't weigh but fifteen pounds."

"Every bit helps, Emma."

"Throw out that bag of seed then. It weighs as much and

· 193 ·

it's cheaper to buy than a new stove. Now you do like I say, Boyd."

Coleman set down the camp stove and rolled the sack of seed to the end of the wagon. He threw it with a mighty splash into the red water.

"Pop," Dennis cried, "that plow's goin' clean out of sight. It's suckin' it right under, Pop."

"You be still, Dennis," Coleman said.

"Boyd," Emma called. "We got to do something. Please."

Coleman came through the wagon-flap and caught up his whip.

"Start your mare, Reuben," he cried. "We'll try it one more time."

Standing erect, he lashed with the whip. His face was pale and a vein on his forehead stood out.

"I sure hate to lose that plow," he murmured, beating at the horses with the whip.

The lariat was stretched to the breaking point as Reuben kept up a constant tattoo with his heels on the fat flanks of the bay mare. Again the wheel-hub rose clear of the sand, above the surface of the water. The team bore off at a tangent, with the front wheels twisting in the sandy bottom, and the wagon rocked back and forth. Slowly it began to move forward and the suction of the quicksand on the mired rear wheel was sickeningly audible above the splashing of the horses.

"Git thar!" Coleman shouted, striking with the whip.

The wagon began to roll forward.

"It's runnin' over the plow, Pop," Dennis cried. "It's rollin' right over the plow. It made a bottom fer it, Pop."

Suddenly the veering tip of the wagon-tongue shot ahead as the wheel rolled clear of the quicksand. One horse stumbled to its knees and floundered with its head raised above the water. Under the furious lash of the whip it struggled to its feet and both horses dashed at a near gallop toward the shore. The wagon rocked and jolted over the uneven bottom. Emma Coleman sat tensely with her hands gripped to the jouncing seat and Coleman lashed unceasingly with the whip. The bay mare was first upon the shore, straining at a full gallop at the rope, next the wagon-tongue raised skyward and the dripping team dug their hoofs into the hard sand of the shore. The wagon rolled evenly up the slope and came to rest on sand so hard the wheel tracks barely marred it. Coleman turned and looked back toward the shelved sand where the wagon had emerged, at the slight ripple of water over the bar of quicksand.

"I sure hate to lose that plow," he said.

Suddenly Emma Coleman screamed, put one hand to her mouth. All color had gone from her face and she turned her frightened eyes to Coleman.

"It's coming, Boyd," she cried. "My God, it's coming now."

Coleman knelt beside her. Reuben rode the bay mare at a lope toward the wagon.

"What's the matter, Mom?" he cried. "Pop, what's the matter?"

"Dennis, you spread the mattress flat," Coleman said. "Quick now."

Dennis' frightened face disappeared from the wagon-flap.

"What's the matter, Pop?" Reuben asked. "Is Mama hurt?"

Emma Coleman screamed again.

"Untie your rope from the wagon, Reuben," Coleman said.

He opened the wagon-flap and aided his wife to the mattress which Dennis had spread out on the wagon-bed.

"Hop out of the wagon, Dennis," Coleman said.

As the boy scrambled from the wagon Coleman rolled a blanket deftly and placed it under Emma's head.

"Now you lie easy, Emma," he said. "I'll run the wagon up the hill into the shade and send Reuben fer water. Rest easy, now."

Reuben on the bay mare led the way up the bank. The sand ended abruptly and the wagon rolled over red clay through an opening in the thicket and then over black soil into the woods. Reuben led the wagon on a circuitous route through the trees, searching a roadway wide enough for its passage. Live-oak trees towered above the wagon, and post-oak and iron-oak. Nearer ground was the thick foliage of elm and hackberry. Vines of the wild grape clung among the boughs and tree trunks as in a jungle, almost shutting out the sun. Birds fluttered among the trees, and a brilliant cardinal flew from branch to branch ahead of the wagon, as if to guide it through the forest. It was so quiet that Coleman could hear the heavy breathing of his wife, her muffled moans.

"He'll be a Texan, Emma," he said, looking back through the wagon-flap. "He'll be born in Texas. Now don't you fret."

From the woods ahead he heard Reuben call. The bay mare had gone from sight.

"Here's a place to camp, Pop," Reuben cried. "Come on."

The wagon team pulled through a dense brake only a few feet high and came out from among the tree trunks upon a plateau on which the grass grew in curly wisps. Beyond stretched a plain and in the distance a line of timber. Coleman halted the horses. Dennis was running barefooted beside the wagon. He caught the reins Coleman tossed to him.

"Unharness the team," Coleman said, "and you and Reuben scare up some fresh water, not from the river, now, There ought to be a spring hereabouts."

Coleman disappeared beneath the wagon cover and Reuben dismounted and unstrapped the saddle-girth. He lifted down the heavy saddle and the sweat-soaked blanket and put them in the shade of a tree, the blanket spread across the saddle. He hobbled the forefeet of the mare with rawhide and helped Dennis unharness the team. They hobbled the work horses and spread the wet harness over the wagon-tongue to dry. Together they went to look for water, Reuben carrying the pail.

"Reuben, what's the matter?" Dennis asked. "What's wrong with Mom?"

"She's all right, Dennis. Don't you worry."

"But she hollered that-a-way."

"She's feeling porely, Dennis, but she'll git all right.—Look now, over yonder by that big rock, where the brush grows so straight down to the river like as if somebody planted it that-a-way. I reckon we'll find water there."

They pushed their way through brambles toward the limestone boulder that jutted out from a claybank. At the foot of the rock they found a spring in an open space carpeted with verdant grass. Dennis got down on his knees and drank. The water tasted of limestome. Reuben filled the pail and when they returned to the wagon Coleman took a dipper-full of water from the bucket.

"Now make a fire, you boys," he said. "I want some of this water heated up—and here, Dennis, take this blanket. You can sleep under the trees tonight."

"Ain't I goin' to sleep in the wagon?"

"Not this evenin', boy. You run along now."

Dennis looked at Reuben.

"You're old enough to sleep out, Dennis," Coleman told him. "You're a Texan now. You got to be a man."

"I will, Pop," Dennis said.

Coleman had taken the camp stove out of the wagon and set it up in an open space under the trees. Reuben went into the woods to gather firewood and Dennis sat down in the shade of an oak tree, leaning against the trunk. A vine of mustang grapes trailed from the tree and a bunch of the large blue grapes hung near Dennis. He plucked it and ate one. His mouth puckered and he spat it out.

Reuben had come back with an armful of bleached driftwood and Dennis held up the bunch of grapes resentfully.

"Even them grapes is sour, Reuben," he said.

"You be still, Dennis," Reuben said, "and help me build this here fire. Bring some twigs and leaves."

As Dennis got to his feet he heard his mother scream. He stopped with his mouth open, staring. Then it was still again but for the constant chirping of the birds in the vines overhead. Dennis moved nearer Reuben and their eyes met.

"Reuben," Dennis said, "is Mom goin' to die?"

"Course not, Dennis. She'll be better tomorrow."

Kneeling, Reuben struck a sulphur match on the side of the stove. The match sputtered a moment, then flamed slowly, and Reuben lit a little pile of leaves and twigs he had put in the stove. When the leaves were burning well he placed twigs and more leaves in the stove and built up the fire with driftwood. He poured water in a kettle and placed it on the stove to heat.

"Call me when it boils, Dennis," he said, and went into the bushes to gather more wood.

Left alone, Dennis stood by the fire, glancing now at the wagon, now at the silent trees that had hidden Reuben from sight. Off in the grove he heard the sound of splintering wood as Reuben broke dead limbs to length with his foot. From the wagon he heard his father's voice, deep and soothing. From time to time he looked at the water in the kettle and when it began to bubble he shouted for Reuben. Emma Coleman's shrill moan echoed his shout, and Coleman put his head through the flap in the back of the wagon cover.

"Dennis, you be still," he said. "What do you want?"

"The water's boilin'," Dennis said.

"Well, don't you holler."

"But Reuben said to call him."

"Take the water off the fire and bring it here."

Dennis pulled out his shirt-tail and wrapped it around the handle of the kettle. He ran with it across to the wagon. Coleman took it and motioned Dennis away and the boy walked slowly back to the fire. Sitting against the trunk of a hackberry tree, with the fire at his feet, he looked out across the prairie. The land sloped away from him in broad undulations, marked here and there by clumps of trees and with the curly mesquite grass a pale blue color in the afternoon sunlight. The sun was nearing the horizon but still was very bright. Far away, above hills faintly tinted with the shades of distance, two round white clouds hung perfectly still against the luminous sky. Dennis plucked another mustang grape. He turned it over in his fingers, then carefully drew back the skin. A quantity of juice flowed upon his hands from where it had been secreted between the pulp and the skin.

Experimentally Dennis put the pulp in his mouth and sucked it. It was sweet and he ate it. He plucked another grape. When Reuben returned he was sitting with a bunch of the wild grapes in his lap and the ground beside him strewn with grape hulls.

"I'm hongry," Dennis said. "I been eating grapes. The inside of 'em is sweet."

"I'll fix you something, Dennis. How about salt pork and hoe-cake."

"I reckon Mom would rather make it, or Pop," Dennis said. "She don't want you to meddle with her pans. She said so, Reuben."

"Tonight don't make a difference," Reuben said. He knelt and thrust more wood into the stove. "Git me the skillet."

Dennis sat alone under the tree while Reuben cooked the meal. From time to time he glanced at the wagon, but he heard only occasional cries from his mother and no word from Coleman. It had been a long time since they came out of the river.

"Reuben," Dennis said as they began to eat, "Texas looks jist the same to me. I don't see no difference in it."

Reuben cooked food for Coleman and his mother and left it in the frying pan on the stove. He and Dennis sat together under the tree, eating from tin plates. Coleman did not come out of the wagon and at sunset Reuben raked the embers from the stove and built a fire of logs in the open. He placed the pan of food on a flat rock near the fire. The sun set far across the plains in brilliant color that seemed to touch every particle of the air. They seemed to be breathing colored air as they sat together by the tree trunk in the orange light watching the huge red sun sink behind gray hills. The sun disappeared behind the line of hills in a space of light sky between the hill-line and the gathering clouds, and it did not begin to get dark until long after the sun had set. As the twilight deepened Coleman remained in the wagon and occasionally they heard their mother's moans. Dennis was frightened.

As night advanced they heard a faint cry across the plains, an answering yelp near at hand. Dennis looked at Reuben. From the trees at the foot of the slope of mesquite grass came a plaintive, prolonged howling. Dennis sat erect.

"Coyotes," Reuben said. "They won't harm you, Dennis."

"I wish they'd let me in the wagon, though."

From the line of trees a chorus of yelps broke out, followed by a series of shrill, slowly dying sounds, in which the stronger tones of one coyote predominated. The other coyotes fell silent as if to listen. Reuben got up and put another log on the fire.

"We'll need more wood," Reuben said, "I reckon . . . "

A scream, louder than the coyote chorus, interrupted him. He looked toward the wagon, and Dennis sprang up and came nearer the fire. All was silent again and even the coyotes at the foot of the hill had quieted momentarily at the sound. Dennis slipped his hand into Reuben's. Together they stood looking toward the wagon. It had suddenly become dark and the white canvas wagon sheet reflected the glow of the fire. One of the horses, grazing on the slope, snorted, the sound so fresh they might almost have felt the spray of its breath. The iron wagon tires caught the high-light of the fire and metal on the wagon-tongue reflected warm light. No sound came from the wagon and the coyotes again were howling down below. Looking across the prairie in the uncertain light, Dennis imagined he saw dark forms, blacker than the night, creeping through the grass. He moved nearer to the fire and with one bare foot pushed a log toward it.

"Reuben," he said, "I'm scared."

The foliage of the trees around them was an inky, fluid black and moss dropping from the straight limbs of a live-oak tree hung in grotesque shapes, lit by the firelight.

"Do you s'pose Mom is all right?" Dennis asked.

Reuben turned to the shadow where the blanket lay. He spread it near the fire on the smooth ground.

"Go to sleep now, Dennis," he said. "There ain't no need to fret. Lie down here."

Dennis stretched himself on the blanket.

"Wrap it around you," Reuben said. "These nights git cold."

"I never slep' out before," Dennis said. His tow hair was quite white in the firelight. He folded the blanket over him and Reuben tucked it beneath his body. The coyotes still were yelping and when Dennis fell asleep Reuben was standing erect by the fire, looking toward the wagon.

When Dennis opened his eyes he did not at first realize that he had been sleeping. Reuben still stood by the fire, but he was looking, not at the wagon, but off toward the prairie. The fire had burned low. Dennis raised himself on one elbow, softly called:

"Reuben."

"Now I thought you was asleep, Dennis."

"I jist woke up. How's Mom?"

"She's all right. She's asleep. Don't make no noise to wake her, Dennis."

"Where's Pop?"

"Over there."

Dennis strained his eyes to see in the darkness.

"He's prayin'," Reuben said. "Keep still, Dennis."

"But where is he, Reuben?"

"Yonder on the prairie."

Dennis fancied he saw a dark form on the slope, outlined by stars so heavy and bright that they seemed to stand out in relief against the background of the sky. Although he could not see Boyd Coleman, Dennis knew how he would look on his knees, hatless, with his hands raised and his closed eyes uplifted. Since he could remember he had seen his father so on Sunday mornings when during prayers in the parlor he had peeked through his fingers. He remembered his father so, with his face raw from shaving and his black hair brushed wet to his forehead, in a clean cotton shirt and black trousers. He had always seemed austere and forbidding to Dennis in the parlor even on bright Sunday mornings and tonight off in the dark, without the familiar background and the known routine, Dennis was frightened and sank back on the blanket.

· 201 ·

"But it's not Sunday, Reuben," he whispered.

"Be quiet, Dennis," Reuben said, and sat down on the blanket beside his brother.

"That's all anybody says—be quiet, Dennis, hold still, Dennis. Say, Reuben, I'm nine years old."

For a long time they stared out into the darkness, which seemed to take moving shapes with their staring. Dennis was getting drowsy and his head had relaxed against Reuben's shoulder when he gasped and sat suddenly upright. A light had flared on the prairie. It flickered an instant, then steadied and took form. Dennis could see it was a lantern light and he saw the dark figure of his father beside it. Coleman set the lantern on the ground and it illumined the tips of the prairie grass and his shining black boots.

"What's he doin', Reuben?" Dennis asked.

Reuben did not answer and Dennis heard the clink of metal on rock, saw his father's figure, grotesquely exaggerated by his shadow behind him, stooping. He watched the shadow shoot swiftly back and forth, now compact and short, now stretching like elastic far beyond the lantern light as his father stooped and straightened. He heard the clink of metal and the soft sound of falling earth.

"Reuben, what's he doin'?" Dennis asked.

"I guess I know," Reuben said. "He took a spade with him."

"You mean he's diggin', Reuben—What?"

"Now don't fret, Dennis. You go back to sleep."

Dennis sprang to his feet and walked to the other side of the fire, staring off toward the lantern.

"Reuben," he said suddenly, coming back to the blanket. He dropped to his knees beside Reuben and whispered, with his face screwed up on the point of tears: "Reuben, is Mama . . . "

"Mom's asleep Dennis. I done told you that."

"Then what is it, Reuben?"

"The stork came, Dennis," Reuben said. "Be quiet now. Here comes Pop."

Both boys got to their feet as Coleman strode into the glow

of the firelight. He passed them and went to the wagon. From the rear of the wagon he picked up something. As he turned toward them, holding the object in his outstretched arms, Dennis saw that it was a rectangular box. He recognized it as the ammunition box which had contained shotgun shells that Coleman had bought in Athens when they started from Arkansas. Coleman paused in the firelight and looked at the boys. He seemed to look through and beyond them and when he spoke Dennis instinctively glanced behind him into the shadows.

"Come with me," Coleman said, "both of you."

He started off toward the lantern. Reuben nudged Dennis and the boys followed their father through the prairie grass. Leaving the black trees Dennis had the illusion of coming into bright light as they walked under the stars toward the lantern. By the lantern they found a fresh hole in the ground, about two feet deep, and a mound of earth beside it. Coleman knelt and put the box in the hole. He remained kneeling beside it a moment, then rose slowly to his feet. He turned and put one hand on Reuben's shoulder. With the other he fondled Dennis' tow head.

"Boys," he said in a low, toneless voice, "that is your little brother, Moses. That was his name."

Dennis looked at the box in the shallow grave. The nailheads glittered in the light and the rough pine boards bore a trader's stamp in black ink which had spread on the soft wood as upon a blotter.

"The Lord would not let him into the land of Canaan," Coleman said. "It was His will."

Dennis stared at his father with his mouth open.

"Kneel down," Coleman said.

Dennis and Reuben dropped to their knees beside the grave. Dennis' eyes were tightly shut and he dared not peek. He heard the rustle of paper and felt through his eyelids an increased intensity of light as Coleman raised the lantern. He was standing on the opposite side of the grave with the Bible open on the palm of his hand, and he began to read, slowly and without emphasis: "*Now after the death of Moses the servant of the Lord it came to pass, that the Lord spake unto Joshua the son of Nun, Moses' minister, saying,*

"*Moses my servant is dead; now therefore arise, go over this Jordan, thou, and all this people, unto the land which I do give to them, even to the children of Israel.*

"*Every place that the sole of your foot shall tread upon, that have I given unto you, as I said unto Moses.*"

Coleman paused for a long time. Dennis' knees hurt from the contact with the hard prairie ground and a chigger bite on his bare leg itched and he longed to scratch it. He spread his fingers slightly and looked at his father. The light of the lantern fell on his face from below, making it seem stern and drawn and his cheek-bones high above hollows in his cheeks. He was staring over Dennis' head into the woods, and from the trees came the distant eerie sound of a hoot owl. Dennis covered his eyes and Coleman began to read: "*From the wilderness and this Lebanon even unto the great river, the river Euphrates, all the land of the Hittites, and unto the great sea toward the going down of the sun, shall be your coast.*

"*There shall not any man be able to stand before thee all the days of thy life: as I was with Moses, so I will be with thee: I will not fail thee, nor forsake thee.*"

Coleman paused an instant as his eyes ran down the page, then he read on in a strong voice: "*Have I not commanded thee? Be strong and of a good courage; be not afraid, neither be thou dismayed: for the Lord thy God is with thee whithersoever thou goest.*"

"Reuben," Coleman said.

Reuben and Dennis raised their eyes.

"Git the spade, boy," Coleman said.

Reuben got up and brought the spade from where Coleman had left it a yard away. The light of the lantern blinded Dennis as he stood up.

"Turn the earth in, Reuben," Coleman said. "Do it easy, boy."

As Reuben shovelled earth over the box, Coleman murmured over and over again in a voice barely audible to Dennis:

"Ashes to ashes and dust to dust. The Lord giveth and the Lord taketh away."

Dennis watched the clods of earth fall crumbling into the grave, hearing the voice of his father and once again the tingling cry of the hoot owl. The fresh earth drew level with the prairie, then raised above it in a small mound. Reuben stood back with the shovel leaning against his hip.

"Boys, I'm buryin' him the best I know how," Coleman said, "in the way I think is fittin'. It ain't regular, maybe, but Moses had no cross to mark his grave, nor your little brother. May he rest in peace."

Coleman lowered his eyes again to the Bible and read slowly in a voice that had gained strength: "*So Moses the servant of the Lord died there in the land of Moab, according to the word of the Lord.*

"*And he buried him in a valley in the land of Moab, over against Beth-peor: but no man knoweth of his sepulchre unto this day.*"

From the line of trees below the sound of coyotes in mournful chorus was raised like the voices of a choir. Coleman closed the Bible. Bending over, he put the lantern at one end of the mound of earth.

"I'll leave this light burn here through the night, boys," he said, "until the oil is gone."

Standing straight, he put his hand on Dennis' shoulder.

"Now, boy, you git some sleep," he said. "We'll make an early start tomorrow if your mother feels up to it. In ten days time we ought to be in Rutherford City."

# *from* HOLD AUTUMN
# IN YOUR HAND

*by* GEORGE SESSIONS PERRY

George Sessions Perry is the author of *Texas: A World in Itself*, etc.
The following selection is from *Hold Autumn in Your Hand*, a novel
principally about a nice guy named Sam Tucker.

WHEN THE CORN HAD BEEN HOED AND IT WAS STILL TOO
soon to do anything to the cotton, Sam said, "Somethin's
been a-worryin me kinda and I just now decided what
it was."

Nona looked up at him silently, patiently, waiting to be told.

"Why, it's dewberry time in the sand hills," he said. "I been
feelin em get ripe in the back o my mind. We got a few days now.
Reckon we ought to go a-pickin?"

"What about the baby?"

"I sort of figgered on us all goin down to your daddy's maybe.
You ain't seen im in a coon's age and there's not no better wild
berries anywhere. Jot could stay at the house."

"Me an him," Granny said. "I'll run the cookin."

"Oh, you'll want to help pick," Sam said. "Be fun. You an
Daisy can run a pickin race."

"I ain't mixin and minglin with no copperhead snakes,"
Granny said. "I'm already wearin one crooked toe them buggers
ruint."

However, when Sam told her she might keep her berries
separate and spend their entire proceeds on snuff, she agreed
to pick.

When Friday afternoon came, the family kept their date

· 206 ·

with Daisy at the railroad crossing where she was to go straight from school, and they all started walking south down the highway. Sam was carrying Jot, Nona a bushel basket with a five-pound sack of two-cent yellow meal in it. Granny, bonneted, complaining of her feet, was carrying an empty gallon sirup bucket in each hand, with which she tried to wave down the passing cars, yelling, "Hold on there, feller! We got a long way to go. N I'm seventy years old and then some." Then as the car would whiz by, she'd yell, "Well, go on, you scalawag! Didn't want to ride in no cheap-johnny car nohow."

Walking on, disgruntled, her pride now hurt by this lordly indifference to her request as much as the pavement was hurting her feet, she'd turn to Sam and say, "It's a mighty funny bunch, it looks like to me, that the Lord seen fit to furnish with cars. Just skin right by you thout so much as a kiss-my-foot."

"Yes'm," Sam said.

Another car was coming. Once more the sirup buckets were flying.

Finally a man in a wagon with no seat in it gave them a lift and by six o'clock they were standing off the dogs in front of Corinth Macey's house.

Old Corinth, whose name derived from the town of his birth in Mississippi, came to the door, saw the bayed Tucker family in front of the house, and said, "Well, for the land's sakes!" To the dogs he called, "Hush yo fuss. Shame o yourseffs."

As the family streamed up on the front porch of the ancient, paintless, leaning house, Corinth made no especial effort to conceal his amazement at this visitation. He was neither more nor less cordial than he would have been to a meteor that had fallen in the front yard. However, as Granny came up the steps, a soft little sigh of despair did escape him. Corinth was, always had been, and always would be, utterly baffled and intimidated by this old woman; so thoroughly, in fact, that his attempt to hide it was futile. In Granny's estimation, and this was no secret either, Corinth was white trash. Whenever they were together, she comported herself like a princess in the presence of a privy-cleaner.

But just now she smiled on him with generous, friendly condescension and said, "Hello, Corinth. Run get me a glass of cool water. I'm tard and hot."

A little miserably Corinth got it and came back, the bewilderment on his face gently asking that it be removed by some explanation.

"We came a-berry-pickin," Sam said. "Just till Monday. We brought our own meal."

That at last was something definite. Corinth looked a little more relaxed.

"Set, everybody," he said, himself sitting (largely at the direction of his shriveling ego) on the floor, though there were chairs and stools enough for all the grown-ups.

Sam had put Jot on the bed, where he lay quietly, gently running his fingers through Zoonie's white hair, looking with a quiet blankness into Zoonie's eyes.

"There's some boiled armadillo meat on the back of the stove," Corinth said humbly, thinking of the old woman and dropping his eyes.

"Oh, is that so?" Granny said with amused haughtiness. "I was hopin we'd find some nice fried house cat."

"You ain't goin to get nothin but some peach-tree tea if you ain't careful," Sam said, confident of the deflationary value of this allusion to the switching Nona had given her.

"Well," Granny said disgustedly, "It's got so it's all a feller's life is worth to crack a little joke any more. I don't mind eatin a dab of armadillo, long as it ain't still got the shuck on it."

"What's wrong with the boy?" Corinth asked.

Sam told him that the child had spring sickness, that the doctor called it pellagra.

"He'll get all right," Corinth said. "Had it about twenty times myself. How's things up on the river?"

He was glad to turn the attention away from himself. In most little gatherings of friends and relatives Corinth was quiet but not uncomfortable. His present uneasiness was just the effect this particular old woman had on him.

Corinth's own wife had long since died of a scratch on her arm that had developed into lockjaw. Now he lived in this house which had been abandoned by its owners and their tenants. It sat on a sterile, weed-grown, sandy-land farm in a neighborhood that was full of them. On the hills the shallow top-soil had washed entirely away, leaving only the clay subsoil and a scattering of ironstone rocks. It was land that had made a few good crops in the late 1800's, immediately after it was cleared. But these crops had soon devoured the land's unstable capital of humus and left it, depleted, to wash away. Even as pasture it was almost entirely worthless. These days it was possessed only by Corinth and the quail and the jackrabbits, its narrow branch bottoms choked by wild vines and bushes.

Corinth, now fifty-eight, blind in one eye by reason of a cataract, listless, possessing not a single gram of initiative, subsisted on home relief. He had all of every day to visit his neighbors or loaf in town or doctor his rheumatism. To a degree that startled him whenever he stopped to think of it, he was a happy man; so much so that he often wore a miserable expression to conceal his own inner serenity from a world that seemed to resent too much happiness in any of its people, and particularly those who lived at public expense.

After a supper of bread and oven-browned armadillo, which had all the tender succulence of a plump young pig, he told his guests a piece of news.

The preceding week he'd spent the night in town, having remained at the domino hall until there was no chance of catching a ride home. He had therefore been obliged to sleep in the depot, but the benches were so uncomfortable that he had not been able to stay there after day broke.

He had hardly left the depot when he heard something come tearing down the street. The morning was still dark blue with left-over night, but in a moment the fast-moving object came close enough to see.

It was Morry Patterson, a second cousin of Harmie Jenkins, who had a notorious way with women.

"So then I seen it was Morry," Corinth said, "whizzin down the street barefooted, with his head thrown back and a shoe in each hand. And then he was gone. Bzzzt! Just like that."

The precise nature of the causes for this act and the personalities involved held their attention until bedtime.

Sunrise next morning found them in the woods—all but Jot and Corinth, who said his rheumatism had flared up slightly and that he'd stay at the house and look after the baby.

The berries on the ditch banks, decorated with sunlight and dew, shone like black-purple glass, except those that were not ripe, and they were jade and coral. Some of the vines were loaded with incredible stores of big, fat, ripe berries. On all the vines there were thousands of tiny thorns that slowly made your fingers smart worse and worse. Where the vines lay thickest, you lifted the whole mass gently with a stick to see if there were any snakes underneath waiting for the flies that the sweet, oozing juice of the berries would attract.

Since Daisy kept ahead of the rest and her sharp eyes found the best vines, Granny watched her like a quail hunter watching his dog. Then when Daisy commenced to pick, the old woman would horn in on Daisy's discovery and get herself sassed infuriatingly, and her feelings hurt. When Sam had adjudicated that dispute, Daisy would go on ahead, make another rich find, and it was all to do over again, until Daisy killed a little snake and kept it as a weapon to dangle at the old woman and put her into screaming, skirt-raising flight.

To Sam the evenings here at his father-in-law's were splendid. It was hard to be anything but content after a supper of dewberry cobbler when you were sitting on an old front porch in the sand hills. Especially after Granny had gone to bed and you knew there would be no further allusions to grown men who had callouses only on their behinds, or childishly heartless witticisms about people who were blind in one eye and couldn't see out of the other. The evenings were delightful because there was, in the long run, no better company anywhere than Corinth.

Not only was no current neighborhood gossip a secret to him,

but he was a man to whom the old times were invariably luminous. Its legends, to him, were not subject to tarnish. He was not
a man who lived by the hour or the day or, any more, by the
season. Corinth's units were lifetimes. The quality of his patience
acted upon and dispelled your own irritations of the present.

Corinth's deathless hero was Fayette Tucker, Granny's
late husband and Sam's grandfather. Fayette was a man who
had met not only life in general but Granny on their own terms,
given them both cards and spades and a superb beating. Or so,
at least, Corinth chose to regard the outcome of Fayette's con-
flict with these forces. For old Fayette had been Corinth's *alter
ego*, had performed the dramatic actions of the non-physical
Corinth that existed only in fancy, but which in fancy raised
what Corinth called "unshirted hell."

"Remember like it was yesterday," Corinth said quietly,
drifting involuntarily and with grace into the past. "I was comin
into town on horseback late one Saturday afternoon and seen
this drove of wagons and buggies and stuff comin down the road.
Thought, 'Funny it's such a big funeral an I ain't heard of it.'
But I couldn't make out no hearse. All these wagons and things
—I reckon fifteen. An then they met me, and Buddy Cruik-
shank was in front an says, 'You might just as well turn an go
back,' an I says, 'How come?' And he says, 'Ole Fayette's comin
home drunk from town, an got a shotgun cross his saddle bows
an's makin everbody turn back the way they come from, an's
a-herdin em down the road.' So I just turnt an joined the bunch
and come on back to the house."

Corinth also recalled the time Granny had tried to lead her
husband to salvation, and how every time the preacher came,
Fayette would grab his gun and run under the house, swearing
that rather than accept salvation, he'd gladly die, and so would
the preacher if he made one false move.

Even more fabulous was the time when Granny had moved
down the river to her parents' place and instituted divorce proceedings. She had won and was threatening to sue for the furniture when Fayette shipped it to her, as he phrased it on a post-

card, by water. He'd just hauled it as far as the bridge, thrown it in, and left its fate in transit and its ultimate safe delivery up to "Edna's friend, God."

"Not a time," Corinth said, "durin their whole married life did she make anything off of Mr. Fayette. He never conquered her, but she'd shore'n hell met her match."

Sam told about one of his childhood visits to his grandparents when the old man, though sober, had been nagged beyond his endurance. It was always a point of pride with his grandfather, and an advertised one, that he had never laid hands on Edna. On this occasion, however, as a substitute, he had picked up the four corners of the tablecloth on which their noon meal was set and thrown the whole thing out the window.

"Oh, he was fierce, all right," Corinth said, smiling with dreamy admiration at the memory of his idol. "A real ring-tailed tooter, if there ever was one."

And though Sam had always been aware of the childishness of the old man's tantrums, he knew they were extenuated by a degree of exasperation that nobody who had not lived with Granny could ever have known.

Thus, in gentle, ever-lively reminiscence, on excursions into the past that Sam could not have made with his black-land neighbors, the evenings at Corinth's slipped away.

Ten o'clock on Monday morning found the Tuckers back in town. Sam sent Daisy on to school and left Granny and Nona and Jot in the shade of a tree by a culvert. He would have liked for Nona to go with him on his berry-peddlin tour, but neither of them was willing to leave the child in Granny's care.

When Sam rejoined them at one o'clock, he brought with him a dime's worth of sliced boloney, a large onion, and a loaf of bread. He also brought enough lemons and sugar to make lemonade for the baby for ten days to come. To Granny, he gave a big brown bottle of Five Dot Garrett snuff. Then he handed Nona a light, flimsy little package.

"What's that?" she asked.

· 212 ·

"Open it," he said.

When she did, she found a pair of shiny tan rayon stockings, which glistened in the sun. Granny's mouth puckered in disapproval.

"They're to go with your shoes and that dress you made," Sam said.

For a long time, standing there on the edge of the culvert, Nona looked at these adornments for her own body. Not necessities, mind you, but luxuries. Exotic, feminine luxuries.

Finally, feeling humiliated by her unimportance in this scene, Granny said irritably, "Well, ain't you goin to say your manners?"

"I don't hardly know how to," Nona said, blushing, starting off toward home, carefully re-wrapping the stockings so that the slick green paper would have the same folds that it had before. Once she looked at Sam timidly, then dropped her eyes, feeling tongue-tied and confused. She did manage to blurt out, "They're pretty."

Just then a man drove up in an empty farm truck, looked them over casually, and drove slowly on.

This was too much for Granny. She threw a bucket at him, but it only landed harmlessly in the truck bed, in which it passed on down the road.

"Well, I'll be jiggered!" she exclaimed, feeling swindled. Then, turning to Sam, she said, "This here's the last trip I'm ever takin. Folks on the road don't behave no better than them at home. I'm just goin back to the house and set and wait for my call to Glory."

# Biography ❧

THE AUTOBIOGRAPHY OF A DURABLE SINNER—
*Owen P. White*

A HICKORY CANE—*Marquis James*

LEAD STEERS AND NECK OXEN—*J. Frank Dobie*

THE FIGHT AT THE O.K. CORRAL—*Stuart Nathaniel Lake*

BELLE STARR: A PRAIRIE AMAZON—*Duncan Aikman*

THEY RODE STRAIGHT UP TO DEATH—*Walter Prescott Webb*

THE GALVESTON STORM—*Sam Acheson*

LORENZO IN TAOS—*Mabel Dodge Luhan*

HERO FOR O. HENRY—*Dora Neill Raymond*

SLEEPY BLACK—*Ross Santee*

CRACK-UP—*Beirne Lay, Jr.*

# *from* THE AUTOBIOGRAPHY OF A DURABLE SINNER

*by* OWEN P. WHITE

Owen P. White, ex-resident of El Paso and long on the staff of *Collier's*, is the author of a number of Southwestern books, most recent of which is the rambunctious story of his own life, *The Autobiography of a Durable Sinner*. It is from that book that the following picture of El Paso, in her wilder and more lurid days, is drawn.

Many Southwestern readers will recall the commotion which took place when Owen P. White wrote a two-part profile of the East Texas oil fields for *Collier's*. This was when thievery and most other kinds of ingenious illegality blossomed in this section with a richness startling even to us in the Southwest, who had previously thought of Spindletop and Burkburnett as first-rate examples of the chicanery which the discovery of vast quantities of petroleum engendered. But Owen White exposed these earlier booms for what they were: piddling adventures in petty larceny. To many a Southwesterner this was blasphemy and sacrilege, and for a while the fur flew with great flamboyance.

A great percentage of Mr. White's writing has been controversial. For that matter, the first printing of *The Autobiography of a Durable Sinner* had to be recalled from the bookstores, in order that the nervous publishers, busy with their snips and shears, might remove certain pages which, had they appeared publicly, might well have brought all concerned into the libel courts. As it was, the book appeared with these dangerous pages deleted, and serenity, so much of a stranger to Owen P. White, did prevail.

---

IN 1879, WHEN IT WAS A TOWN WITHOUT LAW OFFICERS, WHEREIN men could take life straight, as they took their liquor, El Paso was utopian. In 1887 it wasn't. Even I, at the mature age of eight as I stepped from the train, could tell it wasn't. The evidence was before me in the shape of a man with a gold cord on his hat, a badge on his shirt, and a .45 on his hip. He was having a hard time to protect the arriving passengers from the assaults of a riotous mob of hotel runners and hack drivers, who very clearly wanted to sail right in and take us all apart. With the aid of this policeman, who had only one arm—his other one having been shot off in a gun-fight—my father managed to get us through the mob and transport us to the home he had secured for us.

During the time I had been away, what had happened to the town of my birth?

In the year in which I was born, El Paso began to undergo a change of life. In that year four great railroads began laying their tracks in the direction of its barrooms and gaming resorts, the result being that the town at once began to fill up with border parasites coming in to prey upon the railroad payrolls. For the first six or eight months these men, and the few women who were with them, came in a trickle, but by the end of another six, with the railheads drawing nearer and nearer, they arrived in a flood. They came in buckboards, buggies, wagons, stages, on foot, and on horseback. They ate what they could get, drank anything, slept with anybody; worked feverishly during the day erecting shacks to live in, and caroused vigorously throughout the night. This was a wicked period in the life of El Paso. Everything was under control: under control of gals and gunmen, to the end that in one year more killings took place in El Paso than had ever taken place in the entire careers of any of the so-called really tough towns of the frontier. But what of it? These killings were unimportant. No one, not even the relatives of the deceased, gave a damn about them. No one had time to, because everyone's attention was centered on the race between the Santa Fé and the Southern Pacific, which were, each one, trying to beat the other into the town.

The Southern Pacific won: it brought its first train in on May 13, 1881, and immediately El Paso underwent a series of changes that were quick and startling.

Before that train pulled in, there had been but one one-story brick building in El Paso, not a single board floor, and only two panes of window glass; while as for such effeminate luxuries as mahogany bar fixtures and square pianos in the dance halls, they were, of course, unknown. But within just a few months these deficiencies, as well as another of which the innocent old-timers had hitherto been happily ignorant, had been remedied. Brick buildings began to replace adobe ones; ornate bar fixtures and fancy gambling tables ousted the makeshift equipment formerly in use; pine boards took the place of Mother Earth on the floors in the dance halls. At the same time a new element in the life of El Paso, a blondined, hand-decorated, female element, recruited in the East and Middle West and shipped in by the carload, arrived to compete with the brown-skinned, black-eyed señoritas of the earlier day.

From this time on, life in El Paso became indeed alluring. A wonderful prosperity, one that the prophets said would endure for many years, was on the way; and so the Sinners, knowing that plucking the Christians would be easy and profitable, garbed themselves becomingly for the harvest. It was a gorgeous display. The calcimined women, both in the humble cribs and in the big parlor houses which were the pride of the town, donned beautiful gowns—scanty perhaps, but none the less beautiful; the bartenders discarded their flannel shirts in favor of white jackets and thousand dollar diamonds; and the members of the gambling fraternity blossomed out in all the glory of imported, tailor-made suits, fast trotting horses attached to red-wheeled road wagons, and kept women.

Behind all this, of course, was the idea of money. In previous times, when El Paso was really heroic, no one cared a great deal for cash. They didn't have to, because a man's social standing depended far more upon his ability to handle his liquor and shoot straight than upon his financial rating. But now it was different. Whether it wanted to or not, El Paso was doomed to become a great metropolis; and so concurrently with blondes, bar fixtures, and red-wheeled road wagons, the trains now began to disgorge men who planned to embark in more or less legitimate enterprises. These new citizens—and among them came six uncles of mine, all on my mother's side—then got busy as rapidly as they could to turn El Paso into as good a place for the sale of the more sedate things of life as the gals and gamblers had already made it for gay and frivolous entertainment.

Thus by 1887, whenever a cattleman, a cowboy, a miner, a prospector, a merchant, a lawyer, or a thief anywhere in Arizona, New Mexico, or West Texas found an extra dollar in his pocket, he headed hell-bent to El Paso to get rid of it. The town's Christians, who peddled groceries, hardware, mowers, plows, coffins, and mining machinery took unto themselves much credit for this, but deserved none of it. They knew it: they knew that the thing that brought customers from afar into their stores was El Paso's invitation to step right up to the Sinners' bench, and they took advantage of it. They even encouraged it.

It was about four years before the antics of the Sinners began to affect me in any way. I don't know exactly why that was. Perhaps I was too high morally, or too low mentally, to be contaminated; but in either case it is quite true that until I was twelve years old, I took very little interest in what went on outside my own sphere of activity. Within that sphere I was very busy, busier than I had ever been, as I had more to attend to. I had to ride, shoot, trap, go to school, both day and Sunday; have measles, mumps, whooping cough, and chicken pox; and at the same time try to catch up on my reading. I never could. I never have. I've quit trying, because I now realize that it's impossible for me to overcome the three or four thousand years' start that the publishers of this world have on me.

In spite of all this effort and opportunity, so trifling were the achievements of my first four years in El Paso that I hesitate to record them, even as I frequently hesitated, at the time, to mention them to my mother.

The first time that I got drunk, for instance, I tried to conceal it; but how could I? My breath betrayed me, even if my staggering gait did not; and so when she cornered me I had to confess that her youngest son, with whose Sunday School record she was so pleased, had not only had a great deal too much to drink but had even robbed a house in order to get the liquor.

I had jimmied my way into the cellar of an absent neighbor, found there a barrel of wine, and, with the aid of a yard of rubber tubing which was there also, inhaled as much of it as I could hold. For this unparalleled piece of wickedness I was not punished. I knew why. My mother could never wield a switch, a buggy whip, or a paddle when she was convulsed with mirth. But two days later, when I again staggered in after a second trip to the barrel, it was very different. So different that never again did my mother ever see me under the influence of liquor. It was hard to avoid, I admit, but I managed it, even though on one disastrous occasion it cost me several hundred dollars to get by with it.

When this happened, to go a bit ahead of my story, I was nineteen. It was Sunday afternoon, and in Charles Beiswinger's place I encountered a man for whom I had an unbounded admiration. He was Fred Fenchler. He was the best-loved sport in El Paso. As a gambler who would sit in with any company, he was known from El Paso to New York, and from Mexico City to Paris. Naturally, when Fred asked me to have a drink with him, and then followed that up with an invitation to dine with him at his home, I was overcome with gratitude. We dined. It was a wet dinner, very wet, and at its conclusion I was again grateful when my host suggested that I trail along while he went uptown and played a little roulette.

He played in the gambling room back of the Oxford Saloon, buying checks at five hundred dollars a stack. I played also, buying at five, but with far better luck than he did. I won, he lost heavily; and as his was a patronage that was much valued by the house, we were served with all the champagne we wanted. Unfortunately I wanted much more than I could carry; and to relieve myself I retired to the washroom, whither I was followed by two kind strangers, who held my head for me and did everything they could to ease my suffering. When I was feeling slightly better, these good men suggested that they take me home.

"No," I said, remembering my mother, "take me to the Sheldon Hotel." They did so. They took me to the hotel, got me a room, and put me snugly to bed. I was deeply grateful; but in the morning, when I awoke and found that I didn't have even a dime left out of approximately eight hundred dollars, I felt differently. I was mad, but I can see now that I shouldn't have been. I should have remained grateful, because from that experience I learned two valuable lessons. One is that whenever any Good Samaritan offers to do me a free favor, I look him over carefully, search him for the ace up his sleeve; and then (lesson number two) if I don't find the ace, I play safe by turning my back on him anyhow.

Having been baptized into the Episcopal Church shortly before we left Tucson (though I so resented being called a Child of God by the preacher that I bit him), I naturally became one of the lambs in that flock after my return to El Paso. In a way I couldn't help it. My father was not at all religious, nor was my mother disagreeably so; but as she was an Episcopalian—probably because that route to Heaven was broader, smoother, and easier to travel than any other then advertised—I also became one. It was not at all painful. On the contrary, I really enjoyed going to Sunday School. I enjoyed the hymns, I enjoyed the Bible stories; but above all, as I was a conceited young jackass, I enjoyed standing up Sunday after Sunday before the entire Sunday School and cutting loose with the text and the collect for the day. This was easy. It was no trick at all for me, with my spongelike mind, to memorize these short bits of Scripture, and I did it gladly, especially as there was a reward at the end of the route. I didn't know what that reward was to be. I only knew that at Easter a grand prize was to be given to the child who had made the best record on texts and collects, and so I set out to win it. I had but one real competitor: a gifted lad who in later years made quite a name for himself by becoming a piano player in a honky-tonk theater and marrying one of the joint's giddy-looking beer slingers.

I finally beat this fellow, and at Easter, before a church packed with fathers and mothers, I was called up to the pulpit, patted upon the head by good old Dr. Higgins—who later backslid and became a homeopathic physician and a really sincere drinker—and was presented with a prize that was of no more use to me than a nail in my foot. It was a full-rigged ship! Think of it! A ship in the desert, a ship with no sea to sail it on. I carried it home, put it carefully away in the woodshed, and for-ever thereafter religiously refrained from texts and collects. Nevertheless I was very proud of the record I had made, and so was my mother. My father was noncommittal.

For the first four years of it, I enjoyed going to public school as much as I enjoyed going to Sunday School, and for much the same reason. I liked it because, although I was very quarrelsome and, as my father said,

> Felt that day lost whose low descending sun
> Viewed at my hand no bloody battle done,

I enjoyed a competition wherein I was always able to keep my-self near the top of the class without having to do enough study-ing to interfere with my other pursuits. But this was not because I was talented or abnormal. I was neither. I was just an ornery, ordinary kid, who was a great trial to his teachers, largely be-cause my erratic parents had given me a very stiff course in memory training. That was the secret of it; and never, up to the end of his days, did my father relax in his efforts to turn me into an anthology of queer and assorted poetry. For three selfish reasons I never resisted him. I liked him, I liked poetry, and I liked money. Knowing these things, my father would proceed in this way: at the breakfast table he would pull from his pocket a poem that he had clipped from a newspaper or a magazine, would hand it to me, and would say: "Son, learn this, recite it to me when I come home tonight and I'll give you a quarter."

No matter how long the offering I never failed to earn the money and have never regretted it. I doubt if there is another man in the United States today who can recite "The Duel in Cowlick Holler." But I can, and I enjoy doing it, because

> You see, 'twas all a case, sir, of liquor and profanity
> That had struck a sorta snag, sir, in muscular Christianity.

My father's interest in my education was not confined solely to filling me to the muzzle with classical learning. He was also practical. For example, prosperity having begun to shower down upon him, he sold his old bay horse and bought for himself a standard-bred trotting mare from Kentucky. She was a beauty. He named her Tom, after a stunning young lady who was a bookkeeper for the Singer Sewing Machine Company, and a good deal of a high-stepper in her own right. Tom—meaning the mare now—was also wicked. Late every afternoon when my father would turn her head in the direction of the feedbox, she'd run away with him, and he never knew it. I can still see him making the turn into the back lot where the stable was. He was a small man, and there he'd be, with his feet braced against the dashboard, his cigar clenched in his teeth, the lines wrapped twice around his hands, and Tom, traveling at top speed, paying no more attention to him than if he hadn't even been in the buggy. She'd dash up to the stable gate and come to a sliding stop to keep from knocking her own brains out, whereupon my father would unwrap the lines, look down at Ed, the colored man, and at me, and say: "Ed, by God it takes a man to drive a horse like this." Ed would grin and say nothing and neither would I.

In some way my father found out that I was very much afraid of that horse. That settled it. No son of his was ever going to be afraid of any horse on earth, if he could help it; and so one morning at breakfast, without giving me the slightest hint as to his criminal intent, he told me to come to his office that afternoon at half past four. I went, walked in, and he looked up and said: "Go back downstairs, son, unhitch Tom, and drive her home." I did, or rather I went down and unhitched Tom, but I didn't drive her home. She went there herself. She did it every day for weeks. It got monotonous. It got so that the merchants, saloon-keepers, and gamblers on San Antonio Street used to line up on the sidewalks to make bets on whether or not I'd survive the trip. They could set their watches by my regular afternoon runaway. Tom never failed to make it a good one. We took all corners on two wheels, and why I was not killed is still a mystery. But I wasn't. I even got over being afraid of Tom, but never of being afraid of the ridicule my father would heap upon me if I had an accident. Finally I had one, but he never heard of it. One afternoon Tom miscalculated her speed, skidded too far when she came to her sliding stop, and tore the shafts off against a gatepost. This was terrible, or might have been if I hadn't gotten the blacksmith to work far into the night putting in a new pair of shafts which were exact duplicates of the old ones. For all of which I paid out of my own pocket.

Having thus cured me, as he thought (and he was partially right about it) of my fear of wild horses, my father took up the matter of wild women. His procedure was about the same as before. Without giving me any advance warning he again told me to come to his office after school, and of course I went. . . .

But before telling of that afternoon I'll go back to an afternoon some months before. It was a cold day, and when I went into the house I found my father sitting hunched up in front of an open fire. He was crying, real tears glistened on his beard; and when I walked over and stood beside him, he looked up at me and said, fiercely and as if he was filled with rage about something: "Son, Alice Abbott's dead, and by God, even if she wasn't respectable, if she doesn't go to Heaven I don't want to go there. And you don't either. It'll be no place for us."

I knew what he meant. Alice Abbott, a large fat woman, and madam of the swankiest and highest-priced bordello in El Paso, was known by sight to every man, woman, and child in the town. No one could miss her, as it was her habit every afternoon, accompanied by four of her beautiful girls, to drive through the streets in a high stanhope rig drawn by a pair of beautiful white horses. Miss Abbott's reason for doing this was obvious; as obvious as if she had a sign THIS FLESH FOR SALE hung on her rig. Consequently the pious minority in the town looked upon her as such a vile, wicked old woman that they were all glad to hear about it when Miss Kitty Freeman, who ran quite a large bawdy house of her own, shot several holes through her with a .45.

But my father who knew Alice Abbott better than any one in El Paso, was not glad to hear of it. He knew her as the most charitable woman in the town; as the only person in it, in fact, to whom he could go without hesitation and ask for help for poor, sick people, either white or Mexican, who were unable to pay for food and medicine. He always got it, and there was never but one stipulation: "Here, Doc, take it and spend it wherever you want to. The only thing is: don't ever tell anybody where it came from."

And that was why my father was sitting in front of the fire that afternoon crying real tears that he was not ashamed of.

On the afternoon in question, though, he was not crying. Instead his eyes twinkled as he handed me a bunch of about twenty bills and told me to go out and collect them. I looked at the addresses and I gasped. Every one bore a number somewhere on Utah Street. "Why Dad," I said, "you don't mean it. You don't mean that I'm to go down there, and go in those houses, and get this money from those women?"

But he did mean it. He knew what he was doing. He knew that, in common with almost every other normal twelve-year-old kid in El Paso, my feeling regarding the girls on Utah Street was one of overwhelming curiosity mixed up with some kind of a mysterious fear. It was true. Many times, sneaking out at night, I had walked down Utah Street to take in the sights but had always kept strictly to the middle of the road. I didn't dare tackle the sidewalks for fear that some of the semi-naked women, standing in the doorways, or leaning out of the windows, and reaching for the men who went by, would grab me, drag me inside, and ravish me. But, "to be or not to be, that was the question." Did I want to be ravished? I didn't yet know; that was a thing I was beginning to get very curious about; and that was why my father, who knew I was curious about it, wanted me to go down and collect those bills from those women. He didn't explain it to me very fully, but I got his idea when he said in reply to my protest: "Of course, son, I want you to go to those places and collect those bills. Why not? Those women won't hurt you.

They're not nearly as bad as most people say they are; in fact many of them are very good, and the sooner you find that out, and get acquainted with them, the easier it will be for you to get along with them a few years from now, when you'll be calling on them for something other than to collect money."

I'll never cease to be grateful to my father for sending me out with those bills. It cured me of curiosity, because by calling on the Utah Street ladies between three and four in the afternoon, when they were just getting up, many of them nursing hangovers, and all with their warpaint off and their face grease on, and their hair in curlers and their rooms reeking with the odor of liquor and cigarette smoke, I unavoidably came to the conclusion that the beauty of sin, as they peddled it, was entirely mythical. As far as their treatment of me was concerned, sin didn't even exist. In the many months that I collected accounts from them, not one of those women, although they were, as I noticed with detached interest, a bit careless in the matter of clothes, ever said a wicked or a suggestive word to me. Instead, because I was Doctor White's kid and they had a great respect for him, they were all very nice to me, they all paid me, and so in time I really learned to like many of them.

But I was not so deluded as not to know that when they were really practicing their profession they were tough sisters. They had to be, because they had tough men to deal with. Generally those dealings were carried on at night. Sometimes they were not. Sometimes, due to the early arrival in town of men who couldn't wait, hell would begin to heave in the red-light district in the middle of the afternoon. Whenever this happened, my job became very interesting. I'll never forget, for instance, the afternoon when Bass Outlaw, a Deputy U. S. Marshal, Kid McKittrick, and an unknown, who was promptly buried and forgotten, started to shoot up Miss Tillie Howard's very high-class establishment. I was not two hundred feet from Tillie's place, whither I was headed to present bills to a couple of her girls, when the bombardment began. I heard a fusillade of shots, a police whistle, a few more shots, and then, running from Tillie's front door and dashing across the street into an Italian saloon, came the unknown. Behind him, with a gun in his hand, limping badly but making good time nevertheless, came Uncle John Selman. Uncle John crossed the street, pushed open the swinging door of the Italian's saloon, fired one shot, turned, and seeing me, asked if my Dad was in his office. "I reckon so," I said. "What's the matter?"

"Bass Outlaw shot me in the leg," replied Uncle John, and as he hobbled away I went on into Tillie's place to see what had happened. It was easy to assemble the particulars. Early in the day, Outlaw, McKittrick, and the stranger started to lay the foundation for a spree. By three o'clock that preliminary had been completed; and as the ethics of the enterprise demanded that, after a certain amount of liquor had been consumed, a sporting house had to be visited and shot up, the trio chose Tillie's place as the one in which they would put on their show. But no sooner had they arrived and gotten inside and yanked out their guns and cracked loose at the bric-a-brac and the chandeliers than Miss Howard, foreseeing a rough time ahead for everybody, ran out on her back porch and began blowing a police whistle.

Hearing that whistle Constable John Selman, who was playing seven-up in the Monte Carlo near by, responded by running into the alley and starting to climb over Tillie's back fence. That move brought on disaster. As Selman threw his leg over the fence, Bass Outlaw, who had come out on the porch to take Tillie's whistle away from her, saw it and just for the hell of the thing put a bullet in it. No one bullet had ever yet stopped John Selman, and this one didn't. On the contrary, it gave him a personal interest in what was going on inside Tillie's place that he hadn't had before; and so, limping across the yard, he went into the back hall, where he was instantly shot at, and unanimously missed, by the three celebrators. When Selman returned the fire, he didn't miss. With his first shot he got Outlaw, who dropped in the hall; with his second he destroyed McKittrick in one of the parlors; while with his third, as we have already seen, he demolished the stranger, in the saloon across the street.

Obviously this was fine shooting; but when I got inside, where the atmosphere was full of smoke, women, and profanity and the floor was littered up with a couple of dying citizens, it was very clear that neither Miss Howard nor any of the denizens of her joint gave a damn about that part of it. They were just plain mad. Mad because the two dying citizens were bleeding all over some very costly Oriental rugs.

# A HICKORY CANE

*by* MARQUIS JAMES

When a biographer of Marquis James's outstanding ability set to work upon so juicy and incomparable a subject as Sam Houston, something exciting and extraordinarily fine was bound to result. It did. *The Raven*, James's biography of Houston, won the acclaim of the critics, the patronage of the public, and the Pulitzer Prize hands down.

That portion of the book which is reprinted here deals with one of the great turning points in Houston's life. The first such turning point was when, as a youngster, he fought with such striking gallantry and courage in the battle of To-ho-pe-ka that he won the admiration and affection of his commanding officer, Andrew Jackson. Thereafter, propelled by the favoritism of Jackson and his own ability to charm and manipulate the electorate, he quickly rose to the governorship of Tennessee and was regarded as the obvious choice for Jackson's successor in the White House. At this point he married a Tennessee girl from a prominent family, but when the honeymoon was half over, she went home to mama. There was a scandal which, on the wings of rumor, soared to such heights of public concern that Houston resigned and went back to live with his friends, the Cherokee Indians. Here, spurred by remorse and keg whiskey, he was once on the point of repudiating his United States citizenship, unifying all the Indians, and setting up his own nation west of the Rockies. Instead, he accompanied an Indian delegation to Washington, where the following lively events took place.

---

Black Coat, the second Chief, was in charge of the Cherokee delegation with which Sam Houston departed for Washington in December of 1831. Although Houston was not officially a member of the mission, the delegates' instructions and the petition they carried "To Andrew Jackson, Great Father" were in his handwriting. The latter conveyed a recital of grievances, with a paragraph tucked in to regularize a considerable purchase of land Houston had made from "Chouteau's half-breed Indian bastard children," as Agent Vashon phrased it, disliking ambiguities.

For the journey the venerable Creek Chief, Opoth-ley-ahola, gave Houston a handsome buckskin coat with a beaver collar and a hunting knife to adorn the belt. The travelers stopped off at Nashville and Houston showed them through the Hermitage. While inspecting the grounds he used the new knife to cut a hickory sapling about as big around as a man's thumb and fashion himself a walking cane. The party reached Washington in January of 1832 and accommodated themselves at Brown's Indian Queen Hotel on Pennsylvania Avenue. A few days later Houston gave the cane to a friend in Georgetown.

There had been changes in Washington since Houston's last visit. Peggy Eaton was not in town and the place was duller for it. She was in Florida where her husband, by grace of Andrew Jackson, was governor. Echoes of the piquant Peg's political disturbances still resounded in the marble halls, however, as on March 31, 1832, when William Stanbery, Member of Congress from Ohio, in the course of a broad criticism of the Administration, inquired, "Was not the late Secretary of War removed because of his attempt fraudulently to give Governor Houston the contract for Indian rations?"

The words of Mr. Stanbery brought Houston to the foyer of the House chamber determined to "settle" the matter there, but James K. Polk hustled him out into the fresh air. Houston then sent Representative Cave Johnson, of Tennessee, to Stanbery with a note containing the formal inquiries that etiquette required to precede a challenge to a duel. Johnson was made to promise, however, that should Stanbery refuse to receive the note he would not assume the quarrel himself. Stanbery declined to reply to "a note signed Sam Houston." "I'll introduce myself to the damned rascal," said Houston. Mr. Stanbery armed himself with two pistols. Houston put away his evil-looking knife and asked his Georgetown friend if he could take back the cane for a few days.

On the evening of April thirteenth Houston, Senator Buckner, of Missouri, and Representative Blair, of Tennessee, were chatting with Senator Felix Grundy in the latter's room. Houston took his leave, and Buckner and Blair joined him in a walk along the Avenue. The three had covered about half the distance to Brown's Hotel when Blair recognized Congressman Stanbery crossing the street. Whereupon, Mr. Blair turned and walked "rapidly" way.

It was dark, except for the dim street-lamps. Houston approached the man in the street. "Are you Mr. Stanbery?" he asked politely.

"Yes sir," replied the latter.

"Then you are a damned rascal," exclaimed Houston, slamming the Ohioan on the head with the hickory cane.

Stanbery was almost as large a man as Houston. He threw up his hands. "Oh, don't!" he cried, but Houston continued to rain blows and Stanbery turned, as Senator Buckner thought, to run. Houston leaped on his opponent's back and dragged him down. The two rolled on the pavement, Stanbery yelling for help. Houston could not hold and punch at the same time, his right arm having been useless in such emergencies since the battle of To-ho-pe-ka. Stanbery managed to draw one of his pistols. He pressed it against Houston's chest.

Buckner heard the gunlock snap, saw the flint strike fire. But the charge did not explode, and Houston tore the weapon from Stanbery's grasp. Houston then stood up, landed a few more licks with the cane and, as a finishing touch, lifted the Congressman's feet in the air and "*struck him elsewhere*," as Senator Buckner rendered it in his evidence at Houston's trial, ladies being present.

## MOST DARING OUTRAGE AND ASSAULT

was the head-line in General Duff Green's *United States Telegraph*, followed by brutal details. But the article wound up with observations which Houston himself could hardly have improved upon.

"What gives more importance to this transaction is the known relation that Houston bears to the President of the United States. . . . He was the individual who placed in the hands of General Jackson Mr. Monroe's letter to Mr. Calhoun that made so important a part of 'the correspondence' between the President and Vice President. Although he left Tennessee under circumstances that produced the greatest excitement, took up his residence among the Indians and adopted their costume and habits; and although the proof that he contemplated a fraud upon the government is conclusive, yet . . . he is still received at the Executive Mansion and treated with the kindness and hospitality of an old favorite. . . . We have long seen, that tactics of the Nashville school were to be transferred to Washington and that the voice of truth was to be silenced by the dread of the assassin. But we have not yet taken fear as our counsellor."

After this, further reference to a hickory cane cut at the Hermitage was labor of supererogation. General Green, with his powerful newspaper, had quit the Jackson entourage with Mr. Calhoun. Bursting to even the score, he raised the trouncing of Stanbery greatly above the altitude of a common brawl.

3

From his bed Mr. Stanbery dispatched a note to Andrew Stevenson, the Speaker of the House, describing how he had been "waylaid in the street . . . attacked, knocked down by a bludgeon and severely bruised and wounded by Samuel Houston, late of Tennessee, for words spoken in my place in the House of Representatives." This was read to the House, and a resolution was offered for the arrest of Houston.

This parliamentary move brought to his feet James K. Polk, the President's voice in the House of Representatives. Mr. Polk would not admit that the House had the power to arrest Sam Houston in the matter involved, but the vote was one hundred and forty-five to twenty-five for arrest.

On the following day the galleries were crowded and every member was in his seat when the prisoner, wearing his fur-collared buckskin coat and carrying his stick of Hermitage hickory, walked down the aisle of the House chamber beside the sergeant-of-arms. He halted before the Speaker's desk and bowed. Speaker Stevenson, a friend of the accused, read the formal arraignment. Houston asked for twenty-four hours in which to prepare his defense. He was granted forty-eight hours.

Houston reappeared with Francis Scott Key as his attorney, although the defendant virtually conducted his own case. Asked to plead to a charge of assaulting Representative Stanbery for words spoken in debate, Houston said he had not molested Mr. Stanbery for words spoken in the House, but for remarks imputed to Mr. Stanbery by a newspaper. After vainly trying to get Mr. Stanbery to disavow or affirm the published statements, Houston added that on an "accidental" meeting he had given way to his feelings and struck the Congressman with "a common walking cane." This was interpreted as a plea of not guilty and the trial of Sam Houston before the bar of the House of Representatives was set to begin on April nineteenth.

It continued for a month, growing in public interest until everything else in the current news was eclipsed. *Niles' Register*, of Baltimore, which prided itself on its reports of the proceedings of Congress, fell days behind on the regular doings of the Senate and the House, so great was the space required to report the Houston trial. The *Register* was moved to deprecate a public taste so thirsty for details of this raffish proceeding.

4

Mr. Stanbery was the first witness. The bumps on his countenance were Exhibit A. Houston conducted the cross-examination, opening with the statement that the witness had made an accusation of fraud.

"Had you then or have you now," he asked, "any and what evidence of the correctness of such imputation?"

Several of Stanbery's friends objected to the question. Mr. Polk demanded an answer. By a vote of one hundred and one to eighty-two the House ordered Mr. Stanbery to reply.

"It was no part of my intention," he said, "to impute fraud to General Houston."

Senator Buckner told of the encounter as he had witnessed it. Mr. Stanbery characterized the Senator's testimony as "destitute of truth and infamous," but withdrew the statement and apologized. The now celebrated cane was exhibited, hefted and passed from hand to hand. The defense showed that Mr. Stanbery had carried a pistol and had tried to shoot Houston, but the weapon was not introduced in evidence. The cane held the stage, unchallenged by any rival attraction.

On April twenty-sixth Mr. Key made the opening address for the defense. There was little in it to suggest the author of *The Star-Spangled Banner*. He undertook to establish that Houston had not struck Stanbery for words spoken in debate but for words printed in a newspaper. The weak spot in this contention was that the words printed in the paper were a verbatim report of the debate. When he concluded, his client's chances of escaping conviction appeared to be rather slim.

This state of affairs distressed Andrew Jackson, and he sent for Houston. Speaking of it afterward, Sam Houston declared that he had never seen Jackson in such a temper. Houston was wearing the buckskin coat. The President asked if he had any other clothes. Houston said he had not, and Jackson tossed a clinking silk purse to his caller with the advice to dress like a gentleman and buck up his defense. Houston went to a tailor and was measured for "a coat of the finest material, reaching to my knees, trousers in harmony of color and the latest style in cut, with a white satin vest to match."

On the afternoon of May sixth Houston was notified that the defense would be required to close its case on the following day. That night a number of friends dropped into his room at Brown's Hotel. "Gentlemen," Houston is quoted as saying in a reminiscence of the occasion, "we sat late and you may judge how we drank when I tell you that Stevenson [the Speaker of the House, and presiding officer of the trial] at midnight was sleeping on the lounge. Bailey Peyton was out of commission and had gone to his room and Felix Grundy had ceased to be interesting. Polk rarely indulged and left us early."

Houston awoke with a headache. "I took a cup of coffee but it refused to stick." A second cup behaved no better. "After something like an hour had passed I took another cup and it stuck, and I said, 'I am all right' and proceeded to array myself in my splendid apparel."

5

Above the stately entrance to the chamber of the House stood a representation of History, a comely, though alert, young woman, by the hand of an Italian sculptor. Light draperies floated about her. On one knee she balanced a ledger, and gracefully exhibited a pen in perfect readiness to record whatever of interest that should take place within her view. A wheel of the chariot in which she rode served as the face of the clock of the House.

The draped dais of the Speaker faced the clock. At the hour of noon Mr. Stevenson called the House to order. The scene before him was notable. The hall was a noble adaptation of the Greek theater pattern. Shafts of sunlight descended from a glassed dome sixty feet, at its highest point, from the floor. Beneath a sweeping arch at the Speaker's back was a figure of Liberty at whose feet a marble eagle spread its wings for flight. On either side were flag-draped panels, one hung with a portrait of Washington, one with a likeness of Lafayette.

Every seat on the floor was filled and chairs had been placed in the aisles to accommodate the privileged overflow. A solid bank of men pressed against the colonnaded semicircle of wall. For two hours there had been no room in the galleries, where the diplomatic corps, gay with ribbons, the Army, the Navy and Society were authentically represented.

In front of the Speaker's dais the prisoner bowed to his guest of the evening before.

"Mr. Speaker," he said. The tone was one of ordinary conversation, but Houston's rich warm voice reached every part of the chamber. "Mr. Speaker, arraigned for the first time of my life on a charge of violating the laws of my country I feel all that embarrassment which my peculiar situation is calculated to inspire." Houston's perfect composure made this a gracious beginning.

"I disclaim, utterly, every motive unworthy of an honorable man." The tone was suddenly infused with passionate earnestness. If, when "deeply wronged," he had on "impulse" violated the laws of his country or trespassed the prerogatives of the House, he was "willing to be held to my responsibility. All I demand is that my actions may be pursued to the motives which gave them birth."

He stood before the house, he said, branded as "a man of broken fortune and blasted reputation." "I can never forget that reputation, however limited, is the high boon of heaven. . . . Though the plowshare of ruin has been driven over me and laid waste to my brightest hopes . . . I have only to say . . .

> "I seek no sympathies, nor need;
> The thorns which I have reaped are of the tree
> I planted; they have torn me and I bleed."

It was very effective. The galleries applauded, and as Houston awaited an opportunity to resume, a bouquet of flowers dropped at his feet. A woman's voice was heard above the hum: "I had rather be Sam Houston in a dungeon than Stanbery on a throne!"

Amid perfect silence Houston picked up the flowers. He bowed over them but did not raise his eyes.

Houston spoke for half an hour on the perils of legislative tyranny. He mentioned Greece and Rome. The errors of Caesar, of Cromwell, of Bonaparte and of "the Autocrat of all the Russias" were displayed. Blackstone and the Apostle Paul were shown to be on the speaker's side. A well-turned period was closed with a quotation nine lines in length, beginning:

> "There is a proud, undying thought in man
> That bids his soul still upward look. . . . "

From this premise the speaker moved dexterously to the corollary that he had committed no offense for which the Congress could punish him without invading the private rights of a citizen.

Houston paused. His glance met the glance of History, then shifted to the flag that draped the portrait of Lafayette.

"So long as that proud emblem . . . shall wave in the Hall of American legislators, so long shall it cast its sacred protection over the personal rights of every American citizen. Sir, when you shall have destroyed the pride of American character, you will have destroyed the brightest jewel that heaven ever made. You will have drained the purest and holiest drop which visits the hearts of your sages in council and heroes in the field and . . . these massy columns, with yonder lofty dome will sink into one crumbling ruin. . . . But, Sir, so long as that flag shall bear aloft its glittering stars . . . so long I trust, shall the rights of American citizens be preserved safe and unimpaired—till discord shall wreck the spheres—the grand march of time shall cease—and not one fragment of all creation be left to chafe the bosom of eternity's waves."

That was all. Whether Francis Scott Key, who sat in the front row, felt like disowning certain feeble lines of his own, inspired by the bombardment of Fort McHenry, is a detail upon which history is remiss. But Junius Brutus Booth plowed through the crowd and embraced his old friend.

"Houston, take my laurels!"

6

As soon as Speaker Stevenson could restore order, Mr. Harper, of New Hampshire, was recognized. He made a motion.

"*Resolved*, that Samuel Houston now in custody of the Sergeant-of-Arms, should forthwith be discharged."

Mr. Huntington, of Connecticut, was recognized. He desired to amend the motion of Mr. Harper by striking out all but the word "Resolved" and substituting the following:

"That Samuel Houston has been guilty of a contempt in violation of the privileges of this House."

The amendment was debated for four days. Mr. Polk contested every inch of the ground, but the House at length tired of the entertainment and voted one hundred and six to eighty-nine that Houston was guilty. He was sentenced to be reprimanded by the Speaker. The Stanbery wing sought to deprive Houston of the privilege of the floor of the House which he enjoyed as a former member of that body, but Polk struck back and defeated this, one hundred and one to ninety.

The reprimand took place on May fourteenth. Again the galleries were thronged and the aisles packed. Again Houston, the picture of composure, bowed before the Speaker, who bowed back, and began his unwelcome duty. He opened by alluding to the "character and the intelligence" of the accused "who has himself been honored with a seat in this House." "I forbear to say more," concluded Mr. Stevenson, "than to pronounce the judgement of the House, which is that you . . . be reprimanded at this bar by the Speaker, and . . . I do reprimand you accordingly."

But Mr. Stanbery was now showing more fight than he had that evening on Pennsylvania Avenue. He had Houston arrested on a criminal warrant charging assault. Further, he obtained a House investigation of the rations contract maneuvers of 1830. A jury convicted Houston of assault and he was fined five hundred dollars, but for some reason the trial attracted next to no attention. Duff Green seems to have been saving his thunder for the ration investigation which became another national spectacle. Green was so certain that Houston would be convicted of fraud that he announced his guilt in advance.

That was an era of latitude for the press. When Duff Green broke with Jackson, the President needing an organ in Washington, had induced Francis P. Blair to start the *Globe*. Blair was a westerner of the Jackson-Houston stamp in the matter of personal loyalties. His big house near the Executive Mansion was a haven of refuge for an old soldier in ill health, very weary, and at times as near dejection as one of Jackson's unconquerable spirit could be. The President would escape to "Blaar's," as he said it, in the broad North-of-Ireland way, slump into a big chair and smoke his pipe in peace. The *Globe* leaped to Houston's defense in the ration issue, and Andrew Jackson, busy as he was, found time to inspire Frank Blair's blunt pen.

The investigation was conducted by a committee of seven, of which Mr. Stanbery was the chairman. Houston conducted his own defense. The hearings were long drawn out. Stanbery was not impartial. There were many witnesses, some like Auguste Chouteau, from great distances. Duff Green was a tame witness. Houston practically ruined his testimony by a cross-examination conducted with Chesterfieldian courtesy. The evidence showed that Houston was the favored bidder of Eaton and Jackson, and only a failure of plans had prevented his obtaining the ration contract by secretive means and at enormous profit—perhaps aggregating a million dollars. Even so, the government would have saved money, and motives of envy, not patriotism, had kept the contract from Houston. After six weeks the committee reported by a divided vote that "John H. Eaton and Samuel Houston do stand entirely acquitted from all imputation of fraud."

7

These triumphs were far-reaching. They stripped The Raven of his beads and blanket. They buried Big Drunk. They resurrected Sam Houston who passionately embraced as "my country" the land he had so bitterly repudiated only a few months before. Once more he was in the train of the eagle.

Houston understood what had happened. Reviewing the Stanbery episode in after-life he said: "I was dying out and had they taken me before a justice of peace and fined me ten dollars it would have killed me; but they gave me a national tribunal for a theatre, and that set me up again."

No one was more pleased to see Sam Houston set up again than Andrew Jackson. Houston was his friend. He was another good man to use, and what President ever had enough good men? The old intimacy was restored, it was like bygone times. We have the spiteful testimony of Duff Green that Houston practically lived at the Executive Mansion.

Sam Houston was always giving presents. Poor Aunt Rachel must have had a drawerful of such remembrances. The mistress of the President's House at this period was Sarah York Jackson, wife of Andrew Jackson, Jr., the Executive's adopted son. Sam gave her Eliza Allen's engagement ring. From his discarded Indian wardrobe, he presented the President with an elaborate Cherokee ceremonial costume. Jackson had it among his trophies at the Hermitage when he died.

Like old times, indeed: Sam Houston one of the family—a renaissance of the days when this obedient servant traded horses, held offices and fought a duel for Andrew Jackson. His first thought, his constant thought, was to atone for the period of his delinquency. He would do something grand. He would capture an empire and lay it at his old Chieftain's feet—Texas, or the new Estremadura, as Houston used to say when his poetic fancy was on the wing.

# LEAD STEERS
# AND NECK OXEN

*by* J . FRANK DOBIE

Although J. Frank Dobie is a professor of English at the University of Texas, he is known to the nation as the author of *Coronado's Children*, *The Longhorns*, etc. His success as a writer on Southwestern subjects is a result both of his vast and detailed knowledge of the lore of this region and of the fact that his instincts and devotion are so intimately allied with it. He wears his boots and Stetson to school, and carries his leather chaps behind the seat of his Ford coupé.

When World War II began, Frank Dobie, frustrated by the fact that he was not allowed to go kill the enemy, and feeling his teaching to be momentarily beside the point, threw down his hat and in furious dejection declared to the editor of this book, "I'm a damn good mind to go out and grow corn." Subsequently Mr. Dobie has accepted an offer to teach in an English University. When Frank Dobie is stimulated by an occasional bombing, snugly aware that he is sharing in the war's risk and danger, teaching and writing will become fun again. And if the Germans manage to drop a bomb on him, it would be hard to think of a more fitting epitaph than: He never fumbled for the check.

"Lead Steers and Neck Oxen" is a selection from *The Longhorns*.

---

ALWAYS IN ANY GROUP OF ANIMALS, WHETHER MEN OR beasts, certain individuals emerge. The emergers on the trail were mostly lead steers. Trail men talked about them as they talked about cutting horses back home or sure-footed night horses in last night's run. Now and then a steer became so distinguished that his owner would not let him go with the cattle he led but would keep him for leading others. Old Blue, sometimes called Blue the Bell Ox, was known from the Pecos to the Arkansas, in Colorado as well as in Texas. He knew the trail to Dodge City better than hundreds of cowboys who galloped up its Front Street.

Blue was calved down on the Nueces River, near the Texas coast, in the spring of 1870. His mother may have been wild, but, judging by Blue's nature, she was never "snaky." He was four years old before anybody took sufficient notice of him to give him a name, which came from the color the vaqueros call *moro*, or "mulberry."

At the age of three he was put in a herd of other brush cattle bound for New Mexico. Its route was over the Goodnight-Loving Trail. Above Horsehead Crossing on the Pecos, the Apache Indians swooped down one night, stampeded the cattle, and got away with six hundred. In a sharp brush next day six or seven warriors paid for these cattle with their lives, and there was one more cowboy grave on the lone prairie. The remainder of the herd, something over 1500 head, went on ten days farther and were sold to John Chisum at his Bosque Redondo ranch. That fall the Apaches were fierce, and one morning a hand found Blue with an arrow in his rump. It was cut out and the wound healed rapidly. Blue had learned the smell of Indians.

The next spring Charlie Goodnight bought Blue in a "string" of five thousand steers from John Chisum, cut them into two herds, and trailed them on northward to the Arkansas River above Pueblo, Colorado. Blue went in the first herd. He was a mature beef now, four years old. He had seen a lot of the world and from the day the herd trailed out he asserted his natural leadership. Every morning he took his place at the point and there he held it. Powerful, sober and steady, he understood the least motion of the point men, and in guiding the herd showed himself worth a dozen extra hands. The cowboys all noted him. One youngster from Oxford named Hughes, son of the author of *Tom Brown's School Days*, wanted to call him Sir Walter Raleigh, but Blue was the name that stuck.

Instead of sending Blue on up to feed Indians at an agency in Wyoming, as he sent so many steers, Goodnight kept him on his Colorado range. Cattle thieves were bad, and, one morning while trailing a little bunch of cattle through the snow, Blue's owner discovered him and a dozen other steers in a picket corral snugly hidden in the middle of a thicket. Near by was a pile of hides. Blue had escaped having his shucked off, and for reasons that a certain cottonwood limb was drawn into—or drawn from—this particular gang of cow thieves never butchered another animal on the Arkansas.

Goodnight had one of his hands break Blue to the yoke. A man driving an ox wagon to California wanted to buy him, but he was not for sale. The Goodnight herd moved down on the Canadian River to winter.

In the summer of '76 the restless Goodnight decided to pull up stakes in Colorado and return to Texas. So Blue led the herd that stocked the first ranch in the vast Texas Panhandle of the Staked Plains. There were 1600 head of cattle in that first herd, and as they filed down the bluffs, rising nearly a thousand feet above the floor of the Palo Duro Canyon, they must have smelled buffalo. The disassembled wagon and its freight were carried down on mules. Below the pass the canyon opens out ten miles wide, the bluffs on either side making a natural fence. Out of this enclosure Goodnight and his men routed ten thousand buffaloes. Then they blocked up the few trails that led from the plains into the mighty Palo Duro cut, and rode line daily to keep the buffaloes out. The cattle wintered "in clover." Goodnight found a Scotchman, Adair by name, with money. Within ten years their J A brand was showing on the sides of 75,000 cattle and the J A range embraced a million acres of land up and down the waters of the Palo Duro. Meanwhile, other outfits had stocked the whole plains country—and Blue had become the outstanding animal in it.

The outlet for the Palo Duro was Dodge City, two hundred and fifty miles north. It was October 26, 1878, that a herd of 1000 J A steers headed in that direction to trample down the grass over a route thenceforth known as the Palo Duro-Dodge City Trail. Old Blue was in front.

This trip was different from any other he had made. It was

customary to bell the mare leading a horse herd. Away back in the sixties some young men belled an old cow to lead a thousand head of maverick yearlings they had caught on the forks of the Llano River—and after a maverick got used to that bell, he would, if cut off, make haste to get to it. But when Blue's owner decided to bell the leader of a trail herd of steers, he was making an innovation. The leaders were often the wildest old steers of the herd and could never have been managed as Blue was.

His bell was brand new, with green stain and red label fresh upon the brass. The collar was clean and shiny and had the wholesome smell of fresh leather. When Blue got that collar around his neck and heard the *ling-ling-ling* of his bell, he was as proud as a ranch boy stepping out in his first pair of red-topped boots.

The steers soon learned to follow the sound of Blue's bell. Attached to it was a little strap for tying up the clapper. Before the herd was to be bedded down for the night or halted for grazing during the day, one of the cowboys would pitch a rope over Blue's horns, walk up to him and strap the clapper into silence.

After leading a thousand steers all day, Blue believed in exercising the privileges of individuality. He considered himself always as apart from the masses. He would walk right into camp among the pots and pans and eat pieces of bread, meat, dried apples—anything the cook would give him or the boys could steal from the cook. He became a great pet. Often he was hobbled and left to graze with the saddle horses. Sometimes he was staked out at the end of a long rope. He preferred to bed down away from his inferiors—and he had no peer.

The trail work followed a well-established routine. When it was time to travel after the early morning's grazing, Blue nosed out toward one of the point men to have his bell clapper loosened. Then he would give a toss of the head and a switch of the tail, often throwing in a low chuckling bellow to emphasize his pleasure, and stride north. Some waddie with the voice of a bugle horn would sing-song out the old Texas call, "Ho, cattle, ho, ho, ho, ho," and the big steers would soon be strung into line. Blue must have known the North Star, he coursed so unswervingly. He was always "raring to go," and, unless checked, he was apt to walk too fast.

One evening up in the Indian Nation, just beyond Beaver Creek, Blue came near walking right into an unfenced squatter's field, but the point man veered him around it. The squatter came out of his dugout to sell some of the pumpkins he had grown. The J A foreman bought a few and then ordered his men to bed down "away over yonder."

"No, no," pled the squatter, "bed nigh here. I need cow chips for fuel." Blue was just one among many manufacturers of "prairie coal."

When this pioneer herd from the Palo Duro reached the Cimarron River, they found it on a rampage, but Blue shouldered straight into the waters, and after him strung the thousand J A's. After all were across, six of the cowboys swam back to the south bank. Four of them hitched their ropes to the tongue of the chuck wagon; two of them, one on either side hitched ropes to the stays on the bed. Thus pulling and guying the wagon, they helped the cook's team bring it across. It was time to camp, and Old Blue had worked around the herd and was at the bank to meet them when they emerged.

At the Arkansas River, just south of Dodge City, a cold wind was blowing and the north was black. December was at hand. "Every man saddle and tie up," the foreman ordered. "We'll have hell before daylight." About midnight a storm of sleet and snow hit the herd. Every hand went to it. The steers wanted to drift, but the boys held them like a solid wall.

At daylight there was a yell: "Untie Old Blue's clapper and take the river." The water was frozen out from the bank, but plunging into the icy current, the big steers "made the riffle." When they reached the north bank, they felt like running, and harder and faster they crowded Old Blue. Two thousand horns clacked and four thousand feet roared. The frozen ground fairly shook. But if Blue was gentle, he had the speed of a race horse.

Still at the lead of his herd, he headed straight for the twenty-foot gate that opened into the big shipping pens. With one bunch of cowboys to cut, another to count, and a third to run the cattle up the chute into the cars, they were loaded long before noon and on their way to Chicago—all but Old Blue.

He had proved himself far too valuable to be sold for steaks. He stayed with the *remuda* and ate hay while the cowboys warmed their stomachs at a bar and their feet on the floor of a dance hall. After a day and a night of celebration, they had spent themselves empty and were ready to leave. So at Wright & Beverley's store next morning the wagon was loaded with chuck and sacks of shelled corn. The grains in those sacks were colored red, white and blue, and on the road home Blue learned to eat corn; in fact, he loved it, and the colored grains seemed to add to his spirits.

The weather was freezing cold, and as the outfit headed southward, men and horses alike felt like making time. Blue was ready to travel also. He had the stride of seven-league boots and could walk up with any horse. Sometimes the thirty-miles-a-day clip made him trot, but he never tired or lagged. Down on Wolf Creek one night a hungry band of Kiowas rode into camp and, pointing at the big steer, demanded "wohaw" (beef), but Chief Lone Wolf and all his warriors could not have taken Blue away from those Palo Duro cowpunchers.

After this trip up the trail as bell ox, Blue's occupation for life was settled, but besides leading herds to Dodge City, he was put to various uses. When the chuck wagon was out in the spring and summer, Blue would generally follow it, taking choice food the boys would hand him. If an outlaw steer was roped in the cedar brakes and had to be led in, he was necked to Old Blue, the pair was turned loose, and, straight as a crow flies, the bell ox would bring him to camp.

If a wild herd of cattle was to be penned, Blue was put with them to show the way in. Wild cattle upon approaching a pen often circle and try to break away; but the wild ones could not break ahead of Blue, and his course was right into the gate.

Upon entering a pen, range cattle will rush for the opposite side, pushing, hooking, milling. Blue never got into such jams. As soon as he had brought the lead cattle inside the pen, he would step aside and impatiently wait beside the gate until the last animal entered; then he would bolt out.

Once John Taylor and another cowboy took him up on the Canadian River to bring back a pair of young buffaloes. They necked the two to him, both on one side, and, of course, they were contrariness personified. "Old Blue was the maddest steer a man ever saw." He shook his head and bellowed, worked around until he had one of the green buffaloes on each side of himself, and then struck a course. When he wanted to go to water with them, he went; when he wanted to stop and graze, he grazed. He knew every camping place on the route, and when he got to one would stop, whether the men with him wanted to stop or not, and he would not move until his free will motivated him. He tamed the buffaloes thoroughly and in good time brought them into the Palo Duro, where they were turned loose to help make the famous Goodnight herd.

For eight years Old Blue kept at his occupation of leading herds. Some years he went up to Dodge City twice. The horns and legs of the steers he led were growing shorter and shorter, and often the cowboys had to shoe the fine, big short-horns that the J A's were coming to raise, but never once did Blue limp. His hoofs were as hard and bright as polished steel. All told, ten thousand head or more of the J A cattle followed Blue and his bell into the shipping pens of the "Cowboy Capital."

The older he grew, the more philosophical he became. It sometimes made a Spanish cow horse almost laugh, they say, to see him step aside in a night stampede and go to bawling. No slipping of horns, knocking down of hips and running until his tongue lolled out and his rump was chafed green from entrail-emptying for him. "To step aside is human," and Blue was mighty human when a stampede started. If the boys could get the stampeders to milling, Old Blue's bawl had a powerful effect in quieting them. At the head of a herd he never "buggered" when a jack rabbit suddenly jumped up from under a sagebush at his nose, or something like that happened, and thus day and night he was a steadying influence.

When he was twenty years old, he died. For a long time his horns remained in the office of J A headquarters, over the door leading into the vault. They may be seen today in the fine little museum maintained by the Panhandle-Plains Historical Society and the West Texas State Teachers College at Canyon. Like his trail-breaking owner, Old Blue of the Texas Longhorns belongs to history.

Bill Blocker—brother to Ab and John R.—was nineteen years old when he quit school against parental will, borrowed some money on his own hook, and in partnership with two older men put up a trail herd. He went along as a hand with the understanding that he was to have no say-so in the directing of affairs. This was in 1870, and Abilene, Kansas, was the destination.

On the Pedernales River they struck a bunch of wild cattle containing an A P B (Blocker) steer that young Bill immediately decided he had to take along. He was a big bay with black spots, lithe, in fine condition. But it was not his value as a mere bovine that drew young Blocker. "He looked so proud and free," Blocker used to tell long afterwards, "that he reminded me of the way I felt. I wanted him for company." Accordingly he roped the steer, ran the Backwards Seven road brand on him, and turned him loose in the herd.

Before the day was over the big bay was in the lead. Blocker's place was on the northeast corner, the right point. Somehow the bay seemed also to sense something in the free-riding young point man that was kin to his nature. Within ten days this steer, which ran with the wildest bunch in the roughs of his home range, which would still have stampeded at the drop of a hat, and which carried himself so "proud and free," was walking up with Blocker's horse, never quite even with him, but with his noble head so near that the rider could put out his left hand and grasp the right horn. Blocker liked to ride along resting his hand on the powerful horn, and the steer seemed to like to have the hand there. He walked in rhythm with the horse. Blocker called him "Pardner."

No matter where he was, after the cattle had watered or had grazed a while, when the yell arose to hit the trail and string out, Pardner would in a long walk—sometimes trot—pass or go around everything until he was at the point. Plainly he enjoyed the feeling of power and self-assurance that leadership gives and felt himself a kind of peer to the high-headed leader on horseback.

When the outfit got near Red River, they learned that it was on a rampage. Herds were being held out from it, waiting for the water to go down. Several attempts to swim over had failed. Most of the trail bosses considered it useless to try further. Two or three rainy days went by and still the expanse of waters raged. Holding an idle herd is tedious business. Bill Blocker said to his partners, "If you men will let me take charge of this herd, I'll cross." There were responses of half-admiration, half-irony. The herd was turned over to the kid.

His first order was to drive it back, south of the river, three or four miles. Then he swung it around and soon it was strung out in customary formation, headed towards faraway Abilene. Young Blocker rode at his customary place on the north-east corner. The proud and free bay steer stepped up with him in the customary manner, and hand rested on horn.

At the brink of the water neither hesitated. Centaur and steer plunged in together and were soon swimming, the herd coming on like mules strung out behind the bell mare. Other herds had prepared to follow, should the first take the water all right, and now they came on, each on the tail of the other.

That was a rainy year. At the Salt Fork of the Arkansas, the herd got into a mill, out in the middle of deep water. While Blocker was trying to break the mill and save the cattle from drowning each other, a plunging steer pawed his exhausted horse under. Weighed down with boots and leggins, he was making a desperate but losing struggle when the bay leader cut out of the mill and came by him, headed for the north bank. Blocker grabbed his tail and was towed out, the herd following.

After this the proud and free pair seemed to keep step with each other more constantly than before. However, had the man tried to approach the steer afoot, a chasm between them would have opened wider than the Mississippi. It was a great pity to deliver the bay leader along with the herd at Abilene. But what else could be done?

There was a last grasp of hand on horn, and then, "*Adios*, Pardner, I hope you break loose and come back to Texas." But Pardner never got back.

Jack Potter usually named his lead steers after noted characters. "Buckshot Roberts" exhibited the stubborn insolence of that victim of Billy the Kid's gang whose name he took. During a blizzard out in New Mexico, "Lew Wallace" tried one night to get inside Potter's dugout and the next morning demanded a share of the corn meant only for favored horses. A sourdough biscuit filled with black pepper did not break him of hanging around camp. Then one hot afternoon, after having been without water for seventy-six hours, Lew Wallace led the herd down to the Blue Holes of the Pajarito. "Before I realized the long drouth was over," Jack Potter says, "we were in water up to my horse's shoulder. I crawled off and stooped over and tried to drink. I could not swallow. When Lew Wallace had filled up, he looked around at me, and he must have suspicioned something was wrong. He stood there and stuck his tongue out to tell me what to do. So, with my mouth full of tongue, I started throwing water on it with my hand. Finally I got so I could drink. When Lew Wallace thought I had enough, he pushed me with his horn. We went up the bank and cooled off, and after a while we went down and finished our drink."

But I guess Jack Potter's gratitude is strongest towards a rangy steer of the Pecos named after John Chisum. "Ten herds bound for Clayton, New Mexico, were caught by the blizzard of '89," old Jack recalls, "and mine was the only one that got through. The credit goes to John Chisum. We had just finished the fall roundups and nobody was prepared for or expecting such cold weather so early. It proved to be the worst blizzard in the history of that country. Thousands and thousands of sheep and cattle were frozen to death. Several men died. Clayton was without train service for thirteen days and during that time ran about out of food and coal and all out of whiskey.

"When the blizzard struck us, we were traveling north. The cattle, which had been thrown off the trail, began to drift south. After we'd fought them a while, John Chisum gave up resisting, turned his head into the blizzard, held it down between his legs, and, with the other cattle following, kept the direction.

"I knew that if we could get over into the Tremperos Canyon we'd find shelter for the cattle in some protected pens and for ourselves in an old ranch house. Never in my life have I seen such snowflakes as we made into. They were as big as your finger and were driven by a gale blowing sixty miles an hour. We were going up El Muerto Creek, and I kept wondering what traveling would be like when we left it and got out on the naked divide.

"By the time we reached the place to top out, the prairie was covered with snow. The red sand-hill grass was a foot high here. I was piloting the herd, following a newly beat-out road. It wasn't graded or anything like that—just some twisting wagon ruts. The only way I could distinguish it was by noting that the snow was smooth in the ruts and uneven in the grass. I had to pull my hat down over my eyes to protect them from the cutting storm. I could not see ten yards ahead, but I kept the road. I had never been over it, and knew the country only in a general way.

"Then we came to a prong. I figgered one branch led off into the breaks of the Pierdenal—towards shelter. I took it. But old John Chisum, close to my horse's tail, refused to follow. He ducked into the one that seemed to keep on going over the bleak prairie. I was puzzled and commenced to talk to that steer.

" 'You don't seem to realize I am piloting this herd,' I said to him. 'I know a horse has more sense than a man. If you

· 252 ·

give a horse with any sense at all his reins on a dark night or in a snowstorm, he will take you to camp; but you've never been where you are headed, so far as I know. What right has an old, cold-blooded, scalawag steer to be making decisions for a trail boss? If we don't find shelter before night, God knows what will become of all of us. Nevertheless, I'm just guessing too, and now I'm going to let you have your way.'

"John Chisum was right. In twenty minutes we reached a ridge with canyons covered with big pines running off on each side. The trail led down one of these into the Tremperos. As we entered it, four riders from the ranch came out to help us pen and to welcome us to their shelter.

"The storm lulled for a few days, and we floundered on, but if Clayton had been a mile farther off I don't believe my horse would ever have got me there or that John Chisum would ever have led the cattle into the shipping pens. We were holed up for two weeks. All the other herds trying to get to Clayton were drifting and dying. Several men that persisted in hanging with their cattle perished. There seemed to be only one John Chisum on the trails that time—but I do take a little credit to myself for having had sense enough to pay attention to what a good lead steer says."

In the parlance of the range, a lead steer or a lead ox often means a neckin', or neck, animal—one to which wild cattle roped in rough or brushy country are necked and led in. Every ranch of any size in the brush country once had one or more lead oxen. On an occasional ranch where the only cattle, including wild ones, now to be found are of improved blood, one may still find an old Mexican ox for leading in the outlaws. Spanish-blooded steers make the best neck oxen; one well trained has always sold at a premium, though generally he is not for sale.

A good many years ago a cowman who had the "Mustang Pasture" leased, down in the brush country, gave it up. After his brush poppers had worked for weeks driving out what cattle could be handled in a civilized way and roping scores of others, he still had a "considerable sprinkling of snakes" left. He had no idea how many. He contracted with Onie Sheeran to clean the pasture up. Onie took in as partner another noted brush hand named Atlee Weston. His main help, however, was a five-year-old brindle stag named Pavo. The partners were to get five dollars a head for every animal they could deliver alive, and were to turn in the hides of whatever they ran to death. In the course of time they roped one hundred and twenty-five outlaws, tying each one in the brush where it was roped. Pavo by himself led every one of the "snakes" to a pen where a windmill furnished water and the two ropers pitched in prickly pear for the cattle to eat until they were driven away. Without Pavo or some other good lead animal, the men would have been almost as handicapped as without horses to ride.

In Frio County along in the eighties the Martins had two lead oxen named Geronimo and Camino. Geronimo had been a work ox, and scars on both his sides showed how Mexicans had prodded him with burning chunks of wood. An outlaw would be roped somewhere in the brush and tied to a tree—no matter how far from the strongly built trap pasture in which the wild cattle, after being captured, were kept. A *vaquero* would toss his rope over the horns of Camino or Geronimo and strike out for the tied animal, the ox leading like a horse. After he was necked to the outlaw, he would make straight for the trap, not following the trail he had made in coming, but taking an airline, in so far as brush and gullies would permit. He might have to worry with the outlaw considerably, hooking him, going around and around him until the unwilling animal set off in the right direction. Then he would butt ahead with full force, the pair tearing a hole through the brush, running over pear and bushes, knocking down or bending over good-sized mesquites. Usually by next morning the pair would be at the trap gate, the ox impatient to be unnecked and have a treat of burned prickly pear or of cottonseed. If they failed to show up, it was because the outlaw had sulled and died. Then a man must go to where the pair had been turned loose, take their trail, and follow it until they were found, untie the necking rope, and free the lead ox.

Ab Blocker told me that while he was working in the Blanco breaks in 1876–1877, catching old outlaw steers, he had a brown lead ox that did not have to be fed. His inducement for coming in was to be released from his bothersome burden. The Blockers were camping sometimes at one pen and sometimes at another, holding their bunch of wild cattle in a pen at night, herding them by day. This old brown ox would strike the trail of the cattle being kept under herd and follow them to camp, no matter if it had been moved several miles from where he had spent the preceding night.

Old Ben always went to bawling when he got to headquarters with his outlaw. It might be midnight in freezing weather. No matter, a man would go out and free him. If nobody came promptly, he'd bawl louder. Certainly the reward of freedom was his due.

# THE FIGHT
# AT THE O. K. CORRAL

*by* STUART N. LAKE

Stuart Nathaniel Lake was born in Rome, New York, in 1889. By 1909 he'd become a reporter in the Far East, making Manila, Japan, the China Coast, and the Straits Settlements. Back in New York, he went to work on the old New York *Herald* as reporter, rewrite and copy desk man, and assistant city editor. He was Teddy Roosevelt's press agent in the "Preparedness Campaign" (1916–1917), then went with the Army to France.

He came home from France on a stretcher. While in the hospital he wrote ex-soldier stuff, and when he got out, did some silent pictures, among them *Buck Privates*. By now he had also begun to write for the *Saturday Evening Post*. More and more his subjects were drawn from early American history.

At this point his *Wyatt Earp* (from which the following selection is taken) appeared both in the *Post* and between book covers. Four more moving pictures (not counting one collaborative "assist") were completed: *Frontier Marshal, Wells-Fargo, The Westerner, The Man from Tascosa.*

In reading "The Fight at the O. K. Corral," the reader needs to know one or two collateral facts. Wyatt Earp was a United States marshal who had come to Tombstone for the purpose of cooling the acquisitive instincts of a band of rustlers known as "the cowboys." In league with the cowboys and the various elements of local vice was the sheriff. Mr. Lake's story takes up from there.

---

WHISKEY HAS MADE MORE FIGHT-TALK THAN FIGHTS, AND more brag has been slept off with its liquor than ever was made good in battle. Frontier benders pretty generally followed the alcoholic rule, but the red-eye that set Ike Clanton's tongue wagging in the Allen Street saloons during the evening of October 25, 1881, was to precipitate the most celebrated encounter between outlaw and peace officer in the history of untamed Arizona. It was also to furnish Ike with dubious immortality through a gun-fight over which the West has wrangled for half a century, and can still argue as heatedly as while the roar of six-shooters echoed in the streets of Tombstone.

Potency under Ike's belt found vent in loose-mouthed boasts that he would kill Wyatt Earp and Doc Holliday before the setting of the next day's sun. When Farmer Daly and Ed Byrnes suggested that the rustler had laid out quite a job, Ike sneered:

"The Earps are not so much. You'll see, tomorrow. We're in town for a showdown."

About midnight Ike went to the Occidental Saloon where his friends were playing poker. Doc Holliday entered and walked directly to Clanton.

"Ike," Doc said, "I hear you're going to kill me. Get out your gun and commence."

"I haven't any gun," Clanton replied.

"I don't believe you," Doc retorted. "I'll take your word for it this time, but if you intend to open your lying mouth about me again, go heeled."

Morgan Earp, who passed the saloon as Holliday was berating Clanton in picturesque profanity, pulled Doc to the sidewalk. Clanton followed with Tom McLowery, insisting that he was not armed, but promising he soon would be and would shoot Doc on sight. Wyatt and Virgil Earp came along and took Doc to his room, where Wyatt ordered the dentist to keep away from Clanton.

"A gun-fight now, with you in it," Wyatt warned Holliday, "would ruin my chance to round up this bunch."

"All right," Doc promised regretfully, "I'll keep away from him."

Half an hour later, Ike found Wyatt at the Eagle lunch-counter.

"You tell Doc Holliday no man can talk about me the way he did and live," Ike began. "I'm wearing a gun now and you can tell Holliday I aim to get him."

"Doc's gone to bed," Wyatt replied. "You're half-drunk. You'll feel better when you've had some sleep."

"I'm stone-cold sober," Ike retorted. "I'm telling you to tell Holliday I'll gun him the first time I seen him."

"Don't you tangle with Doc Holliday," Wyatt advised. "He'll kill you before you've started."

"You've been making a lot of talk about me, too," Ike said.

"You've done the talking," Wyatt corrected.

"Well, it's got to stop," Ike declared. "You had the best of me tonight, but I'll have my friends tomorrow. You be ready for a showdown."

"Go sleep it off, Ike," Wyatt suggested. "You talk too much for a fighting man."

Virgil Earp came in the door, as Ike started out. Ike paused and shouted over his shoulder:

"I said tomorrow. You're to blame for this, Wyatt Earp. What I said for Doc Holliday goes for you and your so-and-so brothers."

Wyatt and Morgan Earp went home about four o'clock. Virgil went to the Occidental to keep an eye on Behan, Clanton, McLowery, and the other cowboys until their game broke up; he reached home after daylight.

The Earps were awakened in the morning of October 26 by word that Ike Clanton was at Fifth and Allen Street, armed with six-guns and a Winchester, bragging that his friends were on the way to Tombstone to help him clean out the Earps. A second message warned that Billy Clanton, Frank McLowery, and Billy Claiborne had just ridden in to join Ike and Tom McLowery and that five outlaws were at Fourth and Allen Streets. Ike and Frank had been in several saloons asking if the Earps or Holliday had been around that morning. In Vogan's they had boasted they would shoot the first Earp who showed his face in the street.

"Where's Holliday?" Wyatt asked.

"He hasn't been around."

"Let him sleep," Wyatt ordered.

Ike Clanton had not given the Earps much concern, but Billy Clanton, Claiborne, and the two McLowerys, whatever else they might be, were game men, crack shots and killers. The McLowerys were possibly the two fastest men with six-guns in all the outlaw gang. Frank McLowery was admittedly better on the draw-and-shoot than Curly Bill or John Ringo, and held by some to surpass Buckskin Frank Leslie.

Warren Earp was in California with his parents. Jim Earp was physically unable to take a hand. But, outnumbered as they were, none of the three brothers, as he buckled on his guns, had any idea other than that they would go directly to Fourth and Allen Streets.

"You and Morg go up Fremont Street," Wyatt instructed Virgil. "I'll take Allen Street."

He was giving his brothers the better chance of avoiding the outlaws. They knew it, but obeyed, as was their habit.

"If you see Ike Clanton, arrest him," Wyatt said. "But don't shoot unless Ike does. Take his guns away in front of the whole town, if you can, and show him up."

At Fourth Street, Virgil and Morgan turned south and reached the mid-block alley as Ike Clanton eased out of the narrow passage, rifle in hand, eye on the Allen Street corner.

"Looking for me?" Virgil asked in Ike's ear.

Clanton swung around, lifting the rifle. Virgil seized the Winchester with his left hand, jerked a Colt's with his right, and bent the six-gun over Ike's head. Virgil and Morgan lugged their prisoner through the street to Judge Wallace's courtroom, where Morgan guarded him while Virgil went to find the judge. Several persons who had seen Ike arrested went into the courtroom, among them R. J. Coleman, a mining man who figured in later happenings, and Deputy Sheriff Dave Campbell. Ike was raving with fury.

"I'll get you for this, Wyatt Earp!" he yelled as Wyatt came through the door.

"Clanton," Wyatt answered, "I've had about enough from you and your gang. You've been trying for weeks to get up your nerve to assassinate my brothers and me. The whole town's heard you threaten to kill us. Your fight's against me, not my brothers. You leave them out of this. I'd be justified in shooting you on sight, and if you keep on asking for a fight, I'll give it to you."

"Fight's my racket," Ike blustered. "If I had my guns, I'd fight all you Earps, here and now."

Morgan Earp offered one of Ike's sequestered six-guns, butt foremost, to the owner.

"If you want to fight right bad, Ike," Morgan suggested, "take this. I'll use my fists."

"Quit that, Morg," Wyatt snapped. Deputy Sheriff Campbell pushed Ike into a chair.

"All I want with you," Ike shouted, again identifying Wyatt with a few choice epithets, "is four feet of ground and a gun. You wait until I get out of here."

Wyatt walked from the courtroom. At the door he literally bumped into Tom McLowery, hurrying to Ike's assistance.

"You looking for trouble?" McLowery snarled as he recovered his balance.

"I didn't see you coming," Wyatt answered.

"You're a liar!" McLowery retorted.

Bystanders said Wyatt paled an ominous yellow under his tan.

McLowery's gun was at his hip. Faster than the outlaw could think, Wyatt slapped him full in the face. Tom made no move for his pistol.

"You've got a gun on," Wyatt challenged. "Go after it."

McLowery's right hand dropped downward. Wyatt Earp's Buntline Special flashed and the marshal buffaloed Tom McLowery his full length in the gutter. Wyatt turned his back and walked toward Allen Street.

Judge Wallace fined Ike Clanton twenty-five dollars for breach of the peace. As Ike realized he was to get off thus lightly, more of his bravado returned. The courtroom was filled and before this audience the outlaw took a fling at Virgil Earp.

"If I'd been a split-second faster with my rifle," he boasted, "the coroner'd be working on you now."

"I'm taking your rifle and six-guns to the Grand Hotel," Virgil replied. "Don't pick them up until you start for home."

"You won't be here to see me leave town," Ike retorted.

Wyatt Earp had posted himself outside of Hafford's. Frank and Tom McLowery, Billy Clanton and Billy Claiborne passed him, all wearing six-guns, and went into Spangenberg's gun-shop. Virgil Earp came along, carrying Ike Clanton's weapons to the Grand Hotel, and joined Wyatt at a point across Fourth Street from the gunsmith's. They and several Vigilantes who stood with them could see plainly all that went on in the gun-store.

Ike Clanton now hurried into Spangenberg's. He purchased a six-shooter and the five rustlers loaded their cartridge-belts to capacity. Virgil Earp went on to the hotel. Frank McLowery's horse moved onto the walk in front of the gun-store. Wyatt strode across the road and seized the animal's bit. The two McLowerys and Billy Clanton came running from the store.

"Let go of my horse!" Frank shouted.

"Get him off the walk," Wyatt rejoined.

"Take your hands off my horse!" McLowery insisted.

"When he's where he belongs," Wyatt replied, backed the horse into the road and snubbed him close to the hitching-rail.

The three rustlers had their hands on their gun-butts, spectators later testified.

"That's the last horse of mine you'll ever lay hands on!" Frank McLowery assured Wyatt with a string of oaths.

Wyatt turned on his heel and recrossed the street.

The cowboys left Spangenberg's in a group, going to the Dexter Corral on the south side of Allen Street, between Third and Fourth Streets, owned by Johnny Behan and John Dunbar. Wyatt joined Virgil and Morgan at Hafford's corner, where the brothers stood for possibly half an hour while the rustlers made several trips on foot between the corral and near-by saloons, during which most of Tombstone was apprised of their intention to wipe out the Earps.

Captain Murray and Captain Fronck, with half a dozen Vigilantes, were conferring with Wyatt when R. J. Coleman, heretofore mentioned, reported that he had followed the rustlers to the Dexter Corral and on the way back had met Johnny Behan. Coleman said he had told Behan he should disarm the outlaws, as they were threatening to kill the marshal and his brothers, and that Behan had gone on into the corral. As the Earps and the Vigilantes went into Hafford's to get away from the crowd that gathered, Coleman again went down Allen Street to watch the cowboys.

While Virgil Earp was talking with the Vigilantes, Sheriff Behan entered Hafford's and cut into the conversation.

"Ike Clanton and his crowd are down in my corral making a gun-talk against you fellows," Behan said. "They're laying to kill you. What are you going to do about it?"

"I've been hoping that bunch would leave town without doing anything more than talk," Virgil answered. "I guess they've got to have their lesson. I'm going to throw 'em into the calaboose to cool off. I'll put somebody on to see that they don't walk out, too."

"You try that and they'll kill you," Behan warned Virgil.

"I'll take that chance," Virgil replied. "You're sheriff of Cochise County, Behan, and I'm calling on you to go with me while I arrest them."

Behan laughed. "That's your job, not mine," he said, and left the saloon.

Virgil Earp went into the Wells-Fargo office and returned with a sawed-off shotgun, as Coleman came back to Hafford's with word that the rustlers had transferred headquarters from the Dexter to the O. K. Corral and recruited a sixth to their war-party in the person of Wes Fuller, hanger-on and spy for the Curly Bill crowd. Ike Clanton, Tom McLowery, Billy Claiborne, and Fuller had crossed Allen Street to the O. K. Corral without horses, Billy Clanton had ridden his horse and Frank McLowery had led his. All were wearing six-guns, Coleman said, while Billy Clanton and Frank McLowery had rifles slung from their saddles. They had gone past the stalls near the Allen Street entrance to the corral and into the rear lot which opened on Fremont Street. They had posted Wes Fuller on lookout in the alley and Tom McLowery had gone out into Fremont Street, returning within a few minutes.

The reason for Tom's brief absence was established later by Chris Billicke and Dr. B. W. Gardiner, who had been standing on the courthouse steps. Tom walked from the corral to Everhardy's butcher-shop, better known as Bauer's. This business had been placed in Everhardy's name after Bauer was indicted as purchaser of cattle which the Curly Bill crowd rustled, but Bauer continued to work at his block. Chris Billicke and Dr. Gardiner saw Tom McLowery talk with Bauer and stuff a roll of bills into his trousers pocket as he left the shop, revealing as he did so the butt of a six-gun at his belt, an item to be noted.

After Tom's return, Coleman started to walk through the corral yard and was stopped by the cowboys, who asked if he knew the Earps. When he replied that he did, Frank McLowery and Ike Clanton gave him two messages, one for the Earps as a whole, the other for Wyatt, in particular.

"Let's have 'em," Wyatt said.

"They told me to tell the Earps that they were waiting in the O. K. Corral, and that if you didn't come down to fight it out, they'd pick you off in the street when you tried to go home."

The strategy which had moved the outlaws from the Dexter to the O. K. Corral now was apparent.

Allen and Fremont Streets ran parallel with the numbered streets crossing them at right angles, and with an alley running east and west through each block. The O. K. Corral had its covered stalls on the north side of Allen Street, and an open yard across the alley on the south side of Fremont. On Fremont Street an adobe assay office stood at the west line of the corral yard, while to the east was C. S. Fly's photograph gallery.

On the north side of Fremont Street, facing the yard, was the original Cochise County Courthouse, a rambling two-story adobe with courtroom on the ground floor, and on the upper the offices of county officials. These offices opened onto an outside gallery, the west end of which was about opposite the west line of Fly's studio. Then came the *Epitaph* office, and an adobe store occupied by Mrs. Addie Bourland, a milliner.

To return to the O. K. Corral, the alley which ran between the stalls and yard gave onto Fourth Street, and in this passageway Wes Fuller was stationed to keep an eye on the Allen Street corner.

The Earps, in going to and from their homes at First and Fremont Streets, customarily followed Fremont Street past the O. K. Corral yard. The only other direct route available took them by the Allen Street entrance. The Clantons and McLowerys could command with their guns, on a moment's notice, either path; thus outlaw strategy forced the Earps to call the turn or quit the play.

"What's the special message for me?" Wyatt Earp asked Coleman.

"They said to tell you that if you'd leave town they wouldn't harm your brothers," Coleman answered, "but that if you stayed, you'd have to come down and make your fight or they'd bring it to you."

Wyatt looked at Virgil and Morgan. Without a word the three Earps started for the door. Captain Murray stopped them.

"Let us take this off your hands, boys," he offered. "Fronck and I have thirty-five Vigilantes waiting, ready for business. We'll surround the corral, make that bunch surrender, and have them outlawed from Tombstone."

"Much obliged," Wyatt answered for his clan, "but this is our job.

"Come on," he said to Virgil and Morgan.

As the Earps swung out of Hafford's door and started, three abreast, along Fourth Street, Doc Holliday came up on the run.

"Where are you going, Wyatt?" Doc demanded.

"Down the street to make a fight."

"About time," Holliday observed. "I'll go along."

"This is our fight," Wyatt said. "There's no call for you to mix in."

"That's a hell of a thing for you to say to me," Doc retorted. "I heard about this while I was eating breakfast, but I didn't figure you'd go without me."

"I know, Doc," Wyatt said, "but this'll be a tough one."

"Tough ones are the kind I like," the gun-fighting dentist answered.

"All right," Wyatt agreed, and Doc Holliday fell into step with the only person on earth for whom he had either respect or regard.

Holliday was wearing a long overcoat and carrying a cane, as he often did when his physical afflictions bore heavily.

"Here, Doc," Virgil Earp suggested, "let me take your cane and stick this shotgun under your coat where it won't attract so much attention."

Holliday handed over the stick and drew his right arm from the overcoat sleeve, so that the garment hung cape-like over that shoulder. Beneath it he held the short Wells-Fargo weapon. As the four men passed the Fourth Street alley, Wes Fuller ran back into the corral where the Clantons and McLowerys were waiting.

"You ought to have cut him down," Doc Holliday observed.

Beyond this laconic suggestion, not one of the quartet of peace officers spoke as they walked rapidly toward Fremont Street.

Johnny Behan and Frank McLowery had been standing together at the corner of Fourth and Fremont Streets as the Earps left Hafford's. The sheriff and the rustler hurried to the corral yard; Behan talked for a moment with the five cowboys, then hastened back toward the corner, some fifty yards away. He had covered less than half the distance when the marshal's posse came into view.

Tombstone's Fremont Street of 1881 was a sixty-foot thoroughfare with the wide roadbed of the hard-packed, rusty desert sand bordered by footpaths at no marked elevation from the road level. The walks, where buildings adjoined, ran beneath the wooden awnings with their lines of hitching-rails. At the O. K. Corral yard, there was necessarily a gap in the awning roofs and rails, which gave unhindered access for the width of the lot. Johnny Behan apparently expected the marshal's force to follow the sidewalk to the corral and hurried along it to meet them.

Along Fourth Street the Earp party had been two abreast, Wyatt and Virgil in the lead, with Virgil on the outside, Morgan behind him, and Doc Holliday back of Wyatt. Each sensed instinctively what could happen if they rounded the corner of Fly's Photograph Gallery abruptly in close order, and at the street intersection they deployed catercorner to walk four abreast, in the middle of the road.

Half a dozen persons who saw the four men on their journey down Fremont Street have described them. The recollections agree strikingly in detail. No more grimly portentous spectacle had been witnessed in Tombstone.

The three stalwart, six-foot Earps—each with the square jaw of his clan set hard beneath his flowing, tawny mustache and his keen blue eyes alert under the wide brim of a high-peaked, black Stetson—bore out their striking resemblance, even in their attire: dark trousers drawn outside the legs of black, high-heeled boots, long-skirted, square-cut, black coats then in frontier fashion, and white, soft-collared shirts with black string-ties to accentuate the purpose in their lean, bronzed faces. Doc Holliday was some two inches shorter than his three companions, but his stature was heightened by cadaverousness, the flapping black overcoat and the black sombrero above his hollow cheeks. Holliday's blond mustache was as long and as sweeping as any, but below it those who saw him have sworn Doc had his lips pursed, whistling softly. As the distance to the O. K. Corral lessened, the four men spread their ranks as they walked. In front of Bauer's butcher-shop, Johnny Behan ran out with upraised hand. The line halted.

"It's all right, boys. It's all right," the sheriff sputtered. "I've disarmed them."

"Did you arrest them?" Virgil Earp asked.

"No," Behan said, "but I will."

"All right," Virgil said. "Come on."

The politician's nerve deserted him.

"Don't go any farther," he cried. "I order you not to. I'm sheriff of this county. I'll arrest them."

"You told me that was my job," Virgil retorted.

The three Earps and Holliday moved on in the road. The sheriff ran along on the walk.

"Don't go down there! Don't go down there!" he cried. "You'll all be killed!"

The four men in the road cleared the line of Fly's studio. Virgil, Wyatt, and Morgan turned sharply left into the corral, Virgil a few feet in the lead, Wyatt and Morgan following in the order named. The wise Doctor Holliday halted with an uninterrupted sweep of Fremont Street. The door of Fly's gallery banged. Johnny Behan had ducked into the building, where a window gave him view of the corral yard and farther along a side-door opened. Across the lot the five rustlers stood, backs to the assay office wall.

The outlaws were vigorous, sinewy fellows—Ike Clanton, burlier than the rest, wearing, as did each McLowery, a thin mustache in Mexican-dandy style—all with a similarity of attire as marked as, but contrasting sharply with, that of the Earps. Huge sand-hued sombreros, gaudy silk neckerchiefs, fancy woolen shirts, tight-fitting doeskin trousers tucked into forty-dollar halfboots—a get-up so generally affected by Curly Bill followers that it was recognized as their uniform—set off the lean, sunbaked hardness of these desert renegades. Ike Clanton and Tom McLowery wore short, rough coats, the other three, fancy sleeveless vests in the best cow-country fashion.

Billy Claiborne was farthest of his group from the walk, perhaps thirty feet from the street line. Next, on his left, was Ike Clanton, then Billy Clanton, Frank, and Tom McLowery. They had avoided bunching and Tom McLowery was about ten feet from the street. Posted to blank possible fire from the assay office corner were two cow-ponies, one Frank McLowery's, the other Billy Clanton's, each carrying a Winchester rifle in a saddleboot.

One glance at the cowboys revealed that, despite Johnny Behan's declaration, all were armed. Tom McLowery had a six-gun stuck in the waistband of his trousers. Frank McLowery, Billy and Ike Clanton, each had similar weapons slung from their belts. Claiborne had a Colt's at either hip.

The Earps moved in. From the road, Doc Holliday referred to Johnny Behan in one unprintable phrase. Virgil Earp was well into the corral, Wyatt about opposite Billy Clanton and Frank McLowery, Morg facing Tom. Not a gun had been drawn. Wyatt Earp was determined there'd be no gunplay that the outlaws did not begin.

"You men are under arrest. Throw up your hands." Virgil Earp commanded.

Frank McLowery dropped his hand to his six-gun and snarled defiance in short, ugly words. Tom McLowery, Billy Clanton, and Billy Claiborne followed concerted suit.

"Hold on!" Virgil Earp shouted, instinctively throwing up his right hand, which carried Doc Holliday's cane, in a gesture of restraint. "We don't want that."

For any accurate conception of what followed, one thing must be kept in mind: action which requires minutes to describe was begun, carried through, and concluded faster than human thought may pick up the threads. Two witnesses swore that its whole course was run in fifteen seconds, others fixed the time at twenty seconds, Wyatt Earp testified that it was finished thirty seconds after Frank McLowery went for his gun. Also, careful note of that action furnishes, more than any other episode of his life, the key to the eminence of Wyatt Earp.

Frank McLowery and Billy Clanton jerked and fired their six-guns simultaneously. Both turned loose on Wyatt Earp, the shots with which they opened the famous battle of the O. K. Corral echoing from the adobe walls as one.

Fast as the two rustlers were at getting into action from a start with guns half-drawn, Wyatt Earp was deadlier. Frank

McLowery's bullet tore through the skirt of Wyatt's coat on the right, Billy Clanton's ripped the marshal's sleeve, but before either could fire again, Wyatt's Buntline Special roared; the slug struck Frank McLowery squarely in the abdomen, just above his belt buckle. McLowery screamed, clapped his left hand to the wound, bent over and staggered forward. Wyatt knew Frank as the most dangerous of the five outlaws and had set out deliberately to dispose of him.

In this fraction of a second, Tom McLowery jumped behind Frank's horse, drawing his gun and shooting under the animal's neck at Morgan Earp. The bullet cut Morgan's coat. Billy Clanton shot a second and a third time at Wyatt, missing with both as Morgan turned loose on him, aiming for Billy's stomach, but hitting the cowboy's gun hand.

Sensing that Tom McLowery was now the most dangerous adversary, Wyatt ignored Billy Clanton's fire as Tom again shot underneath the pony's neck and hit Morg.

Tom McLowery must be forced into the open. Wyatt shot at the pony behind which the cowboy crouched, aiming for the withers. The pony jumped and stampeded for the street, the excitement taking Billy Clanton's horse with him. As his brother's horse started, Tom McLowery grabbed for the rifle in the saddle-boot, but missed it.

At the upper end of the lot, Virgil Earp had been delayed in going for his gun by the position of his hand and his grasp of Doc Holliday's cane. Before Virgil could jerk his Colt's free, Billy Claiborne fired at him twice and missed. Claiborne started across the corral toward the side-door of Fly's gallery which opened for him, firing point-blank at Virgil as he passed him and missing again. When Ike Clanton saw Johnny Behan open the door for Claiborne, his braggart heart funked. Ike had not drawn his gun; it swung at his hip as in his panic he headed straight for Wyatt Earp.

Tom McLowery's second slug had hit Morgan Earp in the left shoulder, glanced on a bone, ripped across the base of his neck, and torn a gaping hole in the flesh of his right shoulder.

"I've got it!" Morg gasped, as he reeled under the shock.

"Get behind me and keep quiet," Wyatt said.

As Morgan was hit, Virgil Earp fired his first shot in the fight, breaking Billy Clanton's gun-arm as it covered the cowboy's abdomen. Billy worked the 'border shift,' throwing his gun from right to left hand.

Far from obeying Wyatt's command, Morgan, who saw Billy Clanton's maneuver, shot Billy in the chest as Virgil put a slug into Clanton's body, just underneath the twelfth rib.

Before Wyatt could throw down on Tom McLowery, as the pony plunged away, Ike Clanton had covered the few feet across the corral and seized Wyatt's left arm.

"Don't kill me, Wyatt! Don't kill me!" the pot-valiant Clanton pleaded. "I'm not shooting!"

"This fight's commenced. Get to fighting or get out," Wyatt answered, throwing Ike off. The gallery door was held open and Ike fled after Claiborne.

Tom McLowery was firing his third shot, this at Wyatt as Ike Clanton hung to the marshal's arm, when Doc Holliday turned loose both barrels of his shotgun simultaneously from the road. Tom's shot went wild and McLowery started on a run around the corner of the assay office toward Third Street. Disgusted with a weapon that could miss as such a range, Holliday hurled the sawed-off shotgun after Tom with an oath and jerked his nickel-plated Colt's. Ten feet around the corner, Tom McLowery fell dead with the double charge of buckshot in his belly and a slug from Wyatt Earp's six-gun under his ribs which had hit him as he ran.

Frank McLowery was nearing the road, left hand clutching his abdomen, the right working his gun as he staggered on. Billy Clanton was still on his feet and following. Frank shot at Wyatt. The slug struck short. So did another he sent at Morg.

Wyatt heard the crash of glass from the side-window of Fly's gallery, where Claiborne and Sheriff Behan stood. Two shots from the window followed.

"Look out, boys!" Wyatt called. "You're getting it in the back!"

Morgan Earp wheeled to face this new danger, stumbled and fell, but Doc Holliday sent two bullets through the window. Shooting from the gallery stopped. At this juncture Ike Clanton darted from a rear door across the alley and into the stalls of the O. K. Corral, flinging his fully loaded six-gun into a corner of the yard as he ran. Doc sent two shots after Ike, but was a split-second late. Doc wheeled to face Frank McLowery, who had reached the street, drawn himself upright and, less than ten feet away, was steeling himself for steady aim at Holliday.

"I've got you, you so-and-so such-and-such," McLowery snarled.

"Think so?" Doc found wit to inquire.

When Morgan fell, he rolled to bring his gun-arm free and brought up at full length on his side facing McLowery and Holliday.

"Look out, Doc!" Morg called, shooting as he lay.

McLowery's, Holliday's, and Morgan Earp's pistols roared together. Doc winced and swore. Frank McLowery threw both hands high in the air, spun on his boot-heels, and dropped on his face. Morg got to his feet. Morgan's bullet had drilled clear through Frank McLowery's head, just behind the ears; Doc's had hit the outlaw in the heart. Either would have killed him instantly, while Wyatt's first shot, which had torn through his abdomen, would have brought death in another few seconds. Frank's last bullet had hit Doc Holliday's hip-holster, glanced, and shaved a strip of skin from his back.

Meanwhile, as Wyatt sent a bullet into Tom McLowery when he ran, Virgil Earp and Billy Clanton were shooting it out. Billy was making for the street, firing as he went, when he hit Virgil in the leg. Virgil kept his feet and returned the fire as Wyatt shifted his attention to Billy Clanton. Wyatt's shot hit Billy in the hips, and as the cowboy fell, Virgil's bullet tore through his hat and creased his scalp. With his last ounce of gameness, the rustler raised to a sitting posture and tried to steady his wavering gun on his knee. While Wyatt and Virgil hesitated over shooting at a man who plainly was done, Billy Clanton slumped in the dust. The firing ceased. Billy Claiborne ran from the rear of Fly's on through toward Allen Street. Holliday's trigger clicked futilely.

"What in hell did you let Ike Clanton get away like that for, Wyatt?" Doc complained.

"He wouldn't jerk his gun," Wyatt answered.

The fight was over.

Frank McLowery was dead in the middle of Fremont Street. Tom McLowery's body was around the Third Street corner. Billy Clanton was still breathing but died within a few minutes.

Virgil's leg-wound and Morgan's, in the shoulder, were ugly, but not serious. Doc Holliday's scratch was superficial. Four of the cowboys had fired seventeen shots; Ike Clanton, whose brag and bluster brought on the battle, none. They had scored just three hits, not one of which put an adversary out of action.

The three Earps and Holliday had fired seventeen shots, four of which Doc Holliday had thrown at random into the gallery window and after Ike Clanton. The remaining thirteen had been hits. Any one of Frank McLowery's wounds would have been fatal. Billy Clanton had been hit six times, three fatally. Either of Tom McLowery's wounds would have killed him, and Wyatt's shot which stampeded the cow-ponies was a bull's-eye; it served Wyatt's exact purpose, stinging the animal to violent action, but not crippling him beyond ability to get out of the way.

As the smoke of battle lifted, Wyatt turned to look up Fremont Street. A yelling mob was headed toward him. The Citizens' Safety Committee had started for the corral in a column of twos, but excitement overcame discipline.

"I distinctly remember," writes John P. Clum, "that the first set of twos was made up of Colonel William Herring, an attorney, and Milton Clapp, cashier of a local bank. Colonel Herring was tall and portly, with an imposing dignity, while Milton Clapp was short and lean and wore large spectacles. The striking contrast in stature and bearing between these two leaders of the 'column' registered an indelible picture which still intrudes as a flash of comedy in an exceedingly grave moment."

Virgil and Morgan Earp were taken to their homes by the Vigilantes and a guard of twenty posted around the Earp property to prevent retaliation by friends of the dead outlaws. Other Vigilante squads patrolled the Tombstone streets.

Ike Clanton was found hiding in a Mexican dancehall, south of Allen Street, and Billy Claiborne near by. They were taken to the calaboose and guarded to prevent either escape or lynching. Ike, at least, had small desire for freedom; he begged to be locked up and protected.

After his brothers had been cared for, Wyatt Earp walked up Fremont Street with Fred Dodge. Across from the sheriff's office, above the O. K. Corral, Johnny Behan stopped them.

"Wyatt," the sheriff said, "I'm arresting you."

"For what?" Wyatt asked in astonishment.

"Murder," Behan answered.

Wyatt's eye turned cold and his voice hard.

"Behan," he said, "you threw us. You told us you had disarmed those rustlers. You lied to throw us off and get us murdered. *You* arrest *me?* Not today, nor tomorrow either. I'll be where any respectable person can arrest me any time he wants to, but don't you or any of your cheap errand-boys try it."

The sheriff walked away.

That afternoon a coroner's jury refused to hold the Earps and Holliday for death of the cowboys. Johnny Behan, principal witness at the inquiry, was deeply chagrined. At this time Behan thought himself the sole eye-witness to the fight in the corral, other than the participants. He so boasted to C. S. Fly. Fly had seen something of the battle and had noted other witnesses of whom Behan was unaware. Fly was a Vigilante, and close-mouthed. He reported Behan's belief to the Safety Committee, which sagely decided to give the talkative little sheriff all the rope he'd take.

One item which the coroner did uncover was that the three dead outlaws had, among them, more than six thousand dollars in currency, and that Ike Clanton and Billy Claiborne also had carried large sums of cash into the battle. This substantiated subsequent testimony that the rustlers had planned to kill the Earps and Holliday and ride for Old Mexico to stay until public resentment subsided.

The Cochise County grand jury was sitting at Tombstone at the time of the battle in the O. K. Corral and the Vigilantes asked that body to investigate the killings immediately. Behan, still believing there were no non-participating witnesses to contradict him, testified before the grand jury, as did Ike Clanton. Numerous Tombstone citizens were called, but the Earps did not appear. The grand jury announced that it could find no reason to indict four duly appointed peace officers for performance of necessary duty.

# BELLE STARR:
# A PRAIRIE AMAZON

*by* DUNCAN AIKMAN

At the time Duncan Aikman wrote *Calamity Jane and the Lady Wild-cats,* from which "Belle Starr" is excerpted, he was an editorial writer on the El Paso *Times.* In addition to magazine articles, he had also written a volume of essays titled: *The Home Town Mind.* He has, however, subsequently pulled up stakes in the sun-baked capital of the upper Rio Grande and moved to Washington, D. C., where he continues his newspaper career.

I<small>N THE</small> 40's J<small>OHN</small> S<small>HIRLEY WAS RECOGNIZED AS THE FIRST</small> gentleman of the town of Carthage, Missouri—not in spite of his keeping an inn, but because of it. Tavern comforts themselves, on the edge of a wilderness, conferred a distinct glamor; and John Shirley's inn enjoyed in addition the unusual distinction of a worn but highly polished piano belonging to his wife, and a glass case containing enough books—almost a hundred—to make any man's reputation as a scholar in that unliterate frontier.

Too, it took more domestic slaves to run a first-rate tavern in even a small metropolis than were within the means of struggling planters who needed every black arm they could afford for field work; and thus the innkeeper acquired the additional respect due to apparent affluence. From having once held some minor judicial office he had his perpetual title of "Judge"; and he was also the intimate adviser of Congressmen and state political leaders, a sort of minor boss in matters of democratic and extreme pro-slavery patronage.

In such circumstances John and Eliza Shirley presided over

their inn for twenty-five years. One evening late in the first decade of their tenure, the slave service was slightly less organized, and distinctly more excited than usual. The barroom festivities were subdued and early concluded. The ladies' parlor succumbed to an overwhelming nervous tension and excluded gentlemen visitors from its confidence entirely. Next morning grinning black attendants solicited tips in the name of Mrs. Eliza Shirley's new daughter.

She was christened Myra Belle. The border predicted, with a naive pride in the enterprise's possibility, that she would be "raised a lady." It was February 3, 1846.

In that time and place, a lady-like education emphasized ostentation rather than subtlety, mannerisms rather than manners. Being accomplished hardly seemed worth while without showing the accomplishments off. Hence, as Miss Myra Belle learned to read and write fluently, it was necessary for her to prove her cultivation by speaking pieces—the florid declamations of the Old South's romantic sentimentality, spoken flamboyantly and on the most public occasions possible. When she learned to play the piano, the community and the hotel patrons must be reminded of her talent by frequent volunteer performances, which could be arranged almost without solicitation and which were marked more by fury of execution than by studied technique. When she learned to ride, which she did early and on somewhat better mounts than the average, it was not enough for her to trot decorously about the village on a young girl's proper domestic errands and join troupes of chaperoned contemporaries for occasional modest canters about the countryside. She must flaunt her social prominence in spectacular riding habits and feats of break-neck audacity. For patterns she instinctively selected haughty, high-tempered, emotionally reckless heroines out of the novels of the school of William Gilmore Simms.

But a lady's education on the southwestern border included more than the humanities. However much prudish reticences and hysterical aversions might be tests of breeding in eastern salons, dignified poise in southern Missouri required that its possessor be hard to shock.

Miss Myra Belle learned early that the ability to chew and spit tobacco expertly was the normal badge of mature virility. She learned that a gentleman's standing in the local social register was not affected by his getting obscenely and pugnaciously drunk, but that on the contrary many of the best planters and town capitalists paid a sort of left-handed tribute to their state of splendor by occasionally doing it. When they indulged in eye-gouging contests, bowie-knife duels and feuds, eligible young gentlemen did not become fit objects of disgust and the reforming passions of women. In such brawls they merely rose to emotional emergencies in a way that was creditable to their personal honor and high spirit.

She was aware, of course, that no gentleman should address a lady profanely. On the other hand, she learned that it was not her duty to protest against the stream of loose and profane talk which assailed her hardened little ears constantly—on the streets, for instance, or over the thin partitions of the tavern bar, or from the long summer-night talk of rounders and drummers on the verandahs. Finally, she learned that no true lady cherished embarrassing suspicions about certain hard-faced and secretive but lavishly open-handed stockmen who appeared now and then with herds of half-wild cattle and horses for sale—riding in from the Southwest, down Indian Territory way.

In a word, she grew up a hotel child. There was always an audience. Lonely child-loving guests praised her accomplishments beyond their worth. Benevolently befuddled strangers were usually on hand to encourage her extravagances with little gifts and requests for more declamations and concerts; impishly teasing strangers would goad her rather ill-controlled emotions into tantrums one moment and spoil her with flattery the next.

At fifteen, she must have been a little more vain, a little more self-centered, a little more headstrong and theatrical than would have been quite pleasant in so young a "lady" elsewhere than on the southwestern frontier. But she must also have been considerably more resourceful and self-reliant than the average; and the time was coming when she could put such sophistication to use. The spring of her fifteenth year saw the opening of the Civil War.

To southern Missouri the struggle was not so much a volcanic national emergency as an open season for malice. Forty-year-old personal feuds between slavery and free-soil sympathizers now boiled over into a state of permissible killing. Old family hatreds hitherto devoid of political bias drove the antagonists into opposing armies, almost regardless of their opinions concerning slavery and secession, merely for the sake of the new license to murder and despoil. Toughs, bullies and vagabonds whose passions for arson, murder and burglary had thus far been somewhat restrained by the peace officers, now joined volunteer companies which quickly became irregulars—irregulars which degenerated into bushwhackers and land pirates. The marches and occasional minor battles of the regular forces brought to the border almost an air of tranquility. Assassination, plunder and wanton destruction reigned again whenever they left.

A "lady" trained by border standards, Myra Belle was scarcely the one to be horrified by this lawlessness. The atmosphere of hatred appealed to her taste for the violent emotions. The opportunity to ride the countryside as a dashing Confederate virago appealed to her sense of the histrionic. Somewhere in the genteel blood of the Shirleys there was more than a dash of Cherokee; but even without that, pity could hardly have been a controlling emotion with Myra Belle. If a Yankee civilian was murdered now and then by Southern night-riders, his barns burned and household goods plundered, what of it?

Over the line in Kansas a sharp-faced, beady-eyed young man named Quantrill was organizing a band said to be responsible for most of these vengeances. Well, the Yankees deserved all they got. According to the stories Myra Belle and all other Confederates heard, they had begun it. Besides, her brother Ed Shirley himself was off in the swamps with Quantrill. No more than in his teens, he was already a captain. If Myra Belle could find a way to help Quantrill's forces, you could bet your last dollar of Jeff Davis money she would.

The way was found early and rather easily. The Quantrill gang needed, above all other things, information: information about what the Yankee regiments were doing and planning, and where the Yankee home guard companies were, or were not, on their job; information about the gathering of grain, fodder, horses and mules for shipment to the Yankee armies; tips on Yankee farmers and country personages who might have a little silver service or a little hard money in the family sock that would be good for "the cause"—which was to say, young Quantrill's commissary and paymaster departments. A pertly attractive young miss, already something of a privileged character in public places, who knew everybody within a hundred and fifty miles of Carthage who had ever been her father's hotel guest, could, by incessantly using her quick ears, her shrewd wit and her horse-manship, conduct a highly successful tip service. And Miss Myra Belle did.

Twenty-five, fifty, and even more miles away, school-girl friends of Myra Belle and old family intimates of the Shirleys grew accustomed to seeing the dashing young creature in her feathered sombrero and bright-colored riding habit gallop up to their doors on her lathered horse for overnight visits—sometimes for week- and fortnight-long visits. In a country of much generous and casual hospitality there was nothing particularly remarkable about this, except that Myra Belle came unescorted and un-chaperoned. But this was like Myra Belle; and with the war on, the men away and the older women correspondingly busy at home, it was almost inevitable. Some of her hosts were probably in on the secret. But even if they happened to be Yankee sym-pathizers, for a time no doubt they reflected—as their guest sat chattering with girlish enthusiasm about neighborhood gossip, parties, young people's courtships, and not about the war at all— that the little Shirley girl must be a good deal less of a "spitfire" and more of a lady than her reputation suggested. And when she would start home again, her sturdy insistence that she needed no escort would simply remind them that here was an exceptionally independent and resourceful youngster inclined to be considerate of people who had work to do.

But a discreet distance along the way home, Miss Myra Belle would usually leave the main road for some inconspicuous bridle path. And where the bridle path led deepest into the hill country or the backwoods, she was likely to meet a rough-looking, watchful young man on horseback, or possibly half a dozen rough-looking, watchful young men. Then she would impart what her quick ears had picked up and what her shrewd judgment had pieced together from the neighborhood gossip.

Or occasionally she would leave even bridle paths behind her and make her way through swamps and underbrush to a place where the rough-looking young men were camped by scores or by hundreds. Then her brother, Captain Ed, would come and put his arm around her, and young Quantrill would unbend his sullen dignity to pay her sexless but thrilling compliments on her nerve and loyalty. Their "little scout," they called her—for "scouting" was their euphemism for expert spying complicated occasionally with a little treachery to hosts. Nevertheless, she learned from it all how to meet men man-fashion; learned that the admiration of rough and desperate young men had a glamor which the society of chivalrous young Confederate lieutenants in their gray uniforms sometimes lacked.

But before the first year was up the game was growing risky. The Yankees, too, had an intelligence service, and whether or not it was boorish enough to keep track of a prominent debutante's social engagements, it soon suspected something. In a neighborhood given over to rancorous gossip and charges of treachery, and aware that Ed Shirley was hiding out with Quantrill, things would have been suspected even without evidence. But no level heads on the Union side cared to inflame public sentiment by treating a popular young girl unchivalrously. In southern Missouri the Civil War was an exercise as much in propaganda as in bushwhacking, and a girl spy shot or even imprisoned might have affected public sentiment more than a Confederate victory. It seems to have been decided that Myra Belle, for the first time, should be let off with a good scare. After that, all hands could settle back and meet further emergencies as they occurred.

The time selected was an occasion when Ed Shirley was home for a visit. For the Missouri war was as informal socially as it was irregular in other particulars. Men frequently left the marauding bands on both sides to get married, visit wives, do their part in feuds, help with the farming, attend dances, or keep poker engagements. The younger boys now and then even showed up for the short winter school terms. Ed was at home in the winter of 1862, quite openly, simply for a vacation.

He was there so long, in fact, that he ceased to be a novelty, and Myra Belle, early in February, rode over to the village of Newtonia, thirty-five miles away, to pick up the neighborhood gossip. Certainly nothing was further from her thoughts than being interfered with. Nevertheless, one morning a Yankee cavalry squad bore down on her near the Newtonia post office and politely but efficiently arrested her.

They took her to the long, roomy, red-brick house of the town's leading citizen, Judge Ritchery, and there she found that the worst possible thing had happened. She was the prisoner of Major Enos, who besides being in command of an unpleasantly large calvary detachment, was an old neighbor who knew the local ground, the local gossip and all the details of the Shirleys' Confederate connections. Much more than any imported Yankee invader, this home-town scalawag was capable of spoiling everything.

A more suave Myra Belle might have tried to get off by pleading innocence and appealing to old family friendship. But the "little scout" of the Quantrill outfit had been trained to use "scenes" rather than duplicity for getting effects. She clawed at her somewhat amused guardian, kicked him, and made such violent efforts to lay on with her riding quirt that the canny major felt it advisable to throw it out the window. Then she suddenly recalled the long list of picturesque oaths with which her hotel childhood had acquainted her, and generously and sincerely called her captor by all of them. Out of breath, she could remember again that a lady's accomplishments called for something in the way of cultivated defiance. Sitting down at the Ritchery piano, she forced the major to listen to an hour's concert of very loud and very Confederate music.

She gave, no doubt, a peculiarly trying morning to a man who was trying only to scare a little "spitfire" without mortifying her by putting her under a guard of common soldiers. He is thus perhaps to be excused if, when he released her, he remarked somewhat testily: "Get along home now, Myra. And if you meet some of my men on your way back, take a good look at their prisoner. I'll bet you a Yankee dollar against a rebel one that it'll be Ed."

Myra Belle apparently ignored the challenge. To show her indifference she loitered in the garden a whole quarter of an hour with Judge Ritchery's daughter. Then, gathering a bundle of painfully supple cherry switches—the riding quirt had possibly been preserved among the Federal war trophies—she was off. The cavalry troop on Ed Shirley's trail had almost a full half-day's start.

But the cavalry troop knew only the roads on the maps, while Myra Belle knew the short cuts and bridle paths. And whatever her horse did not know about the efficacy of cherry switches, that afternoon she taught him. At sunset she galloped into Carthage, appropriately dishevelled and indignant, but an hour ahead of the Federal cavalry.

When the troop came in with the darkness, she was careful, as became a town heroine on the make, to receive them herself. "If you're looking for Captain Shirley," she told them, "you're very much too late. He had such important business up Spring River that he left a whole half-hour ago—it's much too dark to follow him now, isn't it?"

The whole neighborhood heard about the incident, of course. The Confederates admired in their extravagant fashion, and the Yankees cursed her for a dangerous vixen. At any rate, here she

· 282 ·

was, sixteen and a celebrity. Here was a notoriety that beat speaking pieces and playing exciting gallopades on the piano for the hotel guests; a fame that she could flaunt instead of hiding, as she had had to do with the little secret whispers of notice that came to her from her spying exploits.

Her whole nature had prepared her to make the most of her new prestige—but not, I think, quite agreeably. She was not the girl to be, on account of it, any emotional old Confederate's pet, or even a flirtatious heart-smasher to Quantrill's young men. Instead, she must have swaggered over her deed in a dour, hard-boiled, little fashion and been almost as haughty and distant to those who wished to praise her for it as to pro-Yankee old maids who made up spiteful gossip about her character on the basis of her shocking language to Major Enos. . . . But she liked it, this sensation of being both important and dangerous, better than anything else she had discovered in her whole "lady-like" education. And as the war rolled sullenly on and Quantrill's young desperadoes, now riding in northeastern Kansas, now forced back toward the Territory border, had less and less need of military information from southwestern Missouri, she longed to feel its thrills again and more profoundly.

When the war ended, John Shirley, with an old man's impatience of altered circumstances, abandoned his inn without even bothering to find a purchaser, and went to Texas. Myra Belle of course went with him, though doubtless with some annoyance at leaving a country to which Quantrill's young men were still contributing a good deal of excitement.

But her misgivings, if she had any, soon turned out to be largely unfounded. As Myra Belle before long learned, the north-central Texas farm of Judge Shirley (apparently near Dallas) was destined for a more neighborly relationship with southern Missouri than geography might have suggested.

For instance, when one of Quantrill's young men got into trouble with the authorities by assuming that the war was still going on, it was natural for him to hide out in the wilds of Indian

Territory until the excitement was over, and then ride over into North Texas for a well-earned vacation. Belle doubtless helped entertain a number of such excursion parties, basking pleasantly in the admiration of rough young men who were delighted to be esteemed still as "Quantrill's prowling panthers." Then in 1866 one of the parties brought along Jim Reed.

She had known him before as a Quantrill man and one of Ed's fellow fighters, though apparently almost impersonally. But in Texas Jim found a way to impress her—was it by admiring her small-frontier-town cultivation, flattering her hard pride in dangerous achievement, or reminding her of their mutual homesickness? Whatever his line of approach, within twenty-four hours this young woman of horseback escapades and quick decisions had made up her mind to marry him.

Then, much to their annoyance, Judge Shirley objected. He had plenty of sympathy for the boys who were ostracized, kept out of jobs and chased over the hills by the triumphant Missouri Yankees; and he did not blame them in the least for disturbing the peace of the commonwealth to get a proper vengeance. He was glad to welcome them to Texas, where the carpet-baggers confined themselves to taking the offices and did not try to set the tone for society and monopolize the business openings besides. But marrying Belle off to a fugitive from justice, no matter what justice—this was, to the former first gentleman of Carthage, preposterous.

Nevertheless, while the judge stormed in the conventional manner of Southern fathers, Belle and Jim rode off for an all-day picnic with Jim's excursion party, and were married by a member of the band who boasted a justice's license.

The traditions which follow are so complicated that an authentic account of the romance is almost untraceable. Jim appears to have found it necessary to depart within a day or two after the ceremony for the seclusion of the Indian Territory—possibly because the judge's protective hospitality had been withdrawn. But within four months his Missouri difficulties had cleared up; and he abducted the bride, with her hearty co-operation, to his home at Rich Hill. The unreconciled judge countered promptly by abducting her again to Texas. Jim had to make still another trip to Texas and steal Myra Belle away from the paternal ranch, this time in a shower of birdshot. It was considerably more than a year after the marriage before the Reed household was permanently assembled.

Belle found herself equipped with a husband able to fortify her lady-like education with dashes of Quantrill technique; for as Jim engaged in enough escapades in Missouri to keep him a large part of the time in the Indian Territory, she discovered the prime diversions of matrimony to be visiting him in his hide-outs. Then in 1870 even the Territory became perilous. A rival group of nominally demobilized bushwhackers, the Shannon boys, on the trail of a feudist enemy named Fisher, made the mistake of killing Jim's brother, Scott Reed, in Fisher's stead. Jim refused to accept the explanation of technical error, and killed at least one Shannon in revenge. With an Indian Territory murder warrant out for him, he fled to Los Angeles.

Belle went along with her year-old daughter; and when in 1872 they returned as far as Texas, Judge Shirley had also a year-old grandson. Whether this circumstance reconciled him to a difficult son-in-law, or whether he simply determined to make the best of things, he helped Belle acquire a ranch nine miles from the Shirley place, and the group settled down to unbroken amity. Jim hid out on the prairies of northern Texas to be safer from old warrants and also, it seems, to facilitate certain profitable trading operations in horses of questionable title. Whenever the notoriety of this business made Texas dangerous for him, he retreated to a new hiding place in Indian Territory eighty miles west of Fort Smith, famous already for nearly a generation as the hang-out of Ellis Starr, the bad man of the Cherokees. Old Ellis himself had died earlier, but his son Tom still kept up the family associations; and ex-Quantrill followers, new outlaws of the reconstruction disorder and miscellaneous young men taking vacations from the activities of the new gangs of the James boys and Cole Younger found the place an agreeable resort.

As a frequent visitor from her Texas properties, Belle found there opportunities to enlarge both her acquaintance and her sophistication. Besides riding to dances, after the informal Cherokee Strip custom, with Jim in front of her and the handsome young half-breed boy, Tom Starr's son Sam, holding on to her by the midriff from behind, she seemed to have advanced to first-name intimacy with the Jameses and the Youngers.

But the main business of the establishment was decidedly less idyllic. One night in 1873 a group of Starr retainers came down on the dugout of Watt Grayson, a Creek Indian suspected of having helped himself to the tribal funds, and stretched his neck to a rope seven times and his wife's neck three times until the couple gave up $30,000. Belle was innocently asleep at the ranch near Dallas, but Jim was recognized. His chronic need for concealment was excitingly redoubled.

Belle, however, was equal to the emergency. She found him hiding places in residences of some of the best Dallas families, innocent-appearing jobs at nearby ranches too respectable for sheriffs to question, and, when pursuit became serious, remote retreats in the woods and between the prairie swales. Partly, no doubt, to establish a social center that would also be helpful as an intelligence service, she started a livery stable. Soon Texas society's regard for Jim had been so far restored by her seductive patronage that he could operate again almost openly as a good family provider. The small assortment of farm nags with which Myra Belle had begun business were replaced by spiritied *caballadas* of newly-broken range ponies for which no authentic bills of sale were in evidence.

Belle, in cultivating the community's influential side, found the livery stable on effective point of vantage. She managed to create the impression that the carpet-baggers had made her husband a fugitive, yet here she was with grit enough to stand up for him, and sense enough to run a first-class livery stable and be a lady besides.

The reconstruction passions of rich stockmen and lawyers of the thriving county seat boiled over in chivalrous admiration.

They would see that their wives did something about this; and they did. Belle began to receive calls and to be invited to receptions and suppers. She gave recitations again to delighted audiences, and played the melancholy popular airs of the period on fortunate hostesses' pianos. With just enough reserve amid the gayeties to impress the audience with her heroic firmness under peculiar afflictions, she gained a sympathy which she was careful not to alienate by encouraging philanderers. Even in Dallas's circle of ante-bellum dowagers, it became a moderate social distinction to know the little livery stable keeper intimately.

Her tactics made Jim's open-air stud very profitable. From an ardently-hunted fugitive, he gradually became a husband and father able to cheer his family by appearing often with only the slightest precautions. Even when one of the strings of horses offered for sale happened by some geographical negligence to have been taken on the Texas side, Belle's cultivation of a great lady's social estate proved positively strategic.

The popular young husband's career as a professional reconstruction misfit, however, was nearly over. Federal rewards for his capture dead or alive might not appeal to members of his wife's social circle in Dallas, but they rendered his potential carcass highly attractive to strangers immune to Confederate traditions. Consequently, in the summer of 1875, when he was returning from Mrs. Reed's livery stable to the scene of his Red River operations, a plausible companion by the name of Morris advised him not to offend an eccentric old farmer near McKinney, Texas, by going to dinner in his house with a loaded Winchester.

The confiding Mr. Reed left the weapon outside. Almost immediately Morris, on the chivalrous ruse of pretending to fetch water from the pump for his hostess, walked to the horse corral and procured his own gun. Then, entering the room from the rear, he filled the valuable Mr. Reed full of bird-shot.

But Morris's reckonings failed to take account of the self-control and malevolence of a lady trained in the exercise of vindictive pride. In order to claim the reward for Jim's body, it was necessary to have it identified; and in a Texas summer, the identification had to be made quickly or not at all. Lacking a wide acquaintance in the neighborhood and knowing only its disposition to shield Jim under all circumstances, Morris conceived the strategy of sending for Belle and wringing the identification out of her grief.

Belle came and looked at what was left of Jim dry-eyed and casually, but at Morris scornfully and for an uncomfortably long while.

"Mr. Morris," she said with her best Dallas evening-party irony, "I am very sorry, but you've killed the wrong man. If you want the reward for Jim Reed's body, you will have to kill Jim Reed."

She had learned more things than how to stock a livery stable since she boiled over in the Ritchery parlor and cursed Major Enos.

With Jim gone and no longer in need of her social standing to shield his own operations, Belle's chief motive for discretion was removed, and at the same time she required many things which only shady activities could procure. Her father was dead and her mother's affairs were tangled. She had two children to rear, her taste for luxuries in horses and music—some say books also—to keep up, and, at the moment, a relatively expensive social position to maintain. The only ways she knew of meeting these obligations were Jim's ways.

For a time she seems to have done no more than conduct through her livery stable a tip service for Jim's old associates in border depredations. She moped a good deal over Jim's death, and wrote to his brother in Missouri letters full of complaints about such lady-like ailments as headache and nervousness, urging him to come down to Texas and take proper vengeance. In addition, with her own career as an entertainer to encourage her, she had hopes of making a child dancer of her girl, Pearl, on the Dallas stage. But after a few performances the over-stimulated infant fainted, a prey to some nervous disorder, and returned to the nursery. Belle was back again on her own resources.

She began deserting the livery stable for days at a time to take madcap horseback rides out into the prairies. Dallas, once indulgent when such journeys were known to take her to rendezvous with her husband, now frowned, and gossiped that she was meeting with bands of horse-stealing outlaws. When she let the livery stable virtually drift out of her ownership, and still came back from these expeditions well-provided with money, the tale went around that she was sharing the outlaws' proceeds. From a general favorite, she became first a suspect, and then an object of sinister avoidance. Standing up for Jim had been wifely and proper, but association with outlaws who were rustling Texas horses and cattle was another matter.

By 1877 the town had a nubbin of delectable fact to confirm its worst suspicions. Out on an all-day gallop, Belle and a young girl of harum-scarum reputation named Emma Jones were caught by a Texas norther near a crossroads settlement. They took shelter in the lee of the village store, and when noon came built a fire to warm their coffee, using the rear wall of the building as a backlog. The coffee was successfully made, but in the ensuing conflagration the store was reduced to ashes. Belle next day found herself in the Dallas jail on charges of arson and malicious mischief.

At her first hearing, however, the dignity and refinement of her bearing completely ravished an elderly stockman from the remoter ranges, named Patterson. Stirred to depths of Freudian generosity, the amiable dotard sought her out and inquired how much it would cost to pay her legal expenses and get the charges dismissed. Belle, without batting an eye or making a promise, told him that by the most conservative estimates it would cost $2500. The philanthropic Patterson promptly sold cows and delivered the amount in cash. A day or two later the arson charge was withdrawn (the inevitable outcome all along), and Mrs. Reed was released on payment of a nominal fine for malicious mischief—approximately $2490 to the good.

Mr. Patterson enjoyed her company at one or two innocuous hotel dinners and was put off in his collection efforts with a plea of stupendous legal expenses. Then he sought advice from friends, and was of course urged to file fraud charges and prosecute. But here, one regrets to say, his very excess of doting chivalry led him to blast a lady's reputation.

"Hell, leave her keep it," was his epigram. "I reckon after what she's had to put up with, she's earned every cent of it."

Dallas, promptly assuming with snickers and some indignation that what the widow had "put up with" was advances from the uncomely but notoriously amorous Patterson, cheerfully condemned its former parlor heroine to the ostracism of loose women. Belle had finished with relying on caste to cover her indiscretions.

Yet she took the blow with characteristic strategy, seeming by her dour haughtiness to snub Dallas before it could snub her. With the help of Mr. Patterson's contribution she blossomed out with new thoroughbreds and new and more modish riding habits, so that strangers in the town fancied her to be some eccentric Kentucky or Virginia heiress feeling herself too superior to the normal run of Texans to exchange the common courtesies. She was also using the Patterson money to send her little son to the home of the Reed mother-in-law in Missouri, and Pearl, the retired danseuse, to that of a friend in Arkansas, paying for their board and schooling for two years in advance. Yet in all this she was merely getting ready to prove to Dallas' horrified satisfaction that to call a lady harsh names is a sure way to make her dangerous.

In 1878 she was arrested for horse-stealing: she was getting too bold to stop with acting as fence and tipster for the outlaws, and had begun preying on the neighbors herself. But she was also by now far too contemptuous of the conventions which had ostracized her, to submit to being tried for her crime. In jail she turned the wiles of a distressed and persecuted gentlewoman upon an emotional turnkey. A week later, in the dead of a glamorous spring night, she had eloped with him.

In a month he was back again in the somewhat unsympathetic bosom of his family—a sadder turnkey, and a much wiser one about erotic infatuations. His story is plausible, if only because it is so amusingly consistent with the widow Reed's temperament. For the harassed philanderer insisted that his part in the escapade was not a lover's, but that of escort, cook, horse-wrangler, wood-fetcher and water-carrier, at the point of his own pistol.

That year and the next Belle rode the range of northwest Texas and the Indian Territory Panhandle with as thorough-going a group of desperadoes and cutthroats as ever missed a deserved national celebrity. Jim French, the Blue Duck and Jack Spaniard were their leaders, but all sorts of fugitives from border justice, highwaymen whose gangs had been decimated by prison sentences, half-breeds from the reservations, dangerously Americanized Mexicans from New Mexico, and cowboys gone wrong through rustling, often swelled their numbers to nearly fifty. They picked up mavericks in the Atascosa territory, rustled stampeded cattle from the trail drivers on their way to Kansas shipping points, plied Jim Reed's old specialty of stealing horses from the Indians, held up cowtown banks occasionally, and did a little road-agentry on the stage routes. In general they lived by villainy, and so far as the circumstances of the frontier would permit, lived well. They seem to have maintained some contact, or at least a hospitable acquaintance, with what was left of the Younger and Sam Bass gangs of train robbers.

Belle's own activities with such a remote and secretive group are necessarily somewhat apocryphal. She evidently dominated them a good deal by the force of her will and her proud, increasingly harsh personality. Her commanding airs and her great lady's pose must have made them rustle to do the hard work of the camp for her, so that when she did her share occasionally and with a certain ostentation, she gained credit for immense condescension. Her shrewdness and her astonishing literacy got her standing—if not as a leader of active operations, at least as the brains of the gang.

She knew, too, how to use her frontier harshness sparingly

enough to make it effective. Weeks would go by without her indulging in a word or action unworthy of a lady of the first household of Carthage. But when her hat blew off on a cross-country gallop with the Blue Duck and that scorner of empty mannerisms failed to repair the mishap, he found himself looking down the widow Reed's revolver. "Now, God damn your greasy hide," she threatened him, "you pick up that hat, and let this be a lesson in how to treat a lady that you won't forget." And by the gang's traditions, the Blue Duck never failed in courtesy afterward.

He had reason not to, for Belle shortly paid him more than handsomely for his condescension. The Blue Duck, on a recuperative expedition, borrowed $2000 from the temporarily flush treasury of the band, and lost it in a poker game at Fort Dodge. Belle sympathized with his suspicion that such an expert could not have been deprived of a fortune honestly. Next day, with a gun in each hand, she strolled into the gambling house and raided the pot of $7000. "There's a little change due one of my friends, gentlemen," she informed the players with a flash of her most charming irony. "If you want it back, come down to the Territory and get it."

To this period, too, belongs the legend of her descent on a prosperous cow-country county seat in the character of a genteel Southern widow seeking investment opportunities. She charmed all with her accomplishments and cultivated manners. At the end of the week she had removed from the hotel and taken up her quarters as the guest of the banker's wife.

Then one afternoon the banker himself, sitting in his office with her in a conference on the business outlook, was alarmed to observe that he was covered by her pistol. Still covered, he unlocked the safe, handed over its contents, and submitted to binding and gagging. Mrs. Reed rode off into the prairie darkness. Early next morning when the banker, returned to his home, was still trying to convince a suspicious wife that it was after all not so bad as an elopement, the assets were safe in the gang's treasury.

But the law, having settled with Sam Bass and the James family, was ready to close in on the Blue Duck and Jack Spaniard. With her usual shrewdness, Belle saw the portents, and retired to her late husband's retreat at the Starr ranch in the Cherokee country. But even there danger threatened, or perhaps the charming Sam Starr opened her eyes to the opportunities for rustling near the thriving new cowtown of Ogallala, Nebraska; for they went north early in 1880. When they came back a year and a half later—urged, it is said, by neighborhood suspicions that their herds were increasing by more means than breeding and purchase—they were married.

In a remote spot on the Canadian River, eight miles from the postoffice of Eufaula, the Starrs located a thousand-acre claim and settled down to a life of what, for the Indian country, passed as social leadership. There they brought Pearl, with her vestiges of a stage-child's coquetry. The hostess, prospering from her years with the Blue Duck, ordered sumptuous wardrobes from the St. Louis department stores. From somewhere, too, she acquired the last symbol of frontier cultivation, a piano.

The cabin was plain, with a puncheon floor, and calico print nailed over its log partitions for wall-paper. Buffalo horns and deer antlers did duty in it as the principal decorations; but chance visitors, always easily impressed in the 80's, marvelled at the tastily-chosen bric-a-brac on the rustic mantle. And if we are to believe a lady's most plausible biographer, the intellectual tastes of John Shirley, the first gentleman of Carthage, were represented by rows of books "of a sort as are seen in the best libraries."

Now and then the chatelaine left her half-breed husband and her rustically charming daughter, to visit, it was represented, the popular eastern watering places; likewise, as Harman, the biographer, puts it, to "spend money lavishly and mingle freely with the wealth and culture of the nation." Once at White Sulphur Springs, it is insisted, her playing of doleful ante-bellum popular airs on the piano charmed a circle of old Confederate ladies from Richmond into tears.

Did she really?—or was it simply that Indian Territory admiration could not contemplate the occasional mysterious absence of such splendor without explaining it in a folklore?

The best-authenticated eastern visit, at any rate, was not to a fashionable watering place, nor was it so mysteriously overlaid with tradition. "Now Pearl," Belle wrote to her daughter in 1883, in one of the most genteelly persuasive explanations of a sentence to a reformatory yet penned, "there is a vast difference in that place and a penitentiary; you must bear that in mind and not think of mamma being shut up in a gloomy prison.

"It is said to be one of the finest institutions in the United States, surrounded by beautiful grounds, with fountains and everything nice. There I can have my education renewed, and I stand greatly in need of it. Sam will have to attend school and I think it will be the best thing that ever happened for him. And now you must not be unhappy and brood over our absence. It won't take the time long to glide by and as we come home we will get you, and then we will have such a nice time."

The institution thus eulogized was the Detroit House of Correction. Belle and Sam were sentenced to it, as often ironically happens to famous desperadoes, for a mere peccadillo. The heroine of bank raids and rustling operations by the herd fell before the Federal courts at last for stealing a lone colt.

Belle took the blow with her usual outward calm. She was pale and gently proud before the court, haughtily contemptuous toward newspaper reporters. At the house of correction, her dignified pathos was all but ravishing.

The warden, preparing to instruct her in her duties in the prison factory, invited her to "take a chair, please." He meant for the new inmate to pick up a chair frame and follow him into the workroom where women prisoners were putting the cane seats in place. But Belle replied with a weary sadness: "No, in this place, I think I should stand, thanks"; and when her error was explained to her, smiled tenderly and reproached herself for her thoughtlessness.

Before such graceful tactics the warden melted, and placed her at the lightest work available. The matron wept over the charming wardrobe from the St. Louis department stores when it was replaced by the prison uniforms, talked current literature with her charge in off hours, and urged her to write a book about "the pleasant sides of workhouse life." Belle returned after nine months with a justifiable sense of having secured a new social triumph.

But her poise was weakening. Sam's position in the criminal records grew seriously embarrassing. He had to spend most of 1885 in New Mexico dodging warrants for a post office robbery. When he came back he was first shot up by a posse and then, after he had been arrested and his bond quickly arranged, shot again at a dance in Whitefield in a quarrel over the ownership of his horse.

Too, the neighborhood was filling up with white settlers bringing with them the conventions which had punished Belle at Dallas. With the family's disorderly notoriety, her glamor was becoming every month less and less that of a wilderness social arbitress and more that of a common hell-cat. An acquittal on a horse-stealing charge in 1886, on no better alibi than she had had three years previously, was received by the neighborhood with more signs of annoyance than of sympathy. Even when in the course of the rough-riding exhibitions at the Sebastian County fair in 1887 she picked up the editor of the local newspaper with a wild swoop from the saddle, the crowd which once had feared and paid homage merely jeered.

She was getting fat, dowdy, shrewish-tempered; and worst of all, she was losing her discretion. In 1888 a person of doubtful character named Watson came in vaguely from the southeast with his wife, to become the Starr's tenant. In confidence, Belle wormed it out of the woman that Watson was wanted on a murder charge in Florida.

In the days of her skill at managing men, the mere possession of this secret would have enabled her to attach Watson to her enterprises as long as she had need of him. But she used it now merely to inflame a silly quarrel. Watson took a letter for her at the Eufaula post office and forgot to deliver it. When it turned up a few weeks later she refused his explanations and treated him as a wilful mail-robber. His natural retort was to taunt her with Sam's still pending embarrassment with the Federal authorities over the post office burglary.

"I don't suppose the Federal officers would trouble you," Belle crushed him; "but the Florida officers might."

For the terrorized Mr. Watson the threat was too much. Alone, so that no effective witnesses could be summoned against him, he ambushed her near his house while she was returning from the trial of one of Sam's cousins at Fort Smith for the family vice—horse-stealing. First he knocked her off her saddle with a charge of turkey-shot; then when she was safely on the ground, unconscious, he removed her own weapons and shot her again in the neck and breast until she died.

It was on her forty-third birthday. But one suspects that Belle Starr had already learned all that she cared to know of what a woman may get by taking life with a high hand.

# THEY RODE
# STRAIGHT UP TO DEATH

*by* WALTER PRESCOTT WEBB

Walter Prescott Webb is a Stetson-wearing Texan. He is known to scholars for his economic history *The Great Plains*. To the general public he is best known for *The Texas Rangers*, which is a definitive history of those rugged gents who maintained the law in Texas during the times when to break it was most fashionable and profitable.

As this book is published, Dr. Webb is serving as Harmsworth Professor of American History at Oxford University in England.

As can be seen by the following preface to *The Texas Rangers*, Dr. Webb likes good company, a mess of *frijole* beans, and a mesquite-root fire. He is another example of those robust professors of the Southwest who know as much about the uses of a single-action Colt pistol as of Latin nouns, and who are at least as interested in the history of Sam Bass as in that of Pericles. Just as John Lomax has lifted our native songs from the lips of our people and set them down in print, so, from old records and stories, Webb has assembled, organized, and set down in print the full story of these men who brought lawful order out of the jubilant chaos that was early Texas, when the difference between mine and thine was so often established by the dexterity of mine right wrist and forefinger.

---

I N 1835 THE TEXAS RANGERS WERE ORGANIZED AND GIVEN LEGAL status while Texas was in the midst of revolution against Mexico. Their almost continuous service to 1935, when they were absorbed in a larger organization, indicates that the need for them has been persistent, while their changing functions reflect the evolution of the society they protected from its primitive beginning as a frontier community to a commonwealth of five million people. Though his duties have varied from decade to decade, the Ranger has been throughout essentially a fighting man.

It was Eugene Manlove Rhodes who suggested that the Western man—he was speaking of the cowboy—can be understood only when studied in relation to his work. And so it is with the Ranger. When we see him at his daily task of maintaining law, restoring order, and promoting peace—even though his methods be vigorous—we see him in his proper setting, a man standing alone between a society and its enemies. When we remember that it was his duty to deal with the criminal in the dangerous nexus between the crime and the capture, when the criminal was in his most desperate mood, we must realize that neither the rules nor the weapons were of the Ranger's choosing. It has been his duty to meet the outlaw breed of three races, the Indian warrior, Mexican bandit, and American desperado, on the enemy's ground and deliver each safely within the jail door or the cemetery gate. It is here recorded that he has sent many patrons to both places.

As strange as it may seem in some quarters, the Texas Ranger has been throughout the century a human being, and never a mere automaton animating a pair of swaggering boots, a big hat, and a six-shooter all moving across the prairies under a cloud of pistol smoke. Surely enough has been written about men who swagger, fan hammers, and make hip shots. No Texas Ranger ever fanned a hammer when he was serious, or made a hip shot if he had time to catch a sight. The real Ranger has been a very quiet, deliberate, gentle person who could gaze calmly into the eye of a murderer, divine his thoughts, and anticipate his action, a man who could ride straight up to death. In fatal encounter—the last resort of a good officer—the Ranger has had the unhurried courage to take the extra fraction of a second essential to accuracy which was at a premium in the art and the science of Western pistology. The smoke from such a man's hand was a vagrant wisp and never the clouds read of in books written for those who love to smell powder smoke vicariously.

Men in active service have given me of their *frijoles* and bread and black coffee. They have suffered me to share their camp, ride their best horses, fire their six-shooters, and to feel the companionship of men and horses when the saddle stirrups touch in the solitudes. They are masters of brevity when they speak of themselves—as economical of words as of pistol smoke. "We had a little shooting and he lost" was the way one told the story of a personal encounter. They do not respond to direct questions of a personal nature, and it is best not to ask them. "I have been accused once," responded one whose exploits would fill a book. "We were camped out on the Pecos. A norther came up, I pulled the cover off, and he froze to death."

# THE GALVESTON STORM

*by* SAM ACHESON

Sam Acheson is the author of 35,000 *Days in Texas*, a play *We Are Besieged*, and a biography of Joseph Weldon Bailey. He is a member of the staff of the Dallas *Morning News*, for which he serves as book reviewer and political and editorial writer. He is the brother-in-law of Fanita Lanier (Mrs. Alec Acheson), who made the literary map of the Southwest reproduced as end-papers in this book.

35,000 *Days in Texas* is the story of the birth and growth of the Dallas *News*, one of the Southwest's greatest newspapers. The *News* and its parent, the Galveston *News*, were principal actors in almost every sizable drama or public alarum which has occupied the people of Texas since the early days of the Republic. But there was one of these which the Dallas *News* and the Galveston *News* acting in conjunction could do nothing about, or at least not swerve in its main course. That was the Galveston storm of 1900. Herewith is Sam Acheson's story of the part played by the two newspapers in this titanic catastrophe.

---

AS THE YEAR 1900 OPENED, THE GREAT QUESTION AGITATING Christendom was whether or not the Twentieth Century had been born. There were strict constructionists of the calendar, such as the Vatican, who held that the Nineteenth Century would survive until January 1, 1901. *The News*, weighing the evidence, finally sided with the Papacy. But the year was to prove more epochal in the history of Texas, for toward its close, the state would be visited by the most destructive tropical cyclone in its history, the storm which centered over the city of Galveston and almost destroyed it.

Recorded history is full of accounts of severe coastal storms breaking over the Island of Galveston. As early as 1521, the first white man to tread Texas soil, Cabeza de Vaca, landed there unintentionally because of a shipwreck in such a gale. In more modern times Galveston had suffered, although not seriously, by being on the edge of the storm which wiped out Indianola on Matagorda Bay in 1872. But, in spite of the island's vulnerability—nowhere did it rise as much as twelve feet above high tide and most of the area was even flatter—Galvestonians had little fear of the wind and waters from the Gulf of Mexico. There had been several proposals for a sea wall during the 90's, but none had been entertained seriously. Citizens were totally unprepared, therefore, both physically and psychologically, for the great catastrophe of 1900.

September opened auspiciously for Galveston. *The News* issued its annual September 1 commercial edition to reveal that business and industrial prospects there were the brightest on record. Figures disclosed that the city was now the chief cotton exporting seaport in the world, and rising grain elevators pointed toward the possibility of equal world supremacy in flour and wheat. The Southern Pacific Railway system had recently decided to make extensive investments in terminal railway and steamship-loading facilities. The Census Bureau at Washington had just announced that there were 37,789 men, women and children on the island, a gain of almost thirty per cent in population since 1890. The worst calamity imaginable to the proprietors of *The News* lay in the remote chance that William Jennings Bryan might, on his second try for the Presidency, unseat William McKinley.

As early as Tuesday, September 4, the Galveston weather bureau received its first message regarding a West Indian hurricane, then moving northward over Cuba. Each day thereafter bulletins were posted. By Thursday the slow-moving tropical cyclone (as such disturbances are known to meteorologists) was over southern Florida, from which it changed its course by heading westward in the Gulf. It was centered off the Louisiana coast on the morning of Friday the seventh. The Federal weather reporting station on that day ordered up northwest storm warnings for Galveston. But the great majority of Galvestonians paid little attention to these signs and reports. The first public recognition of the disturbance was in *The News* on Friday morning. Two short, single-paragraph stories on Page 3 reported, under small headlines, that a cyclone had destroyed crops and left natives destitute in the Cuban province of Santa Clara and that the storm, "which has been raging on the South Florida coast for twenty-four hours, is now said to be north of Key West." Even the Saturday morning issue of *The News* contained only a small story on Page 2, also relative to the damage already done by the storm on the Florida coast.

When Galvestonians awoke on the fateful day of Saturday, September 8, the storm was even then upon the city. A high wind was blowing, and the waves on the Gulf side began pounding and wrecking the wooden beach resorts. A heavy tropical rain began to fall. Still, the early morning life of the city moved in its accustomed orbit, although many curious citizens went to the beach to see the grand fury of waves and wind. But weather bureau men on the fifth floor of the Levy Building watched the ominous sinking of the barometer, checked the constant increase on the wind gauge and then noted at 10:10 a.m. that the wind veered suddenly from north to northwest. There was no doubt that the hurricane (as the dreaded tropical cyclone is known popularly) with its opposed quadrants of wind, had borne straight in on the city and enveloped it. It was apparent, in fact, to these trained observers that the whole island was now endangered. Telephone calls poured into the weather bureau office. To the hundreds of anxious inquiries, there was a single answer: "If you live in a low part of the city, move at once to high ground. Prepare for the worst, which is yet to come."

The normal life of Galveston had been paralyzed by early afternoon, with citizens attempting to reach their homes on foot, in carriages, wagons, boats—any way to get through the mounting tide. Half of the city was covered by tidewater at three o'clock; an hour later and the entire community lay buried one to five feet. The wind was howling at more than fifty miles an hour, while the rain continued to fall in blinding sheets. Telegraph connections to the mainland snapped shortly afterward as railroad and wagon causeways swayed and then slumped under the flood; for the first time since the "Old Lady by the Sea" (as the Galveston *News* was called) had established her offspring in North Texas fifteen years earlier, wire communication between the two offices were broken. In Dallas, worried department heads hovered around the dead telegraph instrument and sought vainly for news of the beleaguered city by way of Beaumont, Houston, and even Vera Cruz, Mexico. But the cable between Galveston and the latter city had also lapsed into silence. At the moment communication was severed, City Editor William O'Leary was in the office of Manager G. B. Dealey, proving by *Maury's Geography* that the destruction of Galveston by tropical storm could not happen.

And thus while the world waited and wondered, Galveston passed into its greatest ordeal. By mid-afternoon heads of families who had delayed leaving for home plunged into the storm, wading through water almost to their necks, dodging flying slate from roofs and other missiles whipped through the air by the storm. Several years before Galveston had suffered a disastrous fire; subsequently a city ordinance had been passed requiring slate shingles to be substituted for wooden. A great many people were killed by pieces of slate flying through the air and cutting like so many knives. Still the wind increased in velocity—from sixty to seventy, to eighty, to ninety miles an hour—until at 5:15 p.m. the anemometer on top of the Levy Building registered 96 miles an hour, at which time it was torn from its perch. The wind appeared to begin shifting constantly, calming for a second or two, then resuming with terrific jerks so powerful that it seemed no building could withstand it.

Yet the climax of the storm came only after nightfall. By 8 o'clock, the wind reached a velocity of from 110 to 120 miles an hour, it was estimated by the weather bureau man who stuck to his post in the Levy Building. At the same time the general direction of the wind shifted once more, now from east to southeast and, simultaneously, a tidal wave four to six feet in height swept over the already inundated city. As *The News* reported later in its graphic, first-hand account, this was the moment of greatest destruction. "With a raging sea rolling around them, with a wind so terrific that none could hope to escape its fury, with roofs being torn away and buildings crumbling all around, men, women, and children were huddled like rats in the structures. As buildings crumpled and crashed, hundreds were buried under debris, while thousands were thrown into the waters, some to meet instant death, others to struggle for a time in vain, and yet other thousands to escape death in miraculous and marvelous ways."

Throughout the remainder of Saturday night, there was gradual abatement of the storm. Terror-stricken survivors in homes and buildings that had withstood the elements noted that waters in the first floors began to lower inch by inch. The flood fell back into the bay and into the Gulf more rapidly than it had risen. Sunday morning dawned clear, with bright sunshine flooding the scene of the holocaust. Survivors at first could not comprehend the magnitude of destruction. As yet there was no realization of the frightful toll of life, although soon it was seen that more than a fourth of the area of the city, that nearest the Gulf, had been scraped clean of homes, stores, schools, churches, and orphanages. A huge embankment of compressed wreckage marked the line of the storm's greatest advance toward total annihilation of the city.

The work of rescue and removal of bodies began. Moment by moment the proportions of the tragedy bore in on the dazed minds of the living. By tens, by scores, by hundreds, and then by thousands the death toll mounted. Hospitals were jammed with the injured and dying; public buildings and warehouses were thrown open to provide first aid stations and temporary morgues. With the hot September sun beating down, quick burial of the dead became a necessity. The needs of the living were an even greater problem. With no bridges or wire connections left, word could not be flashed to the outside world of what had happened, yet it was obvious that relief must come, and come quickly, if starvation and pestilence were not to compound the horror.

W. L. Moody's yacht *Pherabe* had miraculously weathered the storm. At 10 o'clock Sunday morning it left the battered docks at Galveston, its improvised crew and passengers hoping to reach Houston fifty miles away by way of the Buffalo Bayou. Richard Spillane and William Delaney were aboard this first vessel, but the ship was unable to go farther than Texas City across Galveston Bay, from whence the two men began walking over five miles of flooded coastal prairie along the railroad track in the direction of Houston. They arrived in time to give details of the destruction to a mass meeting of Houstonians late Sunday afternoon. Shortly before daybreak on Monday a special train left Houston for the stricken city, carrying foodstuffs and clothing and 225 militiamen. Meanwhile, *The News* at Dallas sent two of its most able staff men, Colonel Sterett and George M. Bailey, on the night train for Houston and Galveston.

From late Saturday afternoon the world at large sought an authentic picture of the disaster. By Tuesday a telegraph line had been strung across from the mainland, and one of the first messages was from Charles S. Diehl, general manager of the Associated Press in New York, asking for a statement from Colonel R. G. Lowe. The operating head of *The News* answered with the first authentic estimate of the loss of life and property.

"A summary of conditions prevailing at Galveston is more than human intellect can master," telegraphed the old Scotsman. "The loss of life cannot be computed. No lists could be kept and all is simple guesswork. Those thrown out to sea and buried on the ground wherever found will reach the horrible total of at least three thousand souls. My estimate of the loss of the Island of Galveston and surrounding district is between 4,000 and 5,000 deaths. I do not make this statement in fright or excitement. The whole story will never be told, because it can not be told. The damage to property is anywhere between fifteen and twenty million.

"The necessities of those living are total. Not a single individual escaped property loss. The property on the island is wrecked, fully one half totally swept out of existence. Whatever our needs are can be computed by the world at large from this statement much better than I could possibly summarize them. The help must be immediate."

The response to this cry of distress by State and nation, as well as distant parts of the globe, was memorable and commensurate with the proportions of the disaster. The New York *Herald* took the lead among newspapers of the eastern part of the nation in raising relief funds by popular subscription. To expedite the wise and quick expenditure of relief funds, the New York paper called on the Dallas *News* through its manager, G. B. Dealey, to make purchases and dispatch them to Galveston. Dealey called in the mayor of Dallas, Ben Cabell, and the County Judge of Dallas, Kenneth Foree, to administer these funds with him. Large sums were raised over Texas, and Dallas citizens responded generously to the call for help. Before the task was completed many thousands of dollars were spent in providing emergency relief. The first $500 received were spent for ten carloads of lime, which moved by special train to Texas City and were thence ferried across to Galveston. Dallas drugstores and warehouses were emptied of medicines and disinfectants. For the aftermath of the storm was ghastly, due to the disruption of civic facilities and to the fact that thousands of bodies carried out to sea for burial were washed ashore again by the tide. But martial law was proclaimed by Governor Sayers, threats to public order and public health were soon checked by armed authorities, and within a week the worst of the crisis was over. By September 18, Clara Barton of the American Red Cross had arrived to coordinate disaster relief on the island itself.

The presses of *The News* at Galveston had been stalled, of course, on the afternoon and night of the storm, since the flood waters surrounded the building and climbed well toward the ceiling of the first floor. The customary Saturday night scene of newspaper making had been transformed into one of defenseless watching and waiting, not only by members of *The News'* organization but also by hundreds of other refugees. *The News'* building was perhaps the strongest of its size in Texas and so well built that it went through the storm with damage of only $50— and that was to the iron shutters to doors and windows on the outside. No Sunday paper could be issued, but a small handpress began grinding out handbills later that day. These attempted to list such of the dead as could be identified. It was not until Wednesday morning that *The News* could publish even a semblance of its ordinary edition, yet herein is to be found the first complete story of the catastrophe. What is more, this first edition crystallized the spirit of Galveston, which refused to accept defeat in the face of the appalling experience. Thus its hastily written editorial did as much to restore shattered morale and to plot the future of the seaport as all other agencies combined:

> What *The News* desires most to say to the surviving victims of last Saturday's catastrophe is that, in the knowledge of a world-wide sympathy which is encompassing us, we must not give way to despair. If we have lost all else, we still have life and the future, and it is toward the future that we must devote the energies of our lives.

*The News* also answered the panic of the moment, which counseled removal of the entire city to the mainland:

> Tears and grief must not make us forget our present duties. The blight and ruin which have desolated Galveston are not beyond repair. We must not for a moment think Galveston is to be abandoned because of one disaster, however horrible that disaster has been. . . . It is time for courage of the highest order.

As days and weeks went by, Galveston rapidly righted herself and prepared to make the most of the future. Out of her physical helplessness arose the plan for a great seawall and the raising of the level of the city by hydraulic fill, a protective scheme which proved its success in 1915 when a storm of even greater intensity failed to produce more than a fraction of the havoc of the 1900 hurricane. And, out of the disrupted civic economy, was to evolve the Galveston Plan of city government— a more efficient system of municipal administration which proved a notable advance on the older aldermanic form and was widely adopted in this and other countries. In these and other rehabilitation moves, *The News* again asserted its old leadership on Galveston Island. No better answer could have been given to the report that *The News* would abandon Galveston and "go to live with her daughter at the Three Forks of the Trinity River." But, to scotch the rumor finally and unequivocally, *The News* at Galveston declared in an editorial:

> The Old Lady by the Sea has lived a long time, and she is able not only to hold her own but she has had a life work which she has no idea of abandoning because of the late catastrophe to her people. She will stand with them in the future as she has stood with them in the past; that is until death doth them part.

# *from* LORENZO IN TAOS

*by* MABEL DODGE LUHAN

Mabel Dodge Luhan is best known for the company she keeps. She has long since learned that great people are great fun: perhaps great trouble, but almost without exception the source of great experiences. She maintained a salon of some note in New York before moving to Taos, New Mexico and marrying her present Indian husband, Tony Luhan.

Her most celebrated relationship was that with D. H. Lawrence, author of *Sons and Lovers, Lady Chatterley's Lover,* and many other books, which is told in detail in the following excerpt from her book, *Lorenzo in Taos.* As you will see, the story is written to Mrs. Luhan's friend, "Jeffers."

---

THROUGH THE MONTHS WHILE LAWRENCE AND FRIEDA hesitated about coming to Taos, I willed him to come. Before I went to sleep at night, I drew myself all in to the core of my being where there is a live, plangent force lying passive—waiting for direction. Becoming entirely that, moving with it, speaking with it, I leaped through space, joining myself to the central core of Lawrence, where he was in India, in Australia. Not really speaking to him, but *being* my wish, I became that action that brought him across the sea.

"Come, Lawrence! Come to Taos!" became in me, Lawrence in Taos. This is not prayer, but command. Only those who have exercised it know its danger. And, as before, when I had tried to bring about my wishes, I had Tony with his powerful influence to help me. I told him we must bring Lawrence to Taos because I knew he could do a great deal to help the pueblo. Tony had helped to bring Collier there and he had seen Collier take up the work in behalf of the Indians, and when I told him that if Lawrence came he would bring power for the Indians by his writing, he, too, used his magic to call him. But with some reluctance—just some reluctance to believe that writing about the Indians would help them. His instinct somewhat opposed it. The Indians believe that utterance is loss and that the closed and unrevealed holds power. But I overruled him and he gave way—and together we called Lawrence; and in the darkness and stillness of the night *became* Lawrence in Taos.

In those days it was a long, difficult trip down to Santa Fé over a narrow, dirt road full of ruts and rocks. We always had to rest at least an hour at noon to recover from the bumps and jolts of the car. So when Tony drove me down to Lamy, twenty miles beyond Santa Fé, to the station, we started in the morning and took all day to meet the early evening train.

We stood waiting in the sweet air, all scented as it was from the charcoal kilns burning piñon-wood. That was always the first impression of New Mexico when one got off the train at Lamy station—the thin, keen air full of a smell of incense.

Lawrence and Frieda came hurrying along the platform, she tall and full-fleshed in a suit of pale pongee, an eager look on her pink face, with green, unfocused eyes, and her half-open mouth with the lower jaw pulled a little sideways. Frieda always had a mouth rather like a gunman.

Lawrence ran with short, quick steps at her side. What did he look like to me that first time I saw him? I hardly know. I had an impression of his slim fragility beside Frieda's solidity, of a red beard that was somehow too old for him, and of a nervous incompetence. He was agitated, fussy, distraught, and giggling with nervous grimaces. Tony and I felt curiously inexpressive and stolid confronting them. Frieda was over-expansive, vociferous, with a kind of forced, false *bonhomie*, assumed (it felt so to me, at least) to cover her inability to strike just the real right note. As usual when there is a flurry like that, I died inside and became speechless. Tony is never any help at such a moment, and he just stood there. Somehow I herded them into the lunch room of the station, for we had to eat our supper there because it would be too late when we reached Santa Fé.

We got seated in a row at the counter, the atmosphere splitting and crackling all about us from the singular crash of our meeting. There was a vibratory disturbance around our neighborhood like an upheaval in nature. I did not imagine this: it was so. The Lawrences seemed to be intensely conscious of Tony and somehow embarrassed by him. I made out, in the twinkling of an eye, that Frieda immediately saw Tony and me sexually, visualizing our relationship. I experienced her swift, female measurement of him, and how the shock of acceptance made her blink. In that first moment I saw how her encounters passed through her to Lawrence—how he was keyed to her so that he felt things through her and was obliged to receive life through her, vicariously; but that he was irked by her vision; that he was impatient at being held back in the sex scale. He did not want to apprehend us so and it made him very nervous, but she was his medium, he must see through her and she had to see life from the sex center. She endorsed or repudiated experience from that angle. She was the mother of orgasm and of the vast, lively mystery of the flesh. But no more. Frieda was complete, but limited. Lawrence, tied to her, was incomplete and limited. Like a lively lamb tied to a solid stake, he frisked and pulled in an agony, not Promethean so much as Panic.

Can it be possible that it was in that very first instant when we all came together that I sensed Lawrence's plight and that the womb in me roused to reach out to take him? I think so, for I remember thinking: "He is through with that—he needs another kind of force to propel him . . . the spirit. . . . " The womb behind the womb—the significant, extended, and transformed power that succeeds primary sex, that he was ready, long since, to receive from woman. I longed to help him with that—to be used—to be put to his purpose.

Lawrence scurried to the far seat away from us on the other side of Frieda and she and I sat next each other, with Tony beside me. The meal was an agony—a halt—an unresolved chord, for me, at least, and for Lawrence, I knew. Tony ate his supper with a calm aloofness, unperturbed in the midst of alarm.

Frieda continued her noisy, running ejaculations and breathless bursts of emotional laughter. Lawrence hid behind her big body. I scarcely saw him, but we all knew he was there, all right!

As we made our way out into the dark road where the motor waited, he exclaimed: "Oh! Look how low the stars hang in the southern sky!" It was the first simple, untroubled notice he had taken of anything since they had left the train.

When we reached the automobile, I directed him to the seat beside Tony and took Frieda into the back seat with me, though I wanted it the other way round. But I thought it was easier for Lawrence that way, and that Tony would soothe him down.

As we moved off into the still night, Frieda exclaimed loudly, motioning to Tony's wide back: "He's wonderful! Do you feel him like a rock to lean on?"

"No-o," I answered, hesitantly, unable to confirm her. Her words passed over to Lawrence with a thump. I saw his shoulders twitch. He did not want Frieda to think Tony was a rock to lean on; he could scarcely avoid understanding her unconscious comparison, or feeling again the old, old lack in himself. We ran smoothly on for a little while, and then, quite suddenly, the car simply stopped in the road.

"Well," said Tony. He got out and looked under the hood, though I well knew that, no matter what he saw, he would not understand it. He had never learned much about the motor. Only by having the car checked quite often by garage people, we rarely had any difficulty any more, though when he first learned to drive, things were always going wrong. It was extremely unusual for anything to happen as late as 1922, for Tony had been motoring about the country for four years by that time.

We sat there for ages under the stars while Tony tried different ways to make it go again. We didn't talk much. It was peaceful, but it was growing late and I had not engaged rooms anywhere in Santa Fé. The only hotel possible to stay in then had burned down and I had intended to go to a boarding-house I knew about, for the night. As we sat there, quietly, our emotions subsided, our nerves quieted. Suddenly Frieda cut in: "Get out and see if you can't help him, Lorenzo! Just sitting there! Do get out!"

And Lawrence answered angrily: "You know I don't know anything about automobiles, Frieda! I *hate* them! Nasty, unintelligent, unreliable things!"

"Oh, you and your hates!" she returned, contemptuously.

A moment of silence broken by a vague picking sound out in the front where Tony pried round inside the machinery. And then Lawrence leaned over from the front seat and said: "I am a failure. I am a failure as a man in the world of men. . . . "

Tony got into the car and tried it and it moved again.

"I guess there is some snake around here," he said, as we drove on.

I was flustered when we reached Santa Fé. The city was sleeping. We drove to the Riches' house, where I'd hoped to find rooms, but after rousing the house we were told it was full. Lawrence had unloaded their huge bags onto the sidewalk while they waited for me to go in. Frieda had made him do that. When I came out, I found him stamping his foot in a rage and trying to yell quietly in the night at her: "I won't do it, Frieda! You stop that. . . . "

I interrupted him: "We can't get in there. But I'll tell you what: Witter Bynner knows you're coming. He's always up. He has room. I know he'd love to have you—and we can go to some other friends here."

They were dubious and upset. But there was nothing else to do and we drove over to Bynner's house. Of course he and Spud Johnson were still up. I was so tired by now, I have forgotten how it seemed; anyway, we left the Lawrences to Bynner and we went and slept somewhere else.

"Do you like him, Tony?" I asked, before we closed our eyes.

"I don't know yet," said Tony, but he made a face.

It was a comfortable, jolly scene at Bynner's in the morning. They were finishing breakfast in his gay kitchen, and everyone seemed to be in good spirits.

Frieda and I stood looking at a Chinese painting in the

living-room after they all left the table, and she motioned with her head in her lusty, hearty way: "Un ménage, hein? The young thin one seems rather nice."

We made off as soon as we could, for it was a long, tiring drive we had ahead of us. In the car, Lawrence exploded, peevishly: "These men that leave the world—the struggle and heat of the world—to come and live in pleasant out-of-the-way places—I have little use for them."

"Just what he does himself," I thought. "But he has little use for himself, either. He is a frail cargo that he hauls through life with perpetual distaste."

I find, Jeffers, that I have given you no real, concrete portrait of Lawrence and Frieda. But I have here among their letters a description that a girl wrote of them and sent to a friend and me some time during the year we were all waiting for them to come. This was a girl who had known them in England—the only woman with whom (Frieda told me later) Lawrence was ever "unfaithful" to her! "But it was unsuccessful," she added, with a kind of bitter triumph!

I think I will add this description of them, so you will be able to *see* how he looked:

"Lawrence is tall, but so slightly built and so stooped that he gives the impression of a small man. His head seems too heavy for his very slim body and hangs forward. The whole expression of his figure is of extreme fragility. His movements are quick and sure. He has a very heavy crop of ash-colored hair that is cut round in a bang and falls in sort of Greek-like locks. In contrast to his hair, is a very soft, silky beard of bright red. He has very large, wide-apart grey eyes, a long, slender face with a chin that is out of proportion long, a defect that is concealed by the aforesaid beard. His under-lip protrudes from the dainty decoration of the beard in a violent red that makes his beard look pink. In the midst of all this, is a very podgy, almost vulgar, certainly undistinguished nose. There! Can you see him?

"On the whole, it seems foolish to talk about Lawrence to

anyone who has read his books, for he is all there, more than any other author I ever knew. *Sons and Lovers* is a fairly authentic picture of his own life. I think the events are absolutely true. His mother's death almost killed Lawrence. He had such a frightful mother-complex, and still has, I fancy, that the book *had* to be written. His wife told me that when he wrote the death of his mother, she had a perfectly terrible time with him for many weeks.

"But what you want to know particularly, I suppose, is what he is as a human being. He is one of the most fascinating men I ever met. The first time I ever saw him, he talked for a whole afternoon, almost steadily. He will do this at once and without the slightest self-consciousness if he feels a sympathy in his listener. He talks as brilliantly as he writes, and as frankly. Have you read *Women in Love?* because that *is* Lawrence—his word. It is his final philosophy. It pours out of him like an inspired message, and no matter how much you may differ when you are away from him, or how little able you are to follow his own particular mysticism, he makes you believe it when he is with you.

"But at the slightest touch of adverse criticism or hostility, Lawrence becomes violent. His vituperation is magnificent. I have never heard its equal. He spares none. He has quarreled with everyone. He says he has no friends that he has not quarreled with. And yet all these same friends, I noticed, are very likely to come back for the same treatment again and again. Lawrence is a Puritan, really, and his intellectual reaction against it is so violent that he hurls himself against it with all of himself, destroying himself as he does it. In the marvelously sweet side of his nature, he is inarticulate. And yet he is the gentlest, kindest person in all human relations that anyone could be on this earth. The peasants around where he lived in Cornwall adored him, blindly. They looked upon him as the new Messiah come to lead the world out of the dark into a light that they couldn't understand, but which they had infinite faith in, simply because he was he.

"Lawrence lives the life of a workman. He says that no matter

· 315 ·

how much money he has, he always will live just the same. I think this is true. When I visited them in Cornwall, he and his wife lived in a little stone cottage of three rooms. It was spotlessly clean, mostly done by Lawrence. All their cooking was done on an open fire in the living-room. I have even known Lawrence to do the washing, though they usually sent it out. Money means nothing to Lawrence. He is very frugal, with all the thriftiness of his working-class background, but he would share whatever he had with another without a thought. The little, spotless, sunny house in Cornwall had the most beautiful simplicity that I have ever seen.

"His wife is a big, rosy German, who, as the daughter of a Prussian officer, never knew anything but luxury in her girlhood. She is highly impractical now, and the little she knows of housework, Lawrence taught her. She is an expansive child-nature, very sunny and rich, living only in her emotions. The story of their love life is all to be found in the poems, *Look, We Have Come Through.* She is really all light and sun while Lawrence is dark; there seems to be always a weight on him. He is rarely really gay—he is truly the sombre Anglo-Saxon, which he hates with a bitter hatred.

"After all, Lawrence is best known in his books, for he writes all the things he cannot say. And yet he says such a lot! But the inner tumult wears him out. He is very fragile, physically. He says that he is always well when he is happy. It is said that he has something the matter with his lungs, yet not since he was a child has a doctor ever found any actual lung trouble. When he was a little boy, I believe, his lungs were affected, but he seems to have outgrown it.

"People are always making pilgrimages to him. He hates it, but is infinitely sweet to them. His awareness of other people is unbelievable. When you are with him, you feel that there is not a corner of your mind or spirit or whatever you have that Lawrence doesn't see and be tolerant of. And he bares himself perfectly frankly. When a mood or an impulse is in him, there is no such thing as repression. It all comes out in a mighty gust.

"He cannot live in big cities. The excitement kills him. He is too aware all the time. The war was a horrible thing to him, came darned near killing him, through the intensity of his emotion about it."

We passed alongside the Rio Grande River in the clear morning sunlight. In the warm valleys between Santa Fé and Taos the apples were ripening and the air was sweet from the juicy apricots. Corn, wheat, and alfalfa filled the fields, and the Mexicans and Indians were singing.

The September day was sunny and still about us all the way home, but when we made our final long climb up the mountain to reach the table-land of Taos Valley and pulled round the curve at the top, we saw the Sacred Mountain over behind Taos looming half-darkened by cloud shadows that hastened over it in great eagle shapes. Wide wings of eagles spread, sinister, over the huddling mountain while its peaks, forming a wide bow, held the last red rays of the sun.

Lawrence caught his breath. Everyone is surprised at that first view of Taos Valley—it is so beautiful. The mountains, eighteen miles away, curve half round it in a crescent, and the desert lies within its dark encircling grasp. Taos is an oasis, emerald-green beyond the sage-brush, drinking water from the high mountain lakes and streams.

We had just that one long look at Taos in sunlight and shadow, Jeffers, those few moments of sharp light with the eagle clouds in shadow flight across the face of it, when a long, slow flash of lightning zigzagged out of the sky above the mountain and disappeared into it like a snake. And then came, all of a sudden, a terrific explosion of thunder that seemed to fill the whole valley far and near—out of the stillness, out of the windless sky—with a crash so sharp and wild that we could only cower for an instant and cover our ears with our hands.

Tony stopped the car at once, and as he hurried to get out and put up the side curtains, he threw me a swift, strange look. He was just in time to get us covered, for the rain broke over us in stark sheets, straight down in undivided steel sheets, nipping cold and shutting out all the world around us. It turned almost immediately to hail, battering upon the top of the car like cannon-balls, cracking open on the ground like splitting shells; hail like large stones piled up around the car until the earth was covered with them, and the air was suddenly like a winter night. Crash after crash of thunder, and the lightning zigging now on all sides as though a parent snake had peopled all the world in one immediate creation and filled the universe with serpentine light. East and west and north in turn flashed up out of the rain-darkened land. We saw now Taos, now far Colorado, or the low foot-hills east of Ranchos. Only the south, from where we had come that day, lay open and free of the storm.

In the car, no one spoke till Tony said to Lawrence: "The white people say that the thunder comes from clouds hitting each other, but the Indians know better," and Lawrence giggled in a high, childish, nervous way.

The storm did not last long, but when it was over, all the crops in Taos Valley lay on the ground, ruined. There were practically no harvests taken in and the Indians and Mexicans suffered all that year.

It was dark when we reached our hill, a mile out of Taos village. I was shaking and weary, as always after the long, tiring ride. I led the Lawrences into the house and wished I myself were free to leave them and go to bed. But again we had to eat. I had hoped for so long that Lawrence would like our house. It is a strange house, slow grown and with a kind of nobility in its proportions, and with all the past years of my life showing there in Italian and French furniture, pictures from many hands, books from New York, bronzes from Venice, Chinese paintings, and Indian things. And always a fire burning in the fireplaces—"to make life," as Tony says.

Supper was ready. I saw the candles burning on the table in the big, dim dining-room and I led the way down the five round steps from the living-room. I was in a blind retreat behind my face, as always when I get tired from one thing or another: when there is a weight to pull for too long and things don't flow of themselves. After a little while I don't care any more what happens if things don't go of their own accord. Then I am alone, separated, divested of all wishes, indifferent to the whole outside world, forgetful of my high plans and hopes.

I sat them down at the round table, scarcely aware of anything. Blind, departed, nobody home. When I rang the bell to call Albidia, Lawrence giggled as he looked around into the surrounding dimness, from the island of our lighted space, and he said: "It's like one of those nasty little temples in India!"

I didn't care what he said. I longed to get through—through with the day and away from them to my own room and to sleep— sleep—sleep!

Now this had all been a very inauspicious beginning, hadn't it, Jeffers? And yet when I saw Lawrence the next morning, none of that mattered. He was as sunny and good as a rested child and his wide-apart eyes were blue like gentians.

I was rested, too, and we took a good look at each other, neither of us seeming to be doing so. I'm not going to waste any time saying how or why, Jeffers; you must just take it as a fact when I tell you briefly that, from the first, Lawrence and I knew each other through and through as though we were of one blood. In fact, he told me many times afterwards, both in irritation and in sympathy, that I seemed like his sister. We never knew each other any more than we did at the beginning, for it was complete and immediate in the first hours. I wonder if this is not generally true. We do not know people by experience; experience through the passing of time merely ratifies the first full realization we have received entire. With some people it is a thin surface one penetrates, and bottom is soon reached; pleasant, shallow folk to know and like and find always the same. But of course there is a deep knowing when there is depth to sound. Like a diver and with instantaneous perception one plunges through the universe contained in some people, finding all time and all space, with what the past has won and everything that has bloomed and withered on this earth. Generally, however, sooner or later one touches bottom in them. When I was a girl, I had a friend named Violet. She was only twenty, but she was wise. I lost her, for she died; and since her there have been only two people I never reached the end of: Tony and Lawrence.

"You have gone a long way, but I have gone a longer," Lawrence said to me soon.

I had a friend from Buffalo days staying with me: Bessie Wilkinson. One of those prematurely white-haired widows who skim rapidly about the world like swallows, dipping here and there, enjoying themselves, taking life lightly. Lawrence seemed to like her. There was no danger. She did not make Frieda glower, either. Anything that was likely to make Frieda glower, Lawrence avoided. When he was at outs with her, he was thrown off his balance, for she was the root of his existence. He drew life from her so that when anything shook or disturbed that even flow, he was like a cut flower, drying up.

Bessie and I helped them to settle into Tony's house. They liked it very much, and it looked as though we should all have a happy time together.

They were to take their suppers at our house, and when we finished eating that night, Lawrence started telling us about the people on the boat. He was perfectly horrified at the way movie people go on. There had been a great many Hollywood people among the passengers, coming back, evidently, from making an island picture, and apparently Lawrence had observed them to the last!

Their unrestraint and their wild, care-free love-making amazed and at the same time infuriated him. He became acquainted with some of them. They were like a new species of creature he had never seen before. He watched and registered every move—not like a scientist, with coolness and interest—not like a poet—more like a dog in the manger, really, come to think of it, for he was so angry, so incensed when he told us about them. And evidently he had not got away without an antagonistic scene on board—for in the end he had a scene with some of them, and

· 320 ·

they, angered too—"jeered at him," as Frieda says in the following note.

Lawrence made us *see* that ship; the long, slow passage through the blue sea, the reckless, sensational crowd on board, and his own watching, angry, righteous, puritanical presence among them.

Tony was leaving to go to the Apache fiesta the next day and I begged him to take Lawrence along. Lawrence and Bessie Freeman. I wanted awfully to go, too, but there was not room for Frieda, so I knew I had to stay home with her. Tony didn't want to take Lawrence, but I made him!

He is so good-natured, Jeffers, and I am always *making* him do things that are nice for other people, but that leave him indifferent. You see, I wanted Lawrence to get into the Indian thing *soon*. I counted so much on that. On his understanding, his deep, deep understanding of the mystery and the other-worldness, as he would call it, of Indian life. My need to bring Lawrence and the Indians together was like an impulse of the evolutionary will, apart from me, using me for its own purposes. I could no more help trying to bring this about than I could help staying with Tony. I got tired, bored, indifferent, as with a difficult task; I wished I'd never started it; at such times all I cared for was to rest; but inevitably the same strong compulsion would return after a few hours of quiet.

So Bessie and Tony and Lawrence were to leave for the Apache Reservation, where they would have a dry camp on the side of a hill, opposite the Apache camp, where hundreds of tepees would be set up.

I forget who else was there staying with me at that time, but there were evidently others, for Frieda, in answer to a note from me, speaks of our all going over to her house:

"Dear Mabel—

"I am glad you feel like that. It's true, what you say. I have suffered tortures sometimes when Lawrence talked to people, when they drew him out just to 'see his goods' and then jeered at him. I was happy last night. And for all that, you will detest Lawrence sometimes and sometimes he talks bosh—but that is so human in him that he isn't 'suberbo.' It's a joy to me that Tony wants to go with him—but tell Tony that he is frail, he can't stand so very much! Won't you all come here again after your evening meal? I am cleaning and washing.

Love<br>F.

Yes, I will say if there is anything. I only wish with all my heart we had known you long ago!"

She and I had a long talk that day. She was good company when Lawrence was not there, as is the case with nearly all wives. She talked with heartiness and vigor—always with a real, deep, human warmth, albeit sometimes with such obtuseness, such lack of comprehension. So long as one talked of people and their possibilities from the point of view of sex, she was grand. She had a real understanding of that. But one had to be careful all the time—to hide what one knew—to stay back with her. Any reference to the spirit, or even to consciousness, was antagonistic to her. The groping, suffering, tragic soul of man was so much filthiness to that healthy creature. Offensive. I learned early to keep away from her any sight or sound of unhappiness that was not immediately caused by some mishap of the bed—for really she admitted no other. You see, Jeffers, she was hedged in by her happy flesh, for she had not broken her shell when I knew her. Yet Frieda was very alive to all the simple sights and sounds of the earth. To flowers and birds; to the horses and cows and sheep. She responded to things vigorously with boisterous explosiveness, and with passionate "oh's" and "ah's!"

When we first drove them out to the pueblo and they saw it planted there at the foot of the mountain, solid, eternal, and as though its roots were fastened deep in the earth of which it was built, Lawrence was silent and seemingly unaware; but Frieda expressed herself all over the place: "Oh! It is *wonderful!* How ancient and how perfect! Oh, to think it will probably be spoiled! Oh, Mabel, why don't you *buy* it and keep it like this forever!"

"Oh, Frieda! Don't be vulgar," Lawrence broke in on her delight. "Of course Mabel can't *buy* it. And if it has to go, it will go."

I felt, though, that he was getting it through her, experiencing it, seeing it, and that she was, in a sense, giving it to him. Quite soon afterwards, I think, Frieda and I were alone and again out in the pueblo together, for I remember the cottonwood branches over our heads when these words come back to me. I believe it was while Lawrence was away at the Apache fiesta. I said to her: "Frieda, it seems to me that Lawrence lives through you. That you have to feel a thing before he can feel it. That you are, somehow, the source of his feeling about things."

"You don't know how right you are," she answered. "He has to get it all from me. Unless I am there, he feels nothing. Nothing. And he gets his books from me," she continued, boastfully. "Nobody knows that. Why, I have done pages of his books for him. In *Sons and Lovers* I actually wrote pages into it. Oh, it was terrible when he was writing that one! I thought it would kill him. That mother . . . "

It was no time at all before Frieda's grievance—her great grievance—appeared on the surface. "Everyone thinks Lawrence is so wonderful. Well, I am something in myself, too. The Kot thinks I'm not good enough for him!"

"*Who?*" I broke in.

"Koteliansky. My enemy. He thinks I should just be willing to scrub the floor for Lorenzo. And he would like to separate us. Well, I'd like to see *him* live with Lawrence a month—a week! He might be surprised."

It was right away in these first few days that Frieda and I had together that she told me so much. Afterwards there was nothing between us. This probably added to her old sore feeling of not being appreciated as much as Lawrence was. We started being friends. She was excellent company. She had the gift of immediate intimacy that I had myself, which, compared to ordinary intercourse, is like a live baby beside a talking doll. And there was a quick, spontaneous flow between us. But as soon as Lawrence returned to the scene, he stopped it. He was, in all possible ways, jealous, just as she was. He was annoyed that Frieda and I had become friends, and not only jealous of me, but jealous of her as well. The flow immediately ceased between Frieda and me and started between Lawrence and me. He somehow switched it.

It is terribly difficult for me to explain these things to you, Jeffers, these tides and currents that comprise the relationships between people—the fluid come and go that constitute so different a reality from the solid, staring, fixed appearance of faces.

Sometimes I see all of us human creatures, Jeffers, as so many gases, stimulating, beneficent, or poisonous, occasionally bursting into flame, or transformed from one degree to another by meeting a new element. Anyway, the least that we are appears, actually, in the flesh, and the truth lies behind bone and muscle.

I saw that Lawrence and Frieda tried to hold each other in a fixed, unaltered, invariable combination. Each of them immediately checked every permutation that the undomesticated, wandering instinct in the other sought to indulge. Anything that deflected the flow between them, deprived one or the other of his lawful, oh, so lawful! prey, though neither one nor the other was satisfied with what he or she had.

Frieda told me about the two times Lawrence had evaded her. One time was with the American girl in Cornwall when she was absent for a visit to her mother, I think. She had returned to the little house and found a feeling in the air that she had not left there. She forced Lawrence to tell her about it and then showed the girl the door. It had, or at least so he told her, been a miserable failure, anyway. The other one had been a young farmer, also in Cornwall.

"Was there really a *thing* between them?" I asked.

"I think so. I was dreadfully unhappy," she answered.

"It is a woman's place to hold a man *centered*," Lawrence said one day when he and Frieda were momentarily in harmony. "And it is a man's place to keep the woman centered," he added.

Well, when he came back after that few days with Tony and Bessie Wilkinson and found Frieda and I had flowed together in sympathy, he was in a rage. But it must be admitted once and for all Frieda and I were friends and could have been good friends and had fun together if he had never returned.

That very evening he asked me if I would work on a book with him. He said he wanted to write an American novel that would express the life, the spirit, of America and he wanted to write it around me—my life from the time I left New York to come out to New Mexico; my life, from civilization to the bright, strange world of Taos; my renunciation of the sick old world of art and artists, for the pristine valley and the upland Indian lakes. I was thrilled at the thought of this. To work with him, to give him myself—Tony—Taos—every part of the untold and undefined experience that lay in me like a shining, indigestible jewel that I was unable either to assimilate or to spew out! I had been holding on to it for so long, solitary and aware, but helplessly inexpressive!

Of course it was for this I had called him from across the world—to give him the truth about America: the false, new external America in the east, and the true, primordial, undiscovered America that was preserved, living, in the Indian bloodstream. I assented with an inward eagerness, but with the usual inexpressive outwardness. I saw him, though, reading my joy, and he gave me a small, happy, sympathetic nod.

I have among my papers a part of an article he wrote when he came back from the Apache Reservation. I don't know where the end of the manuscript is or if he ever published it. It does not seem to me to be very good. Was it because Frieda was not along with him on that occasion?

"Supposing one fell on to the moon, and found them talking English; it would be something the same as falling out of the open world plump down here in the middle of America. 'Here' means New Mexico, the South West, wild and woolly and artistic and Indian and sage-brush desert.

"It is all rather like comic opera played with solemn intensity. All the wildness and woollyness and westernity and motor-cars and art and sage and savage are so mixed up, so incongruous, that it is a farce, and everybody knows it. But they refuse to play it as farce. The wild and woolly section insists on being heavily dramatic, bold and bad on purpose; the art insists on being real American and artistic; motor-cars insist on being thrilled, moved to the marrow; high-brows insist on being ecstatic; Mexicans insist on being Mexicans, squeezing the last black drop of macabre joy out of life; and Indians wind themselves in white cotton sheets like Hamlet's father's ghost, with a lurking smile.

"And here am I, a lone lorn Englishman, tumbled out of the known world of the British Empire on to this stage: for it persists in seeming like a stage to me, and not like the proper world.

"Whatever makes a proper world, I don't know. But surely two elements are necessary: a common purpose and a common sympathy. I can't see any common purpose. The Indians and Mexicans don't even seem very keen on dollars. That full moon of a silver dollar doesn't strike me as overwhelmingly hypnotic out here. As for a common sympathy or understanding, that's beyond imagining. West is wild and woolly and bad on purpose, commerce is a little self-conscious about its own pioneering importance—Pioneers, Oh Pioneers!—high-brow is bent on getting to the bottom of everything and saving the lost soul down there in the depths, Mexican is bent on being Mexican and not yet gringo, and the Indian is all the things that all the others aren't. And so everybody smirks at everybody else, and says, tacitly: 'Go on. You do your little stunt, and I'll do mine'—and they're like the various troupes in a circus, all performing at once, with nobody for Master of Ceremonies.

"It seems to me, in this country, everything is taken so damn seriously that nothing remains serious. Nothing is so farcical as insistent drama. Everybody is lurkingly conscious of this. Each section or troupe is quite willing to admit that all the other sections are buffoon stunts. But it itself is the real thing, solemnly bad in its badness, good in its goodness, wild in its wildness,

· 326 ·

woolly in its woollyness, arty in its artiness, deep in its depths, in a word, earnest.

"In such a masquerade of earnestness, a bewildered straggler out of the far-flung British Empire is myself! Don't let me for a moment pretend to *know* anything. I know less than nothing. I simply gasp like a bumpkin in a circus-ring, with the horse-lady leaping over my head, the Apache war-whooping in my ear, the Mexican staggering under crosses and thorns and bumping me as he goes by, the artist whirling colours across my dazzled vision, the high-brows solemnly declaiming at me from all the cross-roads. If, dear reader, you, being the audience who has paid to come in, feel that you must take up an attitude to me, let it be one of amused pity.

"One has to take sides. First, one must be either pro-Mexican or pro-Indian: then, either art or intellect: then, Republican or Democrat: and so on. But as for me, poor lost lamb, if I bleat at all in the circus-ring, it will be my own shorn lonely bleat of a lamb who's lost his mother.

"But I arrived at a moment of crisis. I suppose every man always does, here. The crisis is a thing called the Bursum Bill, and it affects the Pueblo Indians. I wouldn't know a thing about it, if I needn't. But Bursum Bursum Bursum!! the Bill! the Bill! the Bill! Twitchell, Twitchell, Twitchell!! O Mr. Secretary Fall, Fall, Fall! Oh Mr. Secretary Fall! you bad man, you good man, you Fall, you Rise, you Fall!!! The Joy Survey, Oh Joy. No Joy, Once Joy, now Woe! Woe! Whoa! Whoa Bursum! Whoa Bill! Whoa-a-a!

"Like a Lindsay Boom-Boom bellowing it goes on in my unwonted ears, till I *have* to take heed. And then I solemnly sit down in a chair and read the Bill, the Bill, the Printed Bursum Bill, Section one-two-three-four-five-six-seven, whereas and wherefore and heretofore, right to the damned and distant end. Then I start the Insomuch-as of Mr. Francis Wilson's Brief concerning the Bill. Then I read Mr. C's passionate article against, and Mrs. H's hatchet-stroke summary against, and Mr. M's sharp-knife jugglery *for* the bill. After which I feel I'm getting mixed up, and Bear ye one another's Bursum. Then lamb-like, ram-like, I feel I'll do a bit of butting too, on a stage where every known animal butts.

"But first I toddle to a corner and, like a dog when music is going on in the room, put my paws exasperatedly over my ears and my nose to the ground, and groan softly. So doing, I try to hypnotise myself back into my old natural world, outside the circus-tent, where horses don't buck and prance so much, and where not every lady is leaping through the hoop and crashing through the paper confines of the universe at every hand's turn.

"Try to extricate my lamb-like soul into its fleecy isolation, and then adjust myself. Adjust myself to that much-talked-of actor in the Wild West Show, the Red Indian.

"Don't imagine, indulgent reader, that I'm talking *at* you or down to you, or trying to put something over you. No no, imagine me lamb-like and bewildered, muttering softly to myself, between soft groans, trying to make head-or-tail of myself in my present situation. And then you'll get the spirit of these effusions.

"The first Indians I really saw were the Apaches in the Apache Reservation of this state. We drove in a motor-car, across desert and mesa, down canyons and up divides and along arroyos and so forth, two days, till at afternoon our two Indian men ran the car aside from the trail and sat under a pine-tree to comb their long black hair and roll it into the two roll-plaits that hang in front of their shoulders, and put on all their silver and turquoise jewellery and their best blankets: because we were nearly there. On the trail were horsemen passing, and wagons with Ute Indians and Navajos.

" 'Da donde viene, Usted?' . . .

"We came at dusk from the high shallows and saw on a low crest the points of Indians tents, the tepees, and smoke, and silhouettes of tethered horses and blanketed figures moving. In the shadow a rider was following a flock of white goats that flowed like water. The car ran to the top of the crest, and there was a hollow basin with a lake in the distance, pale in the dying light. And this shallow upland basin dotted with Indian tents, and the fires flickering in front, and crouching blanketed figures, and horsemen crossing the dusk from tent to tent, horsemen in big steeple hats sitting glued on their ponies, and bells tinkling, and dogs yapping, and tilted wagons trailing in on the trail below, and a smell of wood-smoke and of cooking, and wagons coming in from far off, and tents pricking on the ride of the round *vallum*, and horsemen dipping down and emerging again, and more red sparks of fires glittering, and crouching bundles of women's figures squatting at a fire before a little tent made of boughs, and little girls in full petticoats hovering, and wild, barefoot boys throwing bones at thin-tailed dogs, and tents away in the distance, in the growing dark, on the slopes and the trail crossing the floor of the hollow, in the low dusk.

"There you had it all, as in the hollow of your hand. And to my heart, born in England and kindled with Fenimore Cooper, it wasn't the wild and woolly west, it was the nomad nations gathering still in the continent of hemlock trees and prairies. The Apaches came and talked to us, in their steeple black hats, and plaits wrapped with beaver fur, and their silver and beads and turquoise. Some talked strong American, and some talked only Spanish; and they had strange lines in their faces.

"The two kivas, the rings of cut aspen trees stuck in the ground like the walls of a big hut of living trees, were on the plain, at either end of the race-track. And as the sun went down, the drums began to beat, the drums with their strong-weak, strong-weak pulse that beat on the plasm of one's tissue. The car slid down to the south kiva. Two elderly men held the drum and danced the *pát-pat, pát-pat* quick beat on flat feet, like birds that move from the feet only, and sang with wide mouths, *Hie! Hie! Hie! Hy-a! Hy-a! Hy-a! Hie! Hie! Hie! Ay-away-away—!!* Strange dark faces with wide, shouting mouths and rows of small, close-set teeth, and strange lines on the faces, part ecstasy, part mockery, part humorous, part devilish, and the strange, calling, summoning sound in a wild song-shout, to the *thud-thud* of the drum. Answer of the same from the other kiva, as of a challenge accepted. And from the gathering darkness around, men drifting slowly in, each carrying an aspen-twig, each joining to cluster close in two rows upon the drum, holding each his aspen twig inwards, their faces all together, mouths all open in the song-shout, and all of them all the time going on the two feet, *pát-pat, pát-pat, pát-pat*, to the *thud-thud* of the drum and the strange, plangent yell of the chant, edging inch by inch, *pát-pat, pát-pat, pát-pat*, sideways in a cluster along the track, towards the distant cluster of the challengers from the other kiva, who were sing-shouting and edging onwards, sideways in the dusk, their faces all together, their leaves all inwards, towards the drum, and their feet going *pát-pat, pát-pat*, on the dust, with their buttocks stuck out a little, faces all inwards shouting open-mouthed to the drum, and half laughing, half mocking, half devilment, half fun. *Hie! Hie! Hie!—Hie—away—awaya!* The strange yell, song, shout rising so lonely in the dusk, as if pine-trees could suddenly, shaggily sing. Almost a pre-animal sound, full of triumph in life, and devilment against other life, and mockery, and humorousness, and the *pát-pat, pát-pat* of the rhythm. Sometimes more youths coming up, and as they draw near, laughing, they give the war-whoop, like a turkey giving a startled squeal and then gobble-gobbling with laughter—*Ugh!*—the shriek half laughter, then the gobble-gobble-gobble like a great demoniac chuckle. The chuckle in the war whoop.

"Listening, an acute sadness, and a nostalgia, unbearable, yearning for something, and a sickness of the soul came over me. The gobble-gobble chuckle in the whoop surprised me in my very tissues. Then I got used to it, and could hear in it the humour, the playfulness, and then, beyond that, the mockery and the diabolical, pre-human, pine-tree fun of cutting dusky throats and letting the blood spurt out unconfined. Gobble-agobble-agobble, the unconfined, loose blood, gobble-agobble-agobble, the dead, mutilated lump, gobble-agobble, agobble, the fun, the greatest man-fun.

"So I felt. I may have been all wrong, and other folks may feel much. . . . "

The article breaks off here; and then I have two other paragraphs descriptive of the happenings of the following day:

"We waited three hours for the race to begin, and it was over in half an hour. Then the two groups of racers clustered on their drums again at opposite ends of the track, the drumming began, the ritual song, and slowly the two groups advanced to meet in the centre of the course. They should dance the bird tread all the way, but only the elder ones do so. The others just shuffle. Like the white boy, who stares with a kind of half-ashamed, half-defiant outcast look from side to side.

"The groups meet in the centre, and circle round each other, continuing the singing, while there is a great whooping of the elders. The crowd presses close, and gorgeous Apache women on big horses fling little round loaves of bread, and apples, and small peaches, at random into the cluster of dancers, who catch and pick up from the ground such things as they want. The daubed racers are dully singing, the two drums thud; only the white boy glowers silent. Then the two sides have passed one another, and proceed to their respective goals. There is one tall, lanky young Indian with a square of red cloth hanging at his rear. One of the elders lifts this hind flap and switches the small, loin-clothed posterior of the lanky one as he passes. . . . "

Lawrence hurried over to our house in the morning ready to begin our work together. As I never dressed early in the morning, but took a sun-bath on the long, flat, dirt roof outside my bedroom, I called to him to come up there. I didn't think to dress for him. I had on moccasins, even if my legs were bare; and I had a voluminous, soft, white cashmere thing like a burnous. He hurried through my bedroom, averting his eyes from the un-made bed as though it were a repulsive sight, though it was not so at all. My room was all white and blue, with whitewashed walls, sunny, bright, and fresh—and there was no dark or equivocal atmosphere in it, or in my blue blankets, or in the white chest of drawers or the little blue chairs. But Lawrence, just passing through it, turned it into a brothel. Yes, he did: that's how powerful he was. We went out into the sun on the long, flat roof. The house seemed to be sailing on a quiet green sea—the desert behind us bordered by the cedar-covered foot-hills, and the alfalfa fields in front, and Taos Mountain north-east of us, looking benevolent that day.

That mountain really seemed to have a conscious life of its own. The Indians, passing upon it all through the centuries, have filled it with greater life, and the Pueblo canyon is full of magic—from the perpetual passage of Indians back and forth upon their mysterious errands. The mountain changes its moods: sometimes it is dark and unfriendly, and sometimes it radiates joy. But it is always alive, always alive.

We squatted down in the hot earth of the roof, and the sun shone on Lawrence's red beard, making it look like the burning bush. He dropped his chin on his chest in a gloomy silence and I waited for him to say something. The birds were singing all around, and the pigeons, cosy on the roofs of their upraised cottages, were roucouling as they paced amorously up and down before each other. Everything was calm and quiet and lovely until Lawrence began to talk.

"I don't know how Frieda's going to feel about this," and he threw an angry look over towards their cottage that lay there, harmlessly enough, like a cat in the sun, with no sign of her about.

"Well, surely she will understand . . . "

"Understand! She can't *understand* anything! It's the German mind. Now, I have always had a sympathy for the Latin mind—for the quick, subtle, Latin spirit that . . . but the north German psyche is inimical to it. The blond conquerors! The soldier soul, strong because it does *not* understand—indelicate and robust!" He ran rapidly on and on. I was immediately on his side. He made a perfect cleavage between the blond, obtuse, and conquering German and ourselves. We were Latin together, subtle, perceptive, and infinitely nimble. And from that moment to this I have been Latin, and Frieda has been Goth.

And also in that spoken sympathy Lawrence drew me to him

and would hold me, I believed, forever, for he knew that he and I were the same kind of people. As we were. As we always were.

In that hour, then, we became more intimate, psychically, than I had ever been with anyone else before. It was a complete, stark approximation of spiritual union, a seeing of each other in a luminous vision of reality. And how Lawrence could see!

I won't try to tell you what we said, Jeffers, because I can't remember. I could invent sentences that would give you an idea of our conversation; I could almost tell you what words passed, but not quite. I will not put into this story, Jeffers, a single thing that I have not actually, whole and real, in my memory. What remains there must be the essential truth for *me*, no matter how slight it may turn out to be. Don't you think so? Don't you think that all that was not ours finally escapes us? I do. I always mistrust, in written or recounted memories, those long, interesting conversations that we sometimes enjoy very much. Because talk, real talk between people, is as unexpected and surprising to them as it is uttered as any movement in nature. It flows through one like the wind. The fire shapes, the forms of clouds, or waves, or sand, are sudden and immediate, and as quickly gone. Does the sea remember every pattern in the sand? One *cannot remember* one's own real talk. One cannot remember the quick, evanescent, exact movements of one's own independent soul. The most one can do is to recall the general feeling or mood of a long conversation in after years.

That is why, Jeffers, in telling you about this thing between us all, I feel I am perhaps quite unconvincing. It is all about the invisible, intangible, real world; and with so very little to make it appear concrete. Curiously enough, I suppose that if I were to fake it a little, I could make it come more true for you, but that, Jeffers, would be art—and I want this to be a real scrap of life itself, for that is the only respectful way to attempt to give you anything of Lawrence.

But it was in that first long talk together that he repudiated Frieda so strongly, with an intention, apparently, to mark forever in my eyes his desperate and hopeless bondage to one who was the antithesis of himself and his predilections: the enemy of life—his life—the hateful, destroying female.

"You cannot imagine what it is to feel the hand of that woman on you if you are sick," he confided in a fierce, lowered voice. "The heavy, German hand of the flesh. . . . No one can know . . ."

A great desire to save him, who could not save himself, was surging in me. I *would* save him!

As we got up to go into the house, his eyes shining blue and seeming to be assuaged, he paused an instant and said: "The burden of consciousness is too great for a woman to carry. She has enough to bear with her ever-recurring menstruation." But I was glad at last for being what I was, for knowing, sensing, feeling all I did, since now it was to have its real, right use at last.

Lawrence went downstairs and I stayed to throw on my dress and my stockings. He was in the big room when I came a few minutes later, and I walked over to his house with him. Being with him keyed one up so that everything was humming and one felt light and happy. We were happy together. We reinforced each other and made each other feel invulnerable: more solid and more sure. When his querulousness left him, he was such fun! He was without fear and without reproach and needed no longer to carp and criticize.

As we strolled over to Tony's gate and entered his alfalfa field, we saw Frieda, in the distance, hanging clothes on the line. "She is mad!" chuckled Lawrence, giggling.

As we got nearer, she saw us coming and stopped what she was doing. The big, bonny woman, she stood there in her pink cotton dress and faced us with her bare arms akimbo. Lawrence was laughing almost delightedly into his beard and bending down his face to hide. At the distance of two or three hundred yards one could read the mounting rage gathering in her, the astonishment and the self-assurance.

"I guess I'll go back," I murmured, and as he did not press me to go on, I turned and retreated before that figure of wrath.

It was not my way to fight in the open—although I certainly would fight!

The long, complete talk on the roof was practically the only time I saw him alone. I had supposed, of course, that he would have his own way about his work at least, but no. I did not see anything more of them that day until evening, but when we met again, they had had it out. There was a tired serenity about both of them when they came over, like pale sunshine on a battlefield. Lawrence looked diminished. He said to me, aside, when he had a chance: "Frieda thinks we ought to work over in our house."

"With her *there?*" I asked.

How could I talk to Lawrence and tell him my feelings and experiences with *Frieda* in the room? To tell him was one thing— that was like talking to oneself—but one couldn't tell her *anything*. She wouldn't understand and she would make one terribly uncomfortable and self-conscious.

"Well, not in the room—all the time. She has her work to do."

Then and there I saw it was over and I should never have the opportunity to get at him and give him what I thought he needed or have, myself, the chance to unload my accumulation of power.

# HERO FOR O. HENRY

*by* DORA NEILL RAYMOND

Dora Neill Raymond was born in El Paso, Texas, and apparently never got over it. She has subsequently become a scholar and biographer of note. She has done much literary criticism and is the author of such learned works as *British Policy and Opinion During the Franco-Prussian War*, *Political Career of Lord Byron*, and *Oliver's Secretary: John Milton in an Era of Revolt*.

And then the apparently indelible El Paso influence went to work on her and she wrote her prize-winning *Captain Lee Hall of Texas*. Captain Lee Hall was a worthy subject, adequately treated. A full perusal of the book will repay any reader interested in the subject, but it seems that the general reader may be more especially interested in the small section devoted to O. Henry's ranch experiences. That section is herewith reprinted.

---

A CHARACTERISTIC OF A TEXAS RANCH IN THE EIGHTIES WAS the large number of the manager's family living on it. Lee Hall had with him on the *D. H. and D.* his brother Dick and wife, his brother Frank, and, in the spring of 1882, his father and mother. The parents came for a visit, bringing for a longer stay Willie Porter, a youth of eighteen. Porter had clerked in his uncle's drugstore and had exercised his story-telling powers by retailing to the youth of Greensboro Dr. Hall's occasional accounts of the activities of his Ranger son. The split-second escapes of the North Carolina Captain lost nothing in the telling.

With uncles and fathers of the small boys, Will was unpopular. He seemed unsocial—a fault they did not share. They did not come to Clark Porter's drugstore to purchase, but to play chess, enjoy the warmth of the big store, smoke free cigars, and pass judgment on the policies of the President of the United

· 336 ·

States. Will Porter caricatured these loungers and wrote a satire to accompany his drawing. After that, it was just as well that he left Greensboro for Texas. Dr. Hall invited him to go to the Ranch because he knew the boy's heritage was tubercular and he was grieved by his anemic condition and hacking cough.

Richard Hall and his wife were occupying the second house that Lee had built, and it was at the sheep ranch of this younger brother that Will Porter lived. In the two years he spent there, he became well. The price was boredom. He described the ranch as bounded by the horizon and situated in the lonesomest part of the sheep country. Existence there made clerking in a drugstore seem a glamorous career. After a man had lived on a ranch for a while, he would split his ribs laughing at "Curfew Shall Not Ring Tonight," and would really enjoy playing cards with ladies. His own sheep, he wrote home, were "doing finely . . . never were in better condition. They give me very little trouble, for I have never been able to see one of them yet."

He spent much time on a canvas cot, shaded by hackberries. There he read and drew, strummed a guitar, and learned the songs of Mexican sheepherders. It was fortunate that his illness called for outdoor treatment. For one of the two rooms in the house was Mrs. Richard Hall's, the other was kitchen or dining room, depending on the dividing line of a heavy curtain.

When he had read through the little stock of books the ranch afforded, he eagerly awaited installments of reading matter supplied by Bessie Hall. He perused almanacs and mail order catalogues and assiduously studied the dictionary. He had no thought of writing, but he caricatured men and animals and described his work with a gusto that gave it double value. One pony seemed to have a "Dante Alighieri face." The rider had tucked chaparral twigs beneath the bridle to keep away deer flies. "Thus crowned, the long-faced quadruped looked more Dantesque than before and judging by his countenance seemed to think of Beatrice."

On an afternoon when Porter lay drawing, a bull snake fell on the cook's ironing board. The Negro left, with voluble expressions of relief at getting away. Porter regarded her as a countess or duchess in disguise from the way the pots and pans made way at her approach. With humility, he volunteered for service at the stove, and wrote the Vesper Club in Greensboro of limited success in cooking mutton steak and gravy. "Please send by express to the ranch," he added, "seventy-five cooks and two hundred washwomen, blind or wooden-legged ones preferred. The climate has a tendency to make them walk off every two or three days, which must be overcome."

Sometimes he rode in to Cotulla, and reported progress there: The town had grown wonderfully—thirty or forty new houses had gone up and thirty or forty barrels of whiskey gone down. The barkeeper was planning to tour Europe next summer and thinking of buying Mexico as a plaything for his little boy.

Whatever he did and wherever he went, Porter stored away impressions. He teased stories from Mexicans and cowboys and beguiled Lee Hall to talk of service on the border—to tell such tales as that of vengeful Blas, his faithless *novia*, and her Ranger lover.

Much later when, as "O. Henry," Porter wrote of the four million and for the four million, the two ranch years proved fecund in material. His practice of exaggeration was not needed to bedizen stories of the patrol of the Nueces and the Rio Grande, but he let his sense of the dramatic enliven the events of No Man's Land, inspired with his imagination figures of Rangers, Mexicans, and outlaws, so that they came to life, and spoke and acted. With the lordly swing of a toreador, he swept around their shapes a shimmering cape of high romance. Of them all, none is more romantic than the Ranger modeled from Lee Hall: "blond as a Viking, quiet as a deacon, dangerous as a machine gun" . . . "agile, broad-chested"—a man who could "heft his sixes in their holsters as a belle gives the finishing touches to her toilette"—a man who had "committed bigamy with trouble."

As soon as he was able, Porter deserted his cot and guitar to bestride a saddle, but he did not ride enough to curve his chaps into the horse collar that marks the leather of the old cowhand—

not enough to appear bow-legged. When horses were to be broken, Porter climbed the fence of the corral to sit as "rail bird." He watched the antics of broncs with "bellies full of bedsprings," and noted the brimstone language of their riders. Porter knew when to yell encouragement and when to be quiet. He heard one cowboy will away his boots, saddle, bridle, chaps, and sombrero, thinking he would be "thrown so far he couldn't get back to his own funeral." It was the horse that died. He ruptured a blood vessel.

Porter learned that ankle-deep mud in the corral was not the only reason why a tenderfoot should keep outside. He learned how to dip his drink from a hole that was nearly dry and not muddy the water for the next fellow. And he made the cowboys like him. They even let him talk about the weather. He could describe a norther with such diversity of incident and epithet as left his listeners gaping.

When his rhetoric became too rambunctious and his criticism too caustic, the cowboys punished him with the excessive courtesy that they reserved for the lowest of the low. And after duly testing him, considering his oddities and weighing them against his grit and stamina, his gift for friendship, his admiration for courage and talent for kindness, the cowboys gave him their initiation. They fired six-shooters, let out wild yells, and one of them, dragging a saddle, galloped across his bed. When he protested, they stretched him over a roll of blankets and thrashed him with leather leggings. After an hour of it, they let him go.

Later, in a lively story, he described it all—"The punchers' accolade. From then on he had won his spurs and would be 'pardner' and stirrup brother, boot to boot."

He added to his costume spurs and a sombrero, and when his hair had grown to pioneer length, he boasted that only a benevolently amiable expression saved him from arrest on general suspicion of murder and horse stealing. The cowboys of Lee Hall's former company were too occupied with fence cutters to consider endangering young Porter's liberty. A force of sixty was making new enclosures and restringing wires previously cut near their staples. Ed Brockman ran their commissary. For a time, Will Porter substituted.

He counted at the tent "nine niggers, sixteen Mexicans, seven hounds, two six-shooters, four desperadoes, three shotguns and a barrel of molasses. Inside there were a good many sacks of corn, flour, meal, sugar, beans, coffee, and potatoes, a big box of bacon, some boots, clothes, saddles, rifles, tobacco, and some more hounds. The work was to issue the stores to the contractors as they sent for them, and was light and easy to do. Out at the rear of the tent they had started a graveyard for men who had either kicked one of the hounds or prophesied a norther. When night came the gentleman whose good fortune it was to be dispensing the stores gathered up his saddle blankets, four old corn sacks, an old coat and a sheepskin, made all the room he could by shifting and arranging the bacon, meal, etc., gave a sad look at the dogs that immediately filled the vacuum, and went and slept outdoors."

For diversion, Will Porter "had an offer to gamble from the nigger cook and was allowed as a special favor to drive up the nice, pretty horses and give them some corn. And the kind of accommodating old tramps and cowboys who constituted the outfit came in to board, sleep, smoke, cuss and gamble, lie and brag, in short, did all they could to make time pass pleasantly and profitably to themselves."

# *from* SLEEPY BLACK

*by* ROSS SANTEE

Ross Santee began writing stories of western men and horses as a by-product rather than an end in themselves. His original interest in these subjects was that of a pictorial artist. But he soon realized that editors were just as interested in stories about horses as in pictures of them and that the two together made a fine combination. He tried his hand at writing and found that it worked.

The reason may easily be seen in the following selection from *Sleepy Black*, which is the story of a western horse. This particular part concerns the moods, interest, and problems of the hero while engaged in the rodeo business. In it is always implicit Ross Santee's understanding of and sympathy for his subject.

In a recent note to the editor, Ross Santee pointed out that he was never very happy anywhere but in Arizona. He also mentioned, among other things, the fact that he was married and added the laconic admission: "Just drop the reins anywhere and I'll stand."

---

THE WORST THING ABOUT THE RODEO TO ME WAS THE shipping an' the long rides on the trains. Like everything else I got used to it but I never enjoyed it any. There was something about the long train rides that made my legs feel queer. It always took a little time to get used to the feel of solid ground again. A good roll an' a little run was the thing that helped the most. To feel the good earth under me again was something I always enjoyed.

Hay an' grain was a regular thing in the rodeo. It was never hard to take. A horse can buck harder on a paunch full of grain than when he is living on grass. As the months went by I could feel myself growing bigger an' stronger than ever.

I was treated well by the punchers. I was never whipped or abused. I came to look forward to the times when I was saddled

· 341 ·

in the shute. There was something about the roar of the crowd I liked. I liked the feel of the music too. The only thing I resented was the feel of the rider's spurs.

There was something about the feel of the spurs that took me back to the ranch. To me it was always the peeler on my back when we came out of the shute.

At the ranch there had been no rules when a puncher made a ride. It made no difference what he did as long as he stuck to the horse. For it was after the horse quit pitching that the real day's work began.

In the rodeo I was seldom used but once a day. The ride was always short. I was given the best of it when I came out of the shute. A rider had to observe certain rules or he was disqualified.

Losing a stirrup or touching leather with his hands disqualified a rider. Riding with his spurs in the cinch always counted against him too. He was disqualified if he changed hands on the halter shank before the whistle blew.

When a rider left the shute he came out with both spurs high in a horse's shoulders. An' he was supposed to kick either way from the cinch as the judges might direct.

The rowels of the puncher's spurs were blunt. They were often wrapped in tape. A rider was disqualified if he locked the rowels of his spurs. Whipping a horse was not allowed, a quirt was never used. The rider was supposed to fan with his hat or keep one hand in motion until the whistle blew.

The whistle was always the signal that the puncher had made his ride. At the sound of it the pick-up men always raced to pick up the horse an' take the rider off.

The old bucking horse knew what the whistle meant as well as the rider did. Many of them quit pitching as soon as the whistle blew. I soon learned what it meant but I could never stop. It took more than a whistle to stop me once I began to buck.

In riding according to the rules many riders were thrown who could have rode the horse to a standstill if they wanted to go to leather an' lock their rowels in the cinch.

A qualified ride on a hard bucking horse was really hard to make. A good rider always wanted the horse to buck as hard as he could so the rider could strut his stuff.

No two bucking horses in a rodeo ever buck exactly the same. Each horse has certain ways of doing things that set him apart from the others.

Some ponies jump pretty high, others buck close to the ground. Some of the prettiest ones to watch are the easiest ones to ride. A pony that pitches close to the ground is sometimes the hardest to ride. He has a way of giving his rider several separate jolts each time he hits with him.

A good rider must anticipate each jump the pony makes. There is always a certain beat or time that a horse keeps up as he bucks. It is when the old pony changes the time that he usually spills the pack. If the rider doesn't change time when the pony does he usually loses his seat.

Once a rider loosens an inch it is seldom he ever gets it back when the pony really knows how to buck. The old bucking horses used in the Rodeo knew what it was all about.

No horse was ever rode until he quit or it would have been just a question of time until the pony refused to buck. Each time a pony threw a rider off it gave him new confidence.

Head Light, the Rawlins Gray, Coyote, Deerfoot an' Old Pinto Pete, just to mention a few, were all old bucking horses. There were over twenty in the string. Some were gentle to handle until they came out of the shute. There were others in the string who mistrusted every man. At some time or other something had gone wrong as far as the pony went. It might have happened years before but the pony had never forgotten.

Deerfoot was one horse like myself that always watched his chance to strike when his rider was on the ground. The pickup men were always riding close when we came out of the shute. Deerfoot had struck two riders after he had bucked them off. They never rode again.

Old Pinto Pete had been an easy bucking horse to ride when he first started out. For a time he was used in the string that was ridden by the girls. But as old Pinto Pete became harder to ride he was given to the men.

Some of the horses came from the North. Others from the Southwest. The northern horses as a rule were bigger than the ponies from the South.

Most of them had started much the way I did. But each horse had made a reputation for himself before he joined the Rodeo.

Yet some of the hardest bucking horses on the range never qualified in a rodeo. The Harper Brown, one of the horses in the rough string at the ranch, would never buck in town. Several times he was taken in when the rodeo was on. But each time the brown horse left the shute he came out with his rider as if he were after a calf.

The crowd an' the strange surroundings might have had something to do with it. For the Harper Brown never failed to buck when he was saddled at the ranch. An' of all the horses in the rough string he was one of the hardest to ride.

To qualify as a bucking horse in a rodeo the horse must not only be hard to ride but he must never fail to buck when he came out of the shute.

Some ponies wouldn't buck when a flask cinch was used. Others refused to buck without. While some who wouldn't pitch without the flank cinch refused to buck when the cinch was a little too tight.

The judges always kept an eye on a puncher when he was saddling his horse. If the saddle was placed too far in front it made an easier ride.

The punchers were always trying something out in order to cheat the rules. Some wore rubber heels on their boots that were fixed in a way that they couldn't lose a stirrup. When a judge was riding on each side of him a puncher had to kick his horse. If a puncher knew only one judge was watching him he kicked on that side with his other spur locked in the cinch.

The girls rode with their stirrups hobbled. With the stirrups tied under a horse's belly it was impossible to lose one of them.

But in riding with hobbled stirrups it often meant a broken leg when the pony happened to fall.

Some of the bucking horses in our string had followed the rodeo for years. Others came an' went. Once a horse left the shute on the run an' refused to buck it was usually just a question of time until he was through as a rodeo horse.

Old Head Light was the oldest bucking horse in the string. He was about twenty years old but the old boy never failed to do his stuff when he came out of the shute.

He was gentle an' kind to handle when a man was on the ground. He always stood quietly in the shute while the rider eased into the saddle an' got all set for his ride. But once the shute gate opened the old boy was dynamite.

Some horses buck the same each time they leave the shute. Once a puncher learns how he bucks, a horse is easy for him. But Head Light always kept a rider on his toes. The old boy knew every trick. Many punchers thought they had the old boy's number after making a ride on him only to pick themselves up with both hands full of dirt the next time they drew the old horse.

No one ever made a qualified ride on Broken Box the first year he was out. Each time he threw a rider off it gave him new confidence. But once a puncher made a qualified ride on him the horse was never the same. It was only a question of a little time until any one could ride him. When the day finally came that he left the shute on the run he was through as a rodeo horse.

Several places where we worked they didn't use the shutes. We were led into the arena an' saddled in front of the crowd. A wrangler snubbed us to the saddle horn while the saddle was laced on. Some horses took it quietly, others struggled an' fought. Often the horse was blindfolded before he could be saddled. When a blind was used there was always a chance that the horse would throw himself when the blind was jerked from him.

If a horse knew what it was all about he didn't struggle much. He eased his injured feelings by bucking with his rider.

· 345 ·

Often a pony fought the handlers so much he was wore out before the ride was made. That was the reason for the shutes. It saved the horse so he could let off his steam while he was really bucking.

The rider drew each day for the horse he was to ride. Some of course were harder to ride. They were always used in the finals. But any puncher who could make a qualified ride on any horse in the bunch had to be a real bronc rider.

The riders like the horses were the pick of all the West. They came from everywhere. When the rodeo first started out the best riders as a rule were usually northern punchers. All of the horses used up there were pretty big an' strong. The southern riders when they started out were used to smaller horses. But after a southern man had been out a while an' became used to the big horses from the North it was hard to choose between them.

But the best calf ropers with few exceptions were punchers from the Southwest. They were usually old brush hands. One could always pick an old brush hand by the size of the loop he threw. It had a way of fitting most any part of a critter the puncher wanted to ketch. The brush hand had learned his stuff in the roughest an' brushiest country where the puncher often jockeyed for a half mile before he could get a throw.

Many of the riders were as familiar to me as the horses in our string. Others came an' went. It was seldom we went through a rodeo without someone getting hurt.

To see a rider carried from the arena became an old story to me. Sometimes I never saw them again. But usually in a few months' time the rider would be back.

Many of the punchers entered in several different events. The more events they entered the quicker they disappeared.

Aside from the trick roping an' riding, calf ropers usually had the safest bets. But there were many different ways a calf roper might be hurt when he was working fast. One puncher snapped his ankle as he quit his flying pony an' raced to tie his calf. One night when a puncher was making his tie the lights confused his horse. For a time both roper an' calf were dragged about the place. Aside from his injured feelings the calf was none the worse. But the roper had to be carried when he was taken from the arena.

In the bareback riding the ponies used were not as tough as the ones that were rode with a saddle. But a man to ride a bucking horse bareback had to be a rider. When the whistle blew it was up to the pick-up men to take the rider from the horse. In taking a man from a bucking horse there were often many slips.

In steer riding the puncher slipped to the ground after he made his ride. If the old steer was on the prod he tried to hook his rider when the puncher quit his back. Often the races were pretty close when the rider ran for the fence. It was not uncommon for a rider to be hooked an' trampled by a steer. But more punchers were hurt in the bull dogging an' bronc riding than in any of the other events.

One could usually pick out a bull dogger by the bandages he wore. Even if he wasn't badly hurt the dogger was always skinned up.

When a rider was thrown clear from a bucking horse it was seldom that he was hurt. A good rider knows how to take a fall an' he knows just when to take it.

But there is always a chance that a spur might hang an' the puncher be hung in the rigging and there was always the danger of a flying hoof when the rider was on the ground.

There was one ride that no one who saw will ever forget, the puncher least of all. The puncher was riding a big stout horse. The whistle had just blown. Before the pick-up men could get to him the saddle turned on the horse. In some way the rider's chaps were hung to the horn an' he was dragged under the horse's belly. Terrified the big horse went to bucking an' kicking at him. The pick-up men were helpless, they couldn't ketch the horse.

The rider knew he was in almost as tight a fix as he would ever be but he didn't lose his nerve. Reaching up he tried to ketch the halter shank thinking he might throw the horse.

Twice the rider reached for the halter shank missing it by just a hair. It was when he reached the third time that the big horse kicked him loose.

There was no roar from the crowd that day as the rider was carried off. The crowd was strangely quiet when the next horse left the shute.

It was months later when we had moved far to the south that a rider climbed onto my shute. There was something familiar about him to me when he settled into the saddle. But so many riders came an' went it was hard to place them all. It wasn't until I heard him speak that I knew who he was.

"Come on, Nigger horse," he said, "an' do yore stuff. I'm all set for another ride. Let's hope the saddle don't turn today like it did on that other goat."

It was the puncher who had been dragged underneath the horse. He was back with the rodeo.

# CRACK-UP

*by* BEIRNE LAY, JR.

Beirne Lay, Jr. was one of the first writers to give effective expression
to the trials and experiences of the pioneers in the American Air Forces
back in the days when the sole establishments of the Air Corps (Randolph and Kelly Fields) were located at San Antonio—which subsequently came to be known as "the mother-in-law of the Air Forces."
Later Beirne Lay did important work in the office of the Chief of Staff
for Air.
"Crack-Up" is a selection from *I Wanted Wings*.

CHRISTMAS HAD COME AND GONE LONG SINCE, AND THE
freezing days of January, when we had tumbled out of
the barracks and gone through calisthenics shivering
and half dead with sleep in the pre-dawn darkness. February,
too, was half-way past.

I had passed my final check with the Flight Commander. It
was little more than a formality, for I had flown with him for
three weeks while Lieutenant George was on leave, and now
only one day's flying remained, a cross-country to Laredo and
return for a group of us whose hop there had been postponed
twice by weather.

Remember the wrecked A-3 that I saw lying near the San
Antonio highway, when I was back on Primary Stage, and how I
wondered what the pilot's sensations must have been when the
ground leapt up at him? "Perhaps it was a premonition," I had
said then.

It was a premonition.

I stood at Laredo Airport watching the ships take off for
Randolph, 160 miles to the northeast, leaving at five-minute

· 349 ·

intervals, so that the students couldn't follow each other. Finally, only two others besides me remained. One of them said: "Tack onto my wings, and we'll fly a three-ship formation."

We taxied out behind him in single file. He swung his ship around into the wind, and we drew up snug inside his wings. He nodded, we rolled along the gravelly sod as one airplane, skimmed along with our collective tail up, and soared into a climbing turn to our compass course for Randolph.

He didn't climb very far. He levelled off at one hundred. Then he gradually nosed down lower, until we were scudding along a few feet above the mesquite. We stayed right with him. I could hear my heart thumping in my ears with the exhilaration of it; this was lower than I had ever hedge-hopped before. For fifteen minutes we sped along down there at 115 miles an hour, with a wind on our tails to help. It was like driving a car over rough country at 130 miles an hour without a jar, and the sensation of speed increased as the ground ahead continued to race under the nose. Occasionally I took a quick look across at the cadet on the other wing, and grinned. He grinned back. The leader was out to give us all a thrill, to celebrate our graduation from Basic Stage.

Presently he pulled up to five hundred feet and gave us a chance to relax, motioning us out to a wider interval, and then he dropped down again, still lower than before. We had to pull up over the houses that blocked our hurtling path. Twice I saw his wheels knock the leaves off a treetop, and once he splashed water as we skimmed over a duck pond.

I had been holding my position several feet above him. "Don't be a sissy," I told myself. "Get down on a level with him." Soon my wheels were not more than three feet above the ground and it was tense going, for the air was occasionally bumpy.

We streaked across a red dirt road, and started down a long, narrow, plowed field that was soggy from recent heavy rains. I was still at three feet, or less, holding myself exactly on a level with the leader. A short, quick air bump bobbed me down.

WHAM!

The seat jumped back under me. The tail whipped up behind me. The ground sprang up before me. I yanked back the stick with both hands—all in one flash, a hair's breadth from nosing over, for the tip of my prop had hooked the top of a high furrow.

One human electric shock from head to toe, I zoomed up to a hundred feet with my excess speed, the prop idling to a stop in front of me, motor abruptly silent as the grave, for the impact had sheared both distributor shafts of the dual ignition system.

A quick look to the right. To the left. Up ahead.

Nothing but mesquite on all sides. Not enough altitude to turn back into the wind. Very little field up ahead. My brain did a dozen back-flips in a fraction of a second. *Was there anything I could do?* I reached down and flipped off the ignition switches and the gas gauges, then held her straight ahead at the slowest possible safe gliding speed—60 miles an hour. That plus the fifteen-mile tailwind made my actual speed 75. I could see that the black furrows running parallel ahead of me were soft. Half paralyzed, for I knew that a crash, a bad one, easily a fatal one, was coming, I sat there and braced myself till the body muscles cramped my ribs and pulled up into my groin.

The wheels touched. For a second or two I rolled along, feeling them sink in. And then. . . .

There was a shuddering thump as the prop caught again; those long, black furrows swung up over the center section like spokes of a gigantic wheel whirring toward me. Instinctively, I kept my head rigid between my shoulders instead of ducking. The black spokes flailed down and struck me squarely on the top of my helmet with a force that jarred my whole skeleton.

I was stunned, but only briefly. In a flash I realized the position of my body. Most of my weight was on my head, and a little of it on my belt. I was sitting upside down on my head, and I couldn't see anything. No wonder. My skull was driven six inches down into the muddy earth, covering my nostrils and almost my mouth, too—I could taste it on my lips.

I put one hand down to support the rest of my body while I

unsnapped the belt with the other. I flipped it open, my knees hit the ground, and I lifted my head. Still I couldn't see. I groped around in the darkness with my fingers and soon discovered why. The cockpit was mashed down flush with the ground, and no light could enter.

There was little possibility of fire—if the ship was going to burn, it would have burst into flames instantly—but it was uncomfortable to be trapped. I burrowed away under the cockpit cowling until I had cleared a hole big enough to thrust my head and shoulders through. When I had wriggled half-way out, the seat of my 'chute caught. It was impossible to get out without removing the 'chute, so into my cramped dungeon I wormed again backward—inches at a time—smelling the hot, black oil that I had seen dripping from the side of the engine into a little puddle on the ground. Inside again, I hustled out of the 'chute harness, and at last I crawled out free into the sunshine. I lay on the ground for a few minutes, panting, then slowly climbed to my feet, rubbing my head in amazement.

I looked at the BT. It was lying there upside down with its back broken, a sorry sight. The fuselage, just to the rear of my cockpit, had been fractured clean through, steel longerons and all. The tail surfaces were smashed like a comedian's cigar after a door has been slammed in his face. The top wing was crushed flat up against the fuselage—a panel of twisted ribs and torn yellow fabric.

Still half-dazed and feeling as though I had just survived a murderous *personal* assault, I wondered what would have happened if the ship had burned during the time it had taken me to dig my way free—a full two minutes, which had seemed like twenty. And slowly it dawned on me that the soft ground had saved me. Hard ground would have snapped my neck like a match-stick, even though I did wear a size-sixteen collar.

I gazed around me, and saw one of my companions trotting across the plowed field toward me, stumbling in his haste, and saw his ship a quarter of a mile away in an adjacent field. I walked across to meet him.

"Are you hurt?" he called out.

"Hell, no!" I shouted with shaky bravado.

"*Positive* you're not hurt?" he said again when only a few yards separated us.

"No." He reached me, holding out his hand.

"Here," he said, "hold me up till my knees stop shaking."

# Criticism

K. LAMITY'S TEXAS TALES—*John S. Bonner*

UNIVERSITIES ON THE MARCH—*Joseph A. Brandt*

DRAMA OF THE SOUTHWEST—*John William Rogers*

THE SOUTHWEST: AN INTRODUCTION—*Henry Nash Smith*

THE SOUTHWEST IN FICTION—*Rebecca W. Smith*

# *from* K. LAMITY'S TEXAS TALES

*by* JOHN S. BONNER

John "K. Lamity" Bonner was editor of *The Harpoon*, a monthly magazine which was the cause of much comment and controversy in Texas near the beginning of the century. This magazine expired neither from lack of talent on the part of its editor, nor because of his inordinate love of fishing, but because of a Negrophobia which came to possess him—as it also did Brann (the iconoclast). This preoccupation so dominated the magazine's pages that it lost much of its interest for the general reader.

---

# REVIEW OF
# LAURA JEAN LIBBEY

In any book store or on any railway train, you will find various alleged novels, bearing the name of Laura Jean Libbey, as authoress.

Did you ever read one of the books written by this young journalistic boll weevil? If not, take my advice and buy one. You will, of course, always blame me for it, but you will never forget your experience.

I am ashamed to acknowledge it, but many years ago I read one of her works entitled *Gushing Gussie, or the Wild Resolve*. That may not be the precise name, but it was on that style. When I finished the book, I intended to write a review of it, but never recovered sufficiently to do so, until recently.

I don't believe Laura Jean ought to write any more novels. The specimens now in print will amply suffice to carry her name sliding down astraddle the banisters of Time, as a gay and giddy young gob of gush, who, if she ever had one sane idea, never put it in print.

# SQUELCHING
# THE LIQUOR TRAFFIC

A subscriber who does not live over 786 miles from Austin has sent me the following letter:

"I subscribed for your paper, and paid for it. The only reason I have for discontinuing the *Harpoon* is because I see you are advertising saloons and beer breweries, and I can not aid in supporting any institution or business that indorses the damnable liquor traffic."

I would add the name of the writer, who is a well known business man, but that would cause some people to think that I had gone back on the motto of the *Harpoon*. I have, however, mailed him a letter of thanks, returning him the one dollar paid for subscription, and erased his name from the list. I will also mail him a marked copy of this issue, just to give him an idea of my opinion of such characters.

To begin with, I will acknowledge that I take advertisements from saloons and "beer breweries." If there were any other kind of breweries in the country I would also take advertisements from them. An editor is not supposed to indorse everything an advertiser states. Any man with as much sense as a grub worm ought to know this. One good reason why I take advertisements from men who engage in the manufacture and sale of liquors is because they never fail to pay their bills promptly. That is at least one point in their favor.

Now, my dear old cranky friend, let me reason with you a moment about this matter. Of course it is difficult to reason with a man whose eyes are so close together that they chafe each other when he winks, but I am going to try it. You are in business. When a saloon man comes into your store and asks for anything from a yard of calico to a pound of bacon, do you sell it to him and take his money, or do you tell him you can not "aid in supporting any institution that indorses the damnable liquor traffic?" Of course you sell it to him, but in doing so, does that act denote that you are indorsing his line of business? No person with half as much sense as a grasshopper will contend that you are favoring the sale of intoxicating liquors because you sell a saloon man a sack of flour. Then why should you jump at the conclusion that I am favoring saloons because I sell a saloon keeper advertising space in the *Harpoon?*

The trouble with your breed of cattle is the fact that their heads are not shaped right. You are too narrow all over, especially between the eyes. You are selfish, egotistical, and think you are smart, when in fact your intelligence will not begin to compare with that of an educated chimpanzee.

Another mistake you make is in fancying you are following in the footsteps of the meek and lowly Nazarene Carpenter when you vent your petty childish spite on your fellow men. If you call that religion, I tell you that hell is full of just such religion. That country is chock full of spite, hate, malice, conceit, selfishness and inhumanity. That is why the place was created. There are no fools in hell, however, so you still have a fighting chance for heaven.

I never have indorsed the liquor traffic. At an early age I got down on the business, and in hopes of saving other people, I tried to drink it all up, but I soon found out that the barkeeper kept running in fresh stock on me, and I got mad and quit. Liquor drinking to excess is bad for any sensible man, though I believe a barrel or two would do you good. It would probably loosen your old driedup hide, and possibly broaden your ideas, if you ever have any.

Remember I am not kicking because you discontinued the paper. Why, God bless you, dear five-karat soul, the paper was never intended for such people. If it was I would try to push the circulation in the lunatic asylums. I want men to read the *Harpoon* whose heads are not shaped like a wedge with the big end down. I want readers who are sensible, conscientious men, who love humanity because they themselves are human—who love God because God loves them. I don't want a lot of narrow minded, selfish, mental misfits who labor under the impression that Atlas has quit work and turned the job over to them.

I don't want you to get mad at me just because you don't indorse the liquor traffic. I don't care whether you take the paper or not, but I like you very much, and want you to call again to see me, and we will discuss the evils of intemperance and possibly I may be able to help you out. As a matter of fact, I believe I can give you some pointers whereby you may induce some one very near and dear to you to adopt my scheme for keeping sober—keeping out of saloons.

I know the thorn in your side. I know where the shoe hurts, but, my dear friend, had you attended in time to your own domestic affairs with the same vigor and enthusiasm that you are now attempting to meddle with other people's affairs, you would have had no personal reason for your war on saloons. Even at this late hour a barrel stave properly applied would undoubtedly have a great moral effect in remedying your former negligence.

Don't fail to call on me when you need advice or aid in squelching the liquor traffic. I am doing all I can to get all the money possible from the liquor sellers, and in that way I may succeed in running them out of business. If I break them they will have to stop, but somehow or other they have a wonderful way of recuperating.

As this is the last *Harpoon* you will get I want you to preserve it, so in the future when you feel gay, you can read it over and see what a colossal jackass an old man can make out of himself when he really tries to do so.

# A PLEA FOR THE HOT TAMALE

An exchange, in speaking of San Antonio, recently said:

"In the Alamo City it is now correctly reported that the hot tamale must go."

*K. Lamity's Harpoon* generally has enough to do to champion its own inalienable rights, without hunting up other people's battles, but I never go back on a friend—as long as he has a dollar—yet when I remember how in all the long years of the past the tamale has stuck to me, I can not refrain from uttering one long, loud, lonesome wail for its safety. It seems to me that of all the towns in Texas, San Antonio should cherish the cultivation and production of the tamale, for I can easily establish the fact that she owes much of her present growth and prosperity to this rare exotic. I remember the good old days when at the first stroke of the clock at 6 p.m., dozens of little donkey carts would suddenly dart from the adjacent alleys into Military Plaza, and in the twinkling of an eye tables were set, stoves were heated, and the luscious shuck-covered fruit was bought steaming hot at the nominal price of 10 cents per dozen.

Coffee, bread, milk (usually goat or burro) and hot tortillas could be had, while the exhilarating chile con carne was on deck in all its tropical warmness. To a stranger, the scene was simply fascinating, while the natives themselves were always there as customers. All night long the square was a scene of jolly, good-natured semi-Spanish life, but at daylight the little carts were backed up, the boxes, tinware, and rubbish tumbled in, and at a signal off they went, leaving the square clean and ready for the day's business.

In all this great business, in which thousands of men, women and children made a living, the tamale was the leading spirit, while other articles were only adjuncts. The tamale was the circus—the coffee and chile, the side shows. Rich and poor alike patronized the smiling, black-eyed señoritas, and maybe those degenerate daughters of Spanish and Aztec parentage didn't know how to flirt with the pale-faced Americanos! Oh, doctor! There you could see the poor laboring man, with whom luck was playing hide-and-seek, seat himself at the table and eat his humble meal, and not enjoying the dainty heterogeneous mass of food, fresh from its shuck corset, a bit better than the wealthy tourist at his side, who not an hour before had eaten a good

· 361 ·

supper at the Hotel Menger, yet could not resist the temptation to try the Mexican tamale—for the hot tamale is no respecter of persons.

You may eat the white man's tamale and may like it, but when you eat the genuine Mexican hot tamale you long for it forever. As the hart panteth for the water brook—as the politician panteth for office—so panteth your soul for the picture wrapped in its shuck Mother Hubbard and done in oil and water colors. You devour the white man's imitation tamale, and like Esau said to Jacob, you exclaim, "I have enough, my brother!"

Let San Antonio beware! When she loses the tamale she loses one of her oldest inhabitants and most enterprising citizen. In the upbuilding of the city, in the feeding of the people, in the fight against hunger, the hot tamale has done more for San Antonio than any other factor in that great city. Give the tamale a show and it will always come to the front. Yet to the beginner I would modestly suggest to not go too heavy on the start, for hot tamales are like strong drink, "which in the end biteth like a serpent and stingeth like an adder."

# ADVICE TO LOVELORN

A San Antonio subscriber asks: "Do you believe in early marriages? If so, how early? (Signed) James _____."

Yes, Jimmie, I am an advocate of early marriages. As to the precise time, of course that depends, but if you want to be safe, I would suggest that you marry about 5 o'clock in the morning. A good, early start is half of the journey.

# UNIVERSITIES ON THE MARCH

*by* JOSEPH A. BRANDT

Joseph A. Brandt is a Rhodes Scholar who started his career on the Tulsa *Tribune*. He next assumed the directorship of the University of Oklahoma Press. Though the subjects of its books were regional, the quality of their scholarship and general interest, their sheer excellence from a decorating and manufacturing standpoint, elevated the Press to national prominence.

The Princeton University Press, needing a director and knowing a good thing when it saw it, went out after Mr. Brandt and got him. But the University of Oklahoma refused to take this loss lying down. With a characteristic Southwestern disdain for half measures, it shot the works and offered to let Mr. Brandt run the whole university. That, when he wrote "Universities on the March," was just what he was doing.

---

THE STATES OF THE SOUTHWEST—ARIZONA, NEW MEXICO, Oklahoma, and Texas—have a common heritage from Spain, but now this heritage is no more apparent than the herds of buffalo which once were hunted from tourist trains. Vestiges of it, it is true, cling to parts of Texas and New Mexico. Oklahoma was only territorially a part of it, and the Spanish explorer, hurrying elsewhere, left no record. But just as in the rest of the section the Anglo-Saxon dominated the Spanish, so were the Five Civilized Tribes absorbed in the Indian Territory, unmourned by all except their Motleys, Grant Foreman and Angie Debo. Outwardly, most of the Southwest has borrowed with little originality from New England and the Middle States, which furnished so much of the population of the region. Among the university cities, Dallas is like Chicago, only noisier; Tulsa like Hartford; and Norman's university campus is a curious Gothic anomaly on the flat red beds.

· 363 ·

There is still in process of resolution the question of which will be dominant, the South or the West. When Oklahoma became a state, a pragmatic approach was suggested in tri-dividing the state, one part to be White, another Indian, the third Negro. This Pandora's box was happily avoided; but the Indian lost his identity, the Negro was put under Jim Crow law. Urban Texas and Oklahoma tend in the main to be Western, but the rural districts and the communities dependent on agricultural wealth, to be Southern. There are communities like Norman, Oklahoma, where Negroes may not stay overnight, or where Whites may not stay, as in Taft, Oklahoma. New Mexico and Arizona are definitely Western, although here again we frequently find the indigenous Spaniard an unwelcome presence.

If the Southwest is making a cultural advance it is principally because its colleges and universities have attracted men and women of unusual vision, to whom they have given as much encouragement as their meager resources permitted. But in education the Southwest has suffered greatly from the growing pains of youth and become almost angrily imitative of its older neighbors. Even now, as the confidence which comes with cultural maturity is beginning to reach the region, there are still distressing symptoms of pioneering rigors. Thus the Oklahoma politician is acclaimed a statesman if he can return to his district and proclaim that he has reduced, to the lowest level in the United States, the appropriation for education. In Texas, similarly, a fabulous endowment is available for education, but according to provisions in the state constitution it must be spent only on buildings.

Despite all handicaps, however, the Southwestern atmosphere seems to have an exhilarating effect on those scholars and writers who are infected by it. Thus, at the same time that the universities tend to be carbon copies of older universities, there are encouraging signs of originality in approaching education, of realistic social science in which today means today. The Webbs, the Sears, the Mathews, the Richardsons, Risters, Foremans, working either in universities or through them, have found a *métier* which has at once challenged their best effort and also produced that best.

The writers and scholars have benefited from the fact that the universities have been publishing sponsors. Southern Methodist University has the *Southwest Review,* and the magazine has kept strictly to its area for its empire. The Universities of New Mexico, Oklahoma, and Texas in varying degree engage in book publication, while Oklahoma sponsors *Books Abroad,* devoted to non-English language publications.

Hence a vigorous literary life in the region. Perhaps its writers have not always been alert to the great stories—it required Steinbeck to tell the dismal Jeremiad of the dust bowl. The difficulty is not so much that the writers of the Southwest lack vision or courage as that they are living in a vast sociological laboratory which the universities have as yet scarcely touched. The historical approach has seemed more natural. Even the historical approach has had its pitfalls in a climate so recently clouded with the smoke from two-gun men. Nor have the South-westerners, engrossed in the frequently bitter task of making a living, been always in a mood to turn their society into a clinic.

It is in this atmosphere that the universities have functioned. In many ways, they have exercised a decisive leadership in a region in which culture has often enough seemed a side show for the much more interesting business of commerce. They have refused to yield to self-seeking leaders and they have exemplified in a striking way the fundamental obligation of universities to society. It is true that they still tremble at the audacious professor who writes too lucidly of problems which society tries to keep around the corner, but to their credit, they seem to breed a sub-stantial number of these courageous persons. Youth, like age, finds the contemporary scene with its dramatic changes a fruitful writing laboratory, and the writing groups you find on almost every southwestern campus have something to say. It is a not unhopeful outlook: perhaps it will be through litera-ture that continental United States may achieve self knowledge, mutual tolerance, and eventually cultural unity.

# DRAMA OF THE SOUTHWEST

*by* JOHN WILLIAM ROGERS

John William Rogers, of Dallas, is prominent both in the artistic
and social circles of that city. Though he writes dramatic criticism, his
chief interest is in writing drama itself. His most recent play, *Where the
Dear Antelope Play*, was a tolerant, not unaffectionate lampoon of local
society, who flocked to see it and enjoyed it after they got there. In
approach and feeling it was not unlike some of J. P. Marquand's
writing about his native Boston. Mr. Rogers is also the author of the
prize-winning one-act play, *Judge Lynch*.

---

IT IS OF NO GREAT SIGNIFICANCE, BUT IT IS PERHAPS INDICATIVE OF
attitudes in the Southwest, that the city of Houston, Texas,
had a theater before it had a church. In the early days, when
people got together after the loneliness of the frontier, they craved
to be amused. Touring companies frequently made the hazardous
journey by water from the United States to the coastal towns of
the Gulf, and inland where these were not available, amateur
productions in which the spirit of fun was the chief virtue, were
accepted in that spirit. In the last decades of the nineteenth
century and the first of the twentieth, famous stars and less
famous—among them Edwin Booth, Frederick Ward, James
O'Neill, the elder Barrymores, the Drews, Sarah Bernhardt, and
Lillie Langtry—were as eagerly attended in their trouping as
they were in the rest of the land.

Any creative expression in dramatic form sufficiently
vigorous to merit more than passing local attention, however, is
a recent manifestation. It came about under the same impulse
that made our painters realize the land about them could be
really exciting to paint and our storytellers perceive that the

· 366 ·

extraordinary variety of civilizations that have flowed together here, is of high human interest. Inadvertently, also, it happens to be a product of little theater activity, which in the twenties spread like a rash over this region.

Only this spring a volume of dramas, *Three Southwest Plays*, was published in Dallas which in striking fashion proves that if original productions have been numerically few, playwrights of this region have seriously felt the urge to express themselves; and that their work has found a responsive audience. A remarkable thing about these plays is that in the whole range of American dramatic literature, it would be difficult to assemble three plays more completely varied in theme and mood.

Anyone who has followed the non-professional theater knows that the vitality which expressed itself in community theaters a dozen years ago has largely passed into the dramatic departments of colleges and universities. The Southwest has reflected this shift. In 1938 an ambitious dramatic department was organized at the University of Texas under the direction of James Parke, where not only have old and contemporary plays been produced, but where E. P. Conkle, the Iowa dramatist—author of *Two Hundred Were Chosen* and *Prelude to Glory*—has been playwright in residence. Mr. Conkle has been practising his craft as well as conducting courses in creative writing. His play *Johnny Appleseed* was presented last year at the University and another new script, *Bill and the Widowmaker*, is in rehearsal for production this spring.

Somewhat less elaborate in its setup is the dramatic department of Baylor University at Waco, Texas, but it deserves special mention because of its activities under the direction of Paul Baker. Mr. Baker is a native Texan, who after studying at Yale and wandering around the world has returned to his native state fired with a creative urge that promises exciting things. Under his leadership and from a design worked out by him, Baylor University has just erected a theater on its campus that is unique. As well as the traditional stage facing the audience, this theater has stages on either side of the auditorium and the seats are comfortable swivel chairs that can be turned to face whatever stage is in use. It is even entirely practical to use the back of the theater for stage action if the occasion arises.

This highly original design, which grew out of the problems in staging R. E. Sherwood's Abraham Lincoln, does not in any way handicap the use of the theater as a conventional playhouse. It simply adds vastly to its flexibility and resources for stage experimentation. It may be added that these extra stages were achieved with surprisingly small additional cost to the price of erecting one more building in the rigid theater tradition.

So favorably impressed has the Rockefeller Educational Foundation been with what Mr. Baker is accomplishing, that last fall the Foundation made it possible for Lynn Riggs, the Oklahoma playwright, to spend three months in Waco in intimate association with the students and teaching a course in creative writing. During the coming year Mr. Baker hopes to import another personality distinguished for creative work in the theater for similar contact with his students.

The little town of Albany in western Texas is achieving a kind of celebrity for two unusual dramatic events that take place there annually. Robert Nail, scion of one of the large landowning families in the community, is a writer and gentleman of the theater who has chosen to keep Albany his home. Each year since 1938, Mr. Nail has written an evening for the theater which he gives the general title of *Fandango*. It is a combination of parade, pageant, and episodic scenes linked together by a narrator over a loud speaker. Two hundred and fifty townspeople and people from neighboring ranches take part in this outdoor performance, supervised in all details by Mr. Nail. And such is the interest in the spectacle that Albany—a town of 2,000 people —furnished an audience of 1,800 spectators.

As well as *Fandango* presented each June, at Christmas Mr. Nail offers a "nativity play" which he has written, presenting episodes from Bible history.

At the University of Oklahoma, for some years Rupel Jones has been carrying on the accepted tradition of university dramatic activities, while at Houston, Texas, not one community theater but two flourish under the energetic direction of a young Texan named Margo Jones. If Houston, in the early days, had a theater before it had a church, a hundred years before the town of Houston was dreamed of, San Antonio had its chain of Spanish missions which can still be seen there. And every holiday season today in San Antonio, Mexican citizens whose ancestors began the custom in Spanish days, present in the original archaic Spanish, a traditional medieval miracle play, *Los Pastores*, dealing with the shepherds who saw the star of Bethlehem and followed it.

# THE SOUTHWEST:
# AN INTRODUCTION

*by* HENRY NASH SMITH

Henry Nash Smith, besides being a brilliant critic, has given encouragement to many younger writers who have come into his sphere. Though still officially a member of the faculty of Southern Methodist University at Dallas, he is at the moment on loan to the English department of the University of Texas. Since 1927 he has been one of the active editors of the *Southwest Review*.

---

EW CHAPTERS IN THE HISTORY OF WESTERN EUROPEAN peoples have offered more impressive testimony to the adaptability of the human species than the American advance across the North American continent. Encountering climates ranging from tropical to sub-arctic, and soils ranging in fertility from the lushness of Gulf Coast riverbottoms to the sterility of the Interior Basin, the American pioneer made his way everywhere, and everywhere devised means of occupying the lands his wanderings had discovered. The need for making such a variety of adjustments to many different environments has yielded the diverse ways of life we observe in the present.

The nineteenth-century American migrants were impatient of petty economies, just as they were not over-nice in their concern for justice in human relations. Some, of course, were not really looking for a place to settle down at all, because they had come to love movement for its own sake. They used the land prodigally, as transients, and passed on. But the whole area, each part in the fashion dictated by its resources, was occupied at last by men who had decided to see what could be made of the country as it stood. They drove out the Indians and the Mexicans; they plowed fields and built fences, or trailed their herds of cattle. They put together social institutions and an economic system, and very recently have begun to build the cities that lie so prodigiously upon the prairie.

They have also begun to reflect upon their experience, and have thus begun to feel the influence of the past, of tradition. It is a force not always for good, but indispensable and inevitable.

The materials collected here deal, quite unschematically, with the three shaping forces of terrain, people, and tradition. They belong on the whole to a rather early stage in the process by which a society becomes aware of its own origins and direction; and they are probably most remarkable for their diversity. The men represented here are interested in widely various aspects of the Southwest: Dobie in the land, and its plants, and the animals, and the men who have in greatest store the knowledge of these things which comes from long intimacy; Webb in history, which is the name for what men in society have made of the land; Lomax and La Farge and Stanley Vestal in the races which have met in the Southwest; DeGolyer and Rebecca Smith in what earlier writers have had to say about the country; George Sessions Perry in the tenant farmer of the Brazos bottoms, in the urgent present; Paul Horgan in the rather amusing efforts at sophistication which have appeared in the Southwest of the twentieth century.

These writers do not constitute a school of artists. For one thing, few of them live close enough together for intimate personal acquaintance. They deal with quite different types of material. And while they have produced some first-rate writing, as a group they are not very self-conscious technicians. Their attitude is, in the painter's sense of the word, primitive: they are —most of them—more deeply absorbed in subject matter than in form. They do not have a common esthetic creed.

But diverse as these writers are in temperament and in background, their common concern with the fate of man in this area gives to their work a certain unity. They are engaged in an informal but truly a joint venture: the effort to reach an under-standing of human experience in a specific geographical setting.

It may well be, as some critics have thought, that much of this Southwestern work is primitive in a bad as well as in a good sense. The past, for example, and the unsophisticated human types who represent the past in the present, may loom larger in this inventory than is quite justifiable. It might be objected that too much attention to untouched nature and to rural life threatens to become idle antiquarianism at a time when the world is at war, and when the region is at the mercy of its incredible demagogues. Or, to phrase the charge differently, perhaps the Southwestern writers have evaded a responsibility when they have paid so little attention to danger signals like the Ford hearings before the NLRB in Dallas and the wretched status of migratory farm workers.

These charges have some weight. It is not enough to say that more than one of the men represented here have come upon the brute fact of evil in their exploration of the Southwest, and have added this perception to our stock of self-knowledge. The betrayal of the people by their politicians, the ugly race preju-dices inherited from the past and made worse by economic stress, the helplessness of men of good will before the anachro-nistic abuses of a delayed industrial revolution—all these are in the Southwest of today and are a part of any complete inventory.

But we must not demand everything of every writer. We should record our gratitude to these Southwesterners for their affirmation of a tradition of honesty and genuineness which makes against most of what we do not like in our surroundings now. And we should value at its true worth the very real achieve-ment of regional writers generally in finding a valid way of interpreting American life outside the urban and industrial areas.

This achievement was more difficult and more necessary than we are likely to realize. Three decades ago, a writer who wished to deal with the life of farm or ranch or small town could draw upon only two fully-developed sets of attitudes, neither of which was well adapted to affirming the positive values of the American experience.

The first of these literary traditions was based on the genteel assumptions which so thoroughly permeated American thought in the nineteenth century. If one accepted the idea that the function of literature was to embody high moral ideals, the best that had been known and said in all the ages of human history, it was difficult to attach any very serious meaning to the American frontier experience, or to the diverse and often crude ways of life that resulted from it. Genteel writers, when they turned their attention to the American provinces in the decades after the Civil War, succeeded in dealing with more primitive types of character only by perfecting the local-color formula, which required the author to prove his unlettered natives had an innate and unaccountable moral virtue acceptable as a substitute for culture.

The other literary mode of dealing with the life of non-metropolitan communities was the embittered "realism" of post-frontier disillusionment—the realism of *Main Travelled Roads*—and H. L. Mencken's flippant revolt against the village. Garland and colleagues of his like E. W. Howe performed a necessary function by offering a corrective for easy optimism of the Colonel Sellers type; and Garland especially made many Americans understand for the first time the exploitation of a rural West by the East. Yet necessary and valuable as this realism and even this bitterness were, they failed as completely as did genteel condescension to express the real values that had been created in the Westward advance of the frontier. The newly settled areas lacked culture, and the dream of a utopia issuing directly from the Homestead Act had been dissipated. But was there no more than this to be said concerning the relentless, half-fantastic pioneering enterprise that had absorbed so large a portion of the nation's energy?

I do not think this question has been fully answered by Southwestern writers. But they have been thoroughly right in insisting that we must set out from man-in-his-environment, and that our goal is neither the discovery of imported virtues, nor a cry of despair at the vanishing of the frontier American Dream, but is rather self-understanding.

The quest for such understanding leads to an interest in particular regions because our experience of the land and of our fellow men necessarily takes place within this framework. This proposition is so simple and obvious that it can hardly require designation as an "ism." It is nevertheless easy to understand why such a program has sometimes seemed to need the support of manifestoes and debates. Conceptions held as widely and as implicitly as was the nineteenth-century notion of culture, with its implied contempt for frontier barbarism, survive for a long time, the error embodied in them, apparently, even longer than the truth. It may therefore not be amiss to say once again that the ideal of a cultivation and refinement of the human being without reference to place and social setting has come to have less and less meaning as we have understood more clearly the human need for a harmonious adjustment to nature—not an abstraction, but a specific, tangible terrain; and to society—not a featureless aggregate, but a concrete group of individual persons engaged in a joint enterprise, governed by shared references to a historical tradition, and bound together by the common conditions of their life.

While such a view inevitably has consequences for literature in general and therefore for a Southwestern literature, we do not need to draw up critical prescriptions, or argue seriously whether this book or that conforms to the rules. The different races of men who have devised ways of life here according to the necessities of the land have conceived many alternative solutions of the human problem. Although human occupation of the Rio Grande valley, for example, is very ancient, the Americans came late, and have even yet not lost all the momentum and restlessness of the great migrations. The occupation of the High Plains hardly dates back of the present century. Oil booms have brought about within the past generation the overnight growth of towns and the improvisation of economic systems that we associate with the California of the gold rush. Yet some of the older Spanish settlements, the German communities of the Fredericksburg area, and towns of the eastern woodland like Nacogdoches have a distinct air of stability and permanence. Cities such as Houston and Dallas, middleclass, sprawling, energetic, and rather closely integrated with the national economic structure, are of course another element—still slightly unreal—in the complex whole. The task of Southwestern writers is first the rudimentary one of making an inventory of the region, and then of interpreting it—not that all the interpretations will agree, but that from a variety of interpretations, gradually emerges a coherent view of the past and some sense of direction for the future.

Such a purpose need not seem trivial even in the midst of a world revolution. Although I have been speaking primarily of regionalism in art, the idea has fully as much meaning for politics and economics. Who can say that a simultaneous increase of both internationalism and regionalism will not be the necessary result of the evident bankruptcy of nationalism? I do not intend to join the prophets who are painting pictures of the world to come, but I cannot end this introduction without repeating a suggestion that has been made elsewhere. The national state, nineteenth-century style, is an institution no longer adequate to serve all the political and economic ends of society. Many of these ends must be served in the future by some international organization, but others will undoubtedly be served by economic and social units corresponding to diversities of physical environment. In our country, these units will be regions rather than the highly artificial states of the Union. Some of them cross international boundary lines; all of them, on the North American continent, are smaller than the areas now controlled by national governments. It is not absurd to think that internationalism and regionalism—resulting from a redistribution of the functions of the present national states—will prove to be necessary counterparts of one another. Lewis Mumford has stated this position tersely, and his statement, made before the official outbreak of the present war, requires no revision now: "We have still to create the adequate political framework for Western Civilization: a framework which will recognize both the universalizing forces and the differentiating forces that are at work."

# THE SOUTHWEST IN FICTION

*by* REBECCA W. SMITH

Rebecca W. Smith heads the English Department of Texas Christian University at Fort Worth, Texas. Besides her teaching activities, she is a distinguished critic, bibliographer, and writer. Despite her scholarly affiliations and achievements, she has wholly avoided any contamination by pedantic snobbism or narrow-mindedness. Nor, in the face of the recurrent hoopla of regionalism in the Southwest, is she prone to judge the value of a piece of writing on a basis of the author's address. It is the good fortune of the students of T.C.U. that their English Department has fallen into the hands of a person with Dr. Smith's endowments of judgment and horse sense—not to mention her charm. Simply to meet her you'd never know, unless someone tattled, that she was a Ph. D.—a distinction which Frank Dobie, in his milder moments, speaks of as "the mark of the beast."

---

BEFORE 1900 FICTION OUT OF THE SOUTHWEST WAS, WITH A few exceptions, written either by popular adventure writers or by literary amateurs. The tales were either imitative in form or merely formless; but they had in them much fresh information about the new frontier life of plains and deserts, Indians and Mexicans.

It is hard to say just when Southwest writing began to catch up with the rest of America in artistic technique and intellectual awareness; but soon after World War I there were growing signs of maturity, with now and then a hint of sophistication. Some of the new Southwest authors of the 1920's were already well known in the world of books when they began to write in and of this area. Others grew up in New Mexico and Arizona and Oklahoma and Texas, and learned their craft working with native materials. Tenderfoot or native, they faithfully chronicled the Southwest scene and legend.

Perhaps the most influential of the already well-known writers was Mary Austin, who built her Casa Querida in Santa Fé in 1925. Her profound feeling for the region expressed itself more fully in other forms of narrative than in the novel; for instance, in the admirable Indian folk-lore of *One Smoke Stories*, and in her autobiography, *Earth Horizon*. Nevertheless, her New Mexico novel, *Starry Adventure* (1931), is rich in landscape and customs, and her presence gave impetus to novel writing as well as to other art projects there.

Willa Cather's *Death Comes for the Archbishop* (1927) marks the beginning of a conscious appreciation of contemporary Southwest literature in the minds of the American public. This beautiful, quiet tale of an austere French priest was the first completely successful work in Southwest fiction, and probably remains the most admired. It is true that Mary Austin, in whose home Miss Cather lived in Santa Fé while writing her book, disapproved of the praise of French culture over Spanish-American. But Miss Cather's story, like the Archbishop's formal cathedral overlooking the disorderly plaza in Santa Fé, continues to dominate the scene.

In 1929 came Oliver La Farge's Pulitzer Prize novel, *Laughing Boy*, another work which focussed popular and critical attention upon the Southwest. Intense and poetic, this account of the modern Navajo as a human being, a sincere follower of beauty, is akin to the romantic concept of the "noble savage." LaFarge, however, did not invent an imaginary red man out of books and theories. He has lived among the Indians, and he created *Laughing Boy* in the firm belief that this youth is the real Navajo.

In the meantime, Harvey Fergusson, of an old Albuquerque family, wrote a series of more realistic novels of the historic eras of the Rio Grande Valley: *The Blood of the Conquerors* (1921), *Wolf-Song* (1927), and *In Those Days* (1929). With the rough candor that characterized the gifted young men of the 20's, he related what he counts the whole truth about the early days of the Valley—loot and lust and courage and defeat—in striking contrast to the extroverted success stories of the "Westerns." Almost simultaneously was published Ruth Cross's *The Golden Cocoon* (1924), containing an indictment of North Texas tenant farm life, one of the first social commentaries to find its way into Southwestern literature. Also from Texas, Dorothy Scarborough, a lady and a scholar, wrote the best novel of her career in *The Wind* (1925). This is the Hardy-esque tragedy of an aristocratic Virginia-born bride in a lonely West Texas ranch house, whom the wind drives mad. This novel likewise is no conventional "Western," and it is said to have aroused the Plains people no end.

A considerable amount of good Southwest fiction continued to appear during the late 20's and early 30's. The titles are familiar: Donald Joseph's beautiful and sensitive *October's Child* (1929), Stanley Vestal's colorful *Dobe Walls* (1929), George Milburn's satiric *Oklahoma Town* (1931), John Oskison's vigorous *Brothers Three* (1935). Competent craftsmanship and vitality are combined in all these stories. Especially brilliant are Milburn's disillusioned tales of Oklahoma small town life, which even their *American Mercury* mannerisms cannot wholly "date."

But by the mid-30's there was something more than merely the promise of a real literature of the Southwest. There was achievement, notably in fiction. Since that time the novel has become perhaps the most adequate literary expression of the region. Santa Fé can claim Mary Austin and Willa Cather by luck and the grace of God; but when a crop of good novelists springs from the soil, then Southwestern literature has come of age. The novels of this new group fit into no neat categories, geographical or social; but they all have in common an intense preoccupation with ways of living that are native.

The development of recent Southwestern fiction may be illustrated by reference to eleven writers whose recent books represent fairly the serious fiction of the region. All of these have had the satisfaction of critical literary recognition beyond their own borders, several of them having won important national awards; all of their work, no matter how various in form, bears the impress of special environment, the land and its social history being a major element in their dramatic conflicts.

John Joseph Mathews in *Sundown* (1934) recounts the failure of an intelligent Oklahoma Osage youth to learn the white man's ways, in spite of or, perhaps because of college and a car and an oil well. The author is himself part Indian; yet there is no bitterness, no romanticizing here. With dignity and honesty he chronicles the maladjustment and human waste among the prosperous Oklahoma Indians. This novel and his earlier *Wah'kon-tah* have established Mr. Mathews as an authentic interpreter of his people to the rest of the world.

Paul Horgan, who now lives in Roswell, New Mexico, won his first literary spurs with a sophisticated novel about upstate New York musicians, *The Fault of Angels*. He next ridiculed the wealthy dilettantes of Santa Fé in *No Quarter Given* (1935), the most effective and almost the only satirical novel of the Southwest to date. Significantly, however, Mr. Horgan has turned from satire to portrayals of the landscape and of pioneering days, and more lately to history pure and simple. His *Figures in a Landscape* (1940) is a poetically conceived study in design, a series of stories about people in the New Mexico country, peasant boys and army officers and old people. Each tale fits into the pattern of human transiency against a changeless landscape. In this mood Mr. Horgan is a philosopher who uses fiction to embody the truth he has discerned: that the shape of the land is more permanent than the achievements of the individuals who dwell on it.

Conrad Richter's *The Sea of Grass* (1937) is a saga of the passing of the cattle kings. Mr. Richter lives in Albuquerque, New Mexico, a good vantage point for understanding the Anglo-Saxon culture of New Mexico, which is his most successful theme. He knows range life as well as any "Western" author, but he goes beyond the outward facts to show the reaction of character to economic change. *The Sea of Grass* is an extraordinary technical achievement, almost the equal of *Death Comes for the Archbishop;* though, as a matter of fact, its closest parallel in Willa Cather's work is with *A Lost Lady.* In *The Sea of Grass* we watch a lusty, magnificent pioneer cattle king, Jim Brewton, lose his land and his exquisite wife. He is broken by the social changes he defies, and beaten by emotional conflicts he is too proud to recognize. Rhythmic style and symmetrical structure give this short novel a formal beauty rare in Southwestern literature.

*Lone Star Preacher* (1941), is by John W. Thomason, author of *Fix Bayonets!* Colonel Thomason is a traditional writer, in both material and style. As a World War I Marine officer he could doubtless instruct the hard-boiled younger men how to be realistic; but he prefers the gracious, slightly formal manner of the old style Southern humorist. In fact, his narrative technique is that of the frontier tale teller, the style that molded A. B. Longstreet and Mark Twain. Colonel Thomason is preserving faithfully the tales that the old-timers told him when he was a boy in Huntsville.

Katherine Anne Porter, it is said, never thinks of herself as a Southwestern writer; yet she was reared near San Antonio, which has much of the Old South in its bloodstream, and in the early 1920's she lived among the newspaper and little theater groups of Dallas and Fort Worth, where legends still go the rounds about her. All that would be no reason for including her here, did she not portray the Southwest in many of her stories with quiet, penetrating truthfulness. Her famous first volume of short stories, *Flowering Judas* (1930), is most effective when the settings go down into Mexico, an extension of the Southwest which belongs as naturally to our artists as the ocean does to New Englanders. *Pale Horse, Pale Rider* (1939), consists of three fine novelettes. The best is *Old Mortality*, the poignant memories of a child in a great Southern family haunted by a past that is not hers. The incisive beauty of Katherine Anne Porter's art belongs to no section.

Laura Krey leads a dual existence: as the wife of professor of medieval history at the University of Minnesota, and as the author of two sound historical novels, —*and Tell of Time* (1938) and *On the Long Tide* (1940). —*and Tell of Time* combines the two sources of her inspiration: the "remembered history" she heard of summer evenings as a child on a South Texas gallery, and her thorough research into records. Like Colonel Thomason, Mrs. Krey believes in the past, and she tells it for truth. If she seems sometimes to be documentary, it is probably that, being a scholar as well as a novelist, she too often finds her facts in books.

In the same tradition of historical fiction as Mrs. Krey's work is Karle Wilson Baker's *Star of the Wilderness* (1942) a full length, carefully woven novel of Texas in the early 1830's. Mrs. Baker skilfully centers the action in old Nacogdoches, headquarters of travel and intrigue on the road from Natchez to Mexico City. The story is rich in local customs and daily routine, and is free from conventional patriotism. Its limitation is its genteel, feminine point of view. Just as Mrs. Baker in *Family Style* (1937) views the modern oil game through a lady's eyes, here she recounts the struggle for empire chiefly as a gentle heroine sees it. Mrs. Baker's forte is manners, not full blooded action.

Edwin Lanham is a cosmopolite, having done his turns in Paris and New York literary circles. He has tried various styles and themes, but succeeds best with full blooded panoramas of North Texas, where his family pioneered two generations ago. After all, a young novelist who can combine his two grandfathers into such a hero as Amon Hall of *The Wind Blew West* had better sit and whittle in the courthouse yard of his home town a while longer. Mr. Lanham did just that when he wrote his latest novel, *Thunder in the Earth* (1941), a buoyant but rather uncritical account of the oil game, about which Mr. Lanham has told the truth, nothing but the bruth, though not the whole truth.

Mary King's *Quincie Bolliver* (1941) is an oil novel, too, and very realistic, but in a different manner. Quincie, child of an itinerant mule driver, comes to live in a shabby South Texas town that an oil boom has swept over. Through her young eyes and heart we come to know what the oil industry does to the boarding houses and shanties of a small community. The novel could have been sordid, but is not. Quincie is one of the memorable characters in all Southwestern fiction. *Quincie Boltiver*, Mary King's first novel, was written on a Houghton Mifflin Literary Fellowship.

Elizabeth Wheaton's *Mr. George's Joint* (1941) is also a first novel, and also a prize book, winner of the Thomas Jefferson Southern Award. Mr. George is a Negro *picaro* on "Tes'as City," which is not so far from Houston. The goings-on in his joint, officially known as the Big Spoon, are recounted for us joyously. no matter how earthy and a-moral they are. The dialect is convincing, and the girl Macknolia is a fine piece of character creation. Mrs. Wheaton creates Negro characters accurately and sympathetically; with the racial problem in the abstract, however, she has no concern.

George Sessions Perry's first novel, *Walls Rise Up*, came out three years ago with no great fanfare. It was a little too much in the vein of *Tortilla Flat*. Recognition has justly been accorded to Mr. Perry's *Hold Autumn in Your Hand* (1941) with the National Book Award. (The Texas Institute Book Award likewise went to Mr. Perry.) This is the beautifully simple chronicle of Sam Tucker, a poor tenant farmer in the Texas river bottoms. The story is as rich as bottom land, full of the smell of the earth and the ritual of the seasons on a farm. The problems of poverty and tenant farming are present, but are subordinated, as perhaps they should always be, to the living presence of the plain man Sam Tucker. *Hold Autumn in Your Hand* is almost the first Southwestern novel to be infused with a sense of sociological awareness. What Ruth Cross and Dorothy Scarborough undertook to do by too obvious exposition, Mr. Perry has accomplished by character and action.

In a fuller discussion than this, a number of other Southwestern novels would inevitably be recalled. Among them would be Anne Pence Davis's *The Customer Is Always Right* (1940), an examination of the small world inside a department store; Edwin Corle's *People on the Earth* (1937), a sympathetic portraiture of the Indians today; Sigman Byrd's *Tall Grew the Pines* (1936), a memorable pattern of small town life in East Texas;

O'Kane Foster's *In the Night Did I Sing* (1942), a story of the frustrated New Mexico Spanish-Americans; and Marcus Goodrich's *Delilah* (1941).

The vigor and greenness of all these books spring from the fact that their roots go deep into the actual life lived in the Southwest. To be sure, sometimes the authors stick overclosely to facts and so miss the universals of great art. The preponderance of hearty, surface pictures in the gallery of this fiction makes the exhibit seem somewhat naive. Only a few of the writers have been attuned to the psychological intensity of the nation's interbellum era. Except in the stories of Katherine Anne Porter and in the literary circles of Santa Fé and Taos there has been little sophistication. There are other limitations, too, in this fiction up to now. Even the best writers have not turned often enough to satire of major significance or to social protest. Meanwhile, another omission is also disturbing. Southwestern novels and short stories have little or no fantasy. The resources of the region are a challenge to creative workers to transmute them into whimsy and allegory.

Even so, of the three fields in which the Southwest has been most articulate—history, folk-lore, and fiction—it is fiction just now which is most alive. The historians and biographers are temporarily involved in the chaos of social change. Folk-lore awaits more writers like Mary Austin and Frank Dobie and John Lomax to harvest its riches. At the moment it is the novelists who are currently expressing the dynamic life of the Southwestern area most fully and honestly.